UNIVERSAL NATURAL HISTORY
AND
THEORY OF THE HEAVENS

Books by Stanley L. Jaki

Les tendances nouvelles de l'ecclésiologie

The Relevance of Physics

Brain, Mind and Computers
(Lecomte du Noüy Prize, 1970)

The Paradox of Olbers' Paradox

The Milky Way: An Elusive Road for Science

Science and Creation: From Eternal Cycles
to an Oscillating Universe

The Road of Science and the Ways to God
(Gifford Lectures, Edinburgh, 1975 and 1976)

Planets and Planetarians: A History of Theories
of the Origin of Planetary Systems

The Origin of Science and the Science of its Origin
(Freemantle Lectures, Oxford, 1977)

Cosmos and Creator

* * * * *

The Ash Wednesday Supper (*Giordano Bruno*)
(translation with introduction and notes)

Cosmological Letters on the Arrangement
of the World-Edifice (*J. H. Lambert*)
(translation with introduction and notes)

Immanuel Kant

UNIVERSAL NATURAL HISTORY AND THEORY OF THE HEAVENS

translated with introduction and notes by

Stanley L. Jaki

SCOTTISH ACADEMIC PRESS

PUBLISHED BY
SCOTTISH ACADEMIC PRESS
33 MONTGOMERY STREET, EDINBURGH EH7 5JX

First published 1981

© Introduction, Translation and Notes Stanley L. Jaki 1981

ISBN 0 7073 0294 3

Printed in Great Britain by
Page Bros (Norwich) Ltd
Mile Cross Lane
Norwich

TO
DOUGLAS GRANT

CONTENTS

INTRODUCTION

I. *A New Translation*

In late July, 1895, on receiving the telegram informing him of his appointment to the Chair of Divinity at the University of Glasgow, the Reverend William Hastie, then fifty-three, had every reason to be elated. Instead, he sank into a state of depression verging on nervous collapse. The turn was somewhat dramatic and, as in most dramas, not without a clue. In Donald Macmillan's *The Life of Professor Hastie*[1] the chapter called "Victory at Last" precedes the one called "Last Years," a sequence suggestive of a drama and also of the clue to it. The former chapter tells of a feverish publishing activity with which Hastie fought his final and successful battle for his life's ambition, a chair in the Divinity Halls of one of the four Scottish Universities. Hastie's earlier failure to achieve this aim may have had something to do with the fact that he accepted in 1878, at the age of thirty-five, the post of Principal at the College which the Missionary Board of the Church of Scotland operated in Calcutta. Within seven years Hastie was in a Calcutta jail, owing to a misinterpretation of his aims and policies by his superiors at home.

By 1888, when in the Courts of Edinburgh Hastie had his reputation finally vindicated, it was clear to him that in the academia he could outweigh his antagonists only by books. These he began to publish in quick succession, both in philosophy and in theology. They were original works as well as translations, mostly from German, and made no small impression. Indeed, the expertise in contemporary German theology and philosophy, which Hastie displayed in those publications, was the reason that a professor at Glasgow greeted the news of Hastie's appointment with the remark: "With Hastie among us, we can meet the learned stranger in the gate without any fear."[2]

Hastie would not have been himself if, after overcoming months of depression, he had slackened in his publishing activity. Perhaps he also felt that time was running out for him. If not an original work, at least a translation left his desk each year. In fact, the year 1900 saw the publication of two of his translations, of which one, *Kant's*

Cosmogony,[3] became his best remembered contribution. The work was greeted with unrestrained enthusiasm in "one of the leading journals," a reference by Macmillan who quoted extensively from that review without naming either the journal or the reviewer.[4] Had the latter only written that "the two works which make up the present volume throw absolutely new light on the subjects with which they deal," Hastie should have felt highly gratified. But more encomiums were in store of *Kant's Cosmogony*. The subjects of the two works translated in it were scientific, and the reviewer could not conceal his astonishment: "Most of us have been so much accustomed to regard Kant as a pioneer in Philosophy that we have overlooked the fact of his being a great discoverer in Science." That Kant was an original and lucid scientific thinker was indeed the primary impression to be gathered from Hastie's lengthy Introduction. The first work was a short essay, which Kant published in June 1754 in a Königsberg weekly, where he argued that owing to the friction of tides against the seabed the earth's rotational period was increasing. The second work was much longer. It contained Kant's theory of the evolution of solar systems and galaxies under the title, *Allgemeine Naturgeschichte und Theorie des Himmels,* which Hastie rendered as *Universal Natural History and Theory of the Heavens.* This title has since been used in English publications.

When a translation is reviewed in "one of the leading journals," a comparison of the translation with the original is *de rigueur*. The reviewer should have been prompted all the more so to make such a comparison as the very title of the short essay in the translation section of *Kant's Cosmogony* was different from the one given in the Introduction.[5] Whether attention to that difference would have led the reviewer to pursue the matter is, however, doubtful. If he had misgivings about the merits of Hastie's translation, they did not concern accuracy. Although the romantic component in Hastie's character was strong enough to make him claim expertise in many and even in some esoteric languages,[6] his command of German was firm. But since the reviewer knew that Kant's writings on metaphysics were not the easiest reading, he wondered concerning the difficulties which any essay of Kant on physics would present to the translator. Acknowledged master of style as Hastie was, his was still the enormous task, the reviewer wrote, of making "what is dark plain, or what is crooked straight, or what is rough smooth."

If such were the three aims in translating scientific works, a cursory reading of Hastie's translation could justify the glowing comment: "To our delight we found that he [Hastie] had succeeded marvellously in doing all three, and that he had, by his able and idiomatic translation of two hitherto obscure but important works of

2

Kant, placed English students under a lasting debt." The translation was certainly idiomatic. Whether it was also an "able" translation was another matter. At any rate, there were ample grounds for criticism of Hastie's Introduction, a piece about two-thirds as long as the translated material itself. But the reviewer was unqualifiedly jubilant: "As a piece of philosophic exposition and criticism nothing could be finer." This appraisal was even more misleading than the one concerning the translation, partly because it matched the reviewer's praises of Hastie's success in unveiling the great scientist in Kant.

The success of *Kant's Cosmogony* was not as unqualified as claimed by Macmillan. William E. Pickering, who reviewed it in *Nature*,[7] took Hastie to task for his obvious intention to make his readers believe that, as Pickering put it, "a greater than Newton is here." Pickering, a director of the Observatories in Liverpool and Oxford, could easily spot the scientific errors that plagued all phases of Kant's cosmogonical theory. He felt impelled to note that "there is a tendency in the very able introduction of Prof. Hastie to explain away these errors, and to contend for a closer agreement between the views of Kant and modern scientific theories than really exists." Pickering was clearly oblivious to Descartes as he praised Kant for getting hold "more clearly than any one who lived before him of the great thought" that the formation of the universe was a mechanical process throughout, free of special supernatural interventions. For that great thought, Pickering argued, much can be forgiven Kant even "if in some of his details he shows a lack of accuracy, or if some of his conceptions are in formal con-tradiction with the principles of mechanics." Such generosity would not have satisfied either Kant or Hastie. Both claimed for the specific articulation of that great thought in the *Allgemeine Naturgeschichte* a much higher validity than the one accorded to it by Pickering in his concluding comment, prompted by Kant's contention that it was more difficult to explain the development of a caterpillar than that of the universe: "If this be true, it may be due to the fact that we know less about the fabric of the Universe than of the caterpillar, and it is consequently easier to be convicted of error in the smaller than in the greater matter. Kant, together with all makers of cosmogonies, enjoys the advantage that the accuracy of the theories cannot be submitted to any adequate test."

It would be interesting to know what Hastie's reaction was to Pickering's review which did not touch on a point which, in a sense, was the very heart of Hastie's message on Kant. A poet at heart, a missionary by necessity, and a theologian by profession, Hastie regarded philosophy as his principal expertise. As a philosopher he was fully aware of the hopelessness of the Neo-Kantians' effort to talk away the philosophical agnosticism lurking between the lines of the *Critique of Pure Reason*. This hopelessness derived, so Hastie argued, from the failure of most Neo-Kantians to see that not only in the *Critique* but also before and after it Kant was above all a scientist! Of course, if one claimed, as Hastie did, that the salvation of philosophy lay in science and that Kant throughout his life had a firm grasp of and attachment to science,[8] Newton's science, that is,—a science along whose lines Kant tried to shore up philosophy,—then the perennial relevance of Kant the philosopher could seem plausible, the agnosticism of the *Critique* notwithstanding. This relevance could but receive support from Hastie's apparent mastery of Newtonian science. As a student at the University of Edinburgh he received high marks in courses of mathematics and physics, although the number and level of courses taken by Hastie in both subjects was another matter.[9] He never, for instance, touched on the question of the conservation of angular momentum in a dynamical system, a question that had been repeatedly aired even in connection with the evolution of the solar system in the closing decades of the nineteenth century.

The historical material, which Hastie brought together in the Introduction concerning the reception during the nineteenth century of Kant's *Universal Natural History*, could seem convincing to anyone ready to be swayed by the lustre of famous names, especially the names of men of science. Arago, Humboldt, Struve, Zöllner, Helmholtz, Wolf, Huxley, Tait, Sir William Thomson (later Lord Kelvin), Lodge, and Newcomb—all mentioned within ten pages of that Introduction[10]—were well known beyond scientific circles. Since all of them were quoted by Hastie as admirers of Kant's cosmogony, his readers could only reach the conclusion that it had at best slight faults. Actually, some of those scientists, as will be seen later, expressed serious reservations which Hastie carefully kept under cover. Most reprehensible in this respect was his reporting of Kelvin's reply to an address by Huxley. Contrary to the impression given by Hastie, Kelvin's fleeting praise of Kant's cosmogony did not merely follow within a short time Huxley's encomium of it, but was in part a scathing criticism of its evaluation by Huxley.[11] Most likely, this point was not brought up in a letter of November 12, 1900, in which Kelvin thanked Hastie for having dedicated *Kant's Cosmogony* to him, because by his own admission Kelvin had not time yet to peruse the freshly printed book.[12] Having had their critical sense dulled by an impressive list of scientists, Hastie's readers could hardly wonder whether the many Neo-Kantians, whose acclaim of Kant the scientist was diligently reported by Hastie, had given any evidence of their expertise in science

4

and in its history. But why should the Neo-Kantians have been suspected on this score, when Hastie's encomiums of Kant seemed to be supported by his references to well known writers, especially British, on the history of astronomy?[13]

The best that can be said of Hastie's long Introduction is that it is a diligent work. It was meritorious at a time when the cultivation of the history of science was still in an unscholarly and uncritical phase. The lack of scholarship derived in part from a scant familiarity with primary material, including even the great classics of science. In constantly referring to Newton without every studying him seriously, Kant himself followed an already hallowed fashion. As Voltaire put it when Kant was still a schoolboy: "Very few people read Newton, because it is necessary to be learned in order to understand him. Yet, everybody talks about him."[14] The lack of critical sense revealed itself in that naive acquiescence with which the men of Enlightenment took it for verity that scientific history abruptly started with the sudden onset of the age of reason. Kant himself made a memorable and most influential contribution to that uncritical viewpoint in the preface of the second edi.ion of the *Critique of Pure Reason* where he saw his critical work in philosophy as the sudden and grand dissipation of darkness by light. His confidence was based on the belief, which he uncritically shared with his age, that something similar had already occurred in physics and chemistry when Galileo and Stahl appeared on the scene. Until the cure for that Deus-ex-machina view of scientific history came sometime after 1900 with the gradual realization that Galileo owed much of his light to others before him, the historiography of science was confined of necessity into very strange moulds, so many breeding places of myths.[15] One such myth was the one fostered about the greatness of Kant's cosmogony, an illusion which Hastie took for a reliable estimate. He rendered it in the phrase which opened his Introduction and which he repeated midway in it: "Kant's cosmogony never stood so high in the estimation of the scientific world as it does today."[16]

That this illusory estimate has retained respectability until now can be seen in the Introductions written to the three reprints of Hastie's translation (reprints in which his Introduction was invariably omitted), published in three successive years beginning in 1968. The first to appear claimed in its title-page that it gave Hastie's translation "revised and edited."[17] Nothing could be further from the truth. The only "revision" made by the editor, Willy Ley, concerned the title of Kant's cosmogonical work. According to Ley it had to be rendered into English as *General* and not as *Universal Natural History*, a point which the copy-editor or the publisher himself graced with the remark

5

that well-founded as the correction was, the translation by Hastie, including its title, was reprinted unchanged "to maintain authenticity."[18] Clearly, Ley did not "revise and edit" Hastie's translation. Had he done so, he might have discovered such inaccuracies as Hastie's rendering on occasion "zenterfliehende Kraft" (centrifugal force) as centripetal force, although the context clearly called for the former. Unlike Ley, whose treatment of the history of his scientific topics betrays no serious scholarship,[19] Milton K. Munitz, author of scholarly books on the philosophy and history of cosmology,[20] could be expected to compare Hastie's translation with the original and in his Introduction[21] to do more justice to the true history of Kant's cosmology than Hastie did. The same also applies to the third reprint, to which Gerald J. Whitrow wrote an Introduction, and all the more so as this reprint appeared as No. 133 in the "Sources of Science" series.[22]

The Introductions written by Munitz and Whitrow merely added the veneer of modern science to the one by Hastie and thus strengthened the respectability of the hollow cliché about the grandeur of Kant's cosmogony. Munitz closed his Introduction with the claim that "Kant's theory, in particular, has served as a model and inspiration for more recent theories with all their refinements and subtleties."[23] This claim is no less inaccurate than the statement of Carl F. von Weizsäcker, himself a proponent of a fascinating but faulty theory of the evolution of the solar system,[24] whom Munitz quoted in support of his own claim. It was a mere exercise in vagueness to state, as Weizsäcker did, that "modern astronomy . . . has returned to views *very similar* to those proposed by Kant." The alleged similarity was stretched beyond recognition when Weizsäcker declared that Kuiper's idea "that some denser parts of the nebula condensed further under the influence of their own gravity . . . is *precisely* what Kant thought"[25] (italics added).

A close look at theories on the evolution of the solar system proposed during the past thirty years reveals that in some cases historical antecedents were in fact sought and Kant seemed to fit the role of forerunner. Prior to those years, there was a relatively brief period, the decades between the two World Wars,[26] when there prevailed a keen awareness of the impossibility of accounting for some basic features of the solar system if one assumed it to have developed from a slowly contracting nebula, let alone from that artificially contrived distribution of particles as imagined by Kant. During that period, which provided no allurement for serious students of the question to find a glorious forerunner in Kant, the Swedish mathematician and cosmologist, C. V. L. Charlier, offered a view about Kant's theory, a view which a hundred and more years earlier some

German astronomers had already intimated in a roundabout way.[27] In his Hitchcock Lectures given in 1924 at the University of California, Charlier minced no words: "Evidently the author [of the *Allgemeine Naturgeschichte*] has not himself studied even the first sections of Newton's *Principia*. . . . I mean that the *Naturgeschichte* is scientifically of very small value . . . I consider the *Naturgeschichte* of Kant unsuitable and even dangerous as inviting feeble minds and minds uninstructed in natural philosophy to vain and fruitless speculations."[28] Those who do not take for a sacrilege Bertrand Russell's unorthodox evaluation of Kant as a mere muddle in the history of philosophy[29] will not hastily take Charlier's appraisal of Kant the scientist for a brazen departure from the "received view."

When seen against Charlier's blunt words, the conclusion of Whitrow's Introduction, which parallels the advice of Hastie (whose translation and Introduction Whitrow always quotes with unqualified approval), should seem strange indeed. According to Whitrow "we should pay somewhat less attention than has been customary to those largely outmoded philosophical works of his [Kant's] later years on which his reputation as a thinker has come to depend, and considerably more attention to those early scientific writings in which he revealed such remarkable physical insight."[30] Hastie's corresponding advice has at least the advantage of specifying what is especially misleading in Kant's philosophical works of his later years. Hastie identified it as Kant's shrinking from the reality of the universe "into the mere spectral phantoms of his own subjectivity." The result was, and here the instinctive realist in Hastie showed at its very best, that Kant "became fatally entangled in his Paralogisms and Antinomies which wound him round and round, and from which he never won entire freedom again."[31]

The paralogisms and antinomies in question are a pivotal part of a book, the *Critique of Pure Reason*, which installed Kant in the Valhalla of philosophy. By 1981, the bicentenary of its publication, there will be a new flood of books and articles on it, in most of which a small note in the *Critique* will be conveniently ignored as has been the case in the past. The note is offered by Kant as an illustration of the respective merits of teleological and mechanistic explanations. The equatorial bulge of the earth, Kant warns, can, though not in a strict sense, be taken as a means directly provided by the Creator to prevent the changing of the axis of the earth's rotation by the volcanic upsurge of matter in places far from the equator. But Kant is quick to add that "we felt no scruples in explaining it [the formation of that bulge] from the formerly fluid mass of the earth."[32] This absence of scruples derived from Kant's robust belief which throughout his long

7

career animated him in the definitive truthfulness of all major points of his cosmogony. In few other cases would scruples and mistrust have been more in order. Kant's suggestion that volcanic explosions could change the direction of the earth's axis was no better physics even in his time than was the warning which Adlai Stevenson issued in October 1956 on behalf of his presidential campaign about the eventual dislocation of that axis through continued testing of nuclear bombs. For his blunder Stevenson could possibly blame his scientific advisors who should have remembered some basic laws of dynamics. Kant, who considered himself another Newton, had for excuse only his amateurism in physical science.

Tenacious amateurism was not to be denied a lucky guess or two even in Kant's case. The first of them appeared in his essay on the rotation of the earth published in 1754. There he not only argued, as was already mentioned, that owing to the tides caused by the moon, the period of the earth's rotation must gradually increase, but he also concluded that the increase would go on until the earth's and the moon's rotational periods would be equal so that just as we now see always the same side of the moon, the same side of the earth would always be seen from the moon.[33] Here Kant's originality was much greater than was the case with his other lucky guess, his explanation of the visual appearance of the Milky Way. The latter was in the air, and Kant himself, as will be seen later, did not unambiguously claim originality for that explanation. His identification of nebulae as other Milky Ways should, when taken in its context, seem to be not so much a bold scientific vision as a visionary view blind to its self-defeating aspects and lack of scientific rigor. The former relate to the gravitational and optical paradoxes of infinity. The latter is especially evident in Kant's calculation of the period of the rotation of Saturn's ring, a calculation which he held to be the touchstone of the truth of his cosmogony. Apart from its few insights the *Allgemeine Naturgeschichte* offers at times very wilful and often confused speculations, not science.

Such an evaluation will shock anyone accustomed to the cliché about the grandeur and fruitfulness of Kant's cosmogony and will be vehemently disputed by admirers of Kant, the philosopher and/or the scientist. Efforts to weaken them in their conviction would be largely wasted unless they first recognize that the moment of philosophical truth comes not from mere conceptual criticism, which never gives one reality, not even one's own reality, but from one's primordial commitment to reality as existing independently of and prior to one's voicing anew Kant's critical question whether knowledge is possible. Philosophers trapped in Kant's starting point will at best spin a universe out of their minds, but mostly will, *à la* Kant, do their best to claim that the universe is intrinsically elusive to a mind imbued with the spirit of criticism. But so will elude them its science, cosmology, and with cosmology all science insofar as all science is cosmology. As regards efforts to find in Kant's cosmogony the anticipation of modern theories on the origin of the solar system, the dry remark of Johann Heinrich Lambert, a contemporary of Kant, seems most appropriate. On being told in Nürnberg in 1761 that Thomas Wright of Durham had already developed ideas similar to the ones in his own *Cosmologische Briefe* just published, Lambert replied that his ideas would not make their impact "until an astronomer shall discover something in the sky that could not be explained otherwise; and when the system will be found demonstrated a posteriori, the lovers of Greek literature will come and have no rest until they can prove that the whole system had already been known to Philolaus, Anaximander or some other Greek pundit, and that recently it was only rediscovered and embellished. These are the people who find everything in the ancients provided one tells them what they should look for."[34]

Neither such explorers of scientific history nor philosophers overawed by Kant are of concern here, numerous as they may be. Fortunately, large enough is the number of those who belong to neither class and are ready to break through that hard crust of glory that has accrued around Kant the philosopher-scientist. It is to their benefit that this new translation of Kant's cosmogony is offered. Its principal aim is not "to make what is dark plain, or what is crooked straight, or what is rough smooth." It aims above all at utmost faithfulness to the often cumbersome and convoluted, and at places unintelligible, original which caused enduring headaches to its critical editors, headaches about which Hastie kept silent, to say nothing of the editors of the three reprints of his translation.

Faithfulness to the original would, of course, be honored in the breach if this new translation too were to stop at the point where Hastie's translation did, a procedure for which he offered, as will be seen, a patently lame excuse. Not even that much was done by the three editors in question.[35] Such was, needless to say, the best course to follow by anyone intent on presenting the author of *Allgemeine Naturgeschichte* as a sober scientific mind sparkling with originality. The last fifty-six pages of the work, which Hastie translated but left unpublished, not only show that Kant was not such a mind, but that he did not write a scientific work, his explicit claim to the contrary notwithstanding.[36] That the omission of at least one-fifth of the *Allgemeine Naturgeschichte* had reasons deeper than technical and financial is amply revealed by the fact that Hastie and his publisher found place in *Kant's Cosmogony* for a long Introduction and for three Append-

9

ices, one of which was both superfluous and void of scholarly merit.[37] To justify the omission, Hastie claimed that those pages, which were ready for the press and which "will be given if another opportunity occurs," were not needed for a grasp of Kant's cosmogony and that Kant himself had chosen to omit them forty years after the first publication.[38] Hastie, who firmly believed in the basic correctness of Kant's theory, wanted to conceal the fact that those pages contained a series of boasting (at times of rather bad taste) by Kant about the necessary truth of his theory.

The omission of those pages by Hastie and his re-editors should seem all the more unscholarly as they comprise the Eighth Section of the Second Part and the entire Third Part, the former of which was singled out by Kant in the Preliminary Discourse as a propedeutic to the entire work. In that Section Kant makes it all too clear that the purpose of his book was a reformulation of teleology on the basis of mechanistic science, an obviously philosophical enterprise. According to Kant, while nature was not purposeful in an anthropomorphic sense, it still had to evolve through its mechanical laws into an infinite number of habitable globes to display through its infinite plenitude the very infinity of God. Whatever the merits of the justification of teleology on such a basis, it was Kant's emphatic advice that most readers of his book would do well to start with that Section, which cannot, therefore, be considered expendable by a translator as long as he wants to remain faithful to Kant's own precepts. Once Kant's book is seen in its essentially teleological perspective, the publication in English of the Third Part, in which Kant specifies with affected diffidence the physical and moral characteristics of the denizens of the *necessarily habitable* globes of the solar system, must appear imperative if the English reader is to have a full grasp of Kant's cosmogonical perspective and the science which it inspired.

Since that intrinsically teleological perspective can hardly appear scientific to anyone enamored of Kant the champion of pure scientific reason, crusaders, like Hastie and others, on behalf of that Kant could only keep those pages under cover. That even in the late 1960s the omission was taken in stride, suggests something of the subjective motivations that can play havoc with studies of scientific history. These subjective factors will clearly be at play in connection with the forthcoming celebrations of the bicentenary of the *Critique of Pure Reason*. Despite Kant's parading in the cloak of pure rationality, the *Critique* was the product of a highly subjective mind which sparked both the thorough subjectivism of German Idealism and the dialectical wilfulness of its materialistic counterpart. This should be no suprise. Nothing affects more deeply the thinking subject than its relation to reality and to the totality of reality, the universe. A misconception about that relation can especially ruin, as the history of Kant's influence shows, the subject's main source of balance, his attitude to reality and to its totality, the universe. A subjective starting point can only issue in an a priori approach to reality, which is no less true of the post-critical than of the pre-critical Kant. Such an approach will first yield—the *Allgemeine Naturgeschichte* is the proof—a pretentious and often contradictory notion of the universe, and then land one in the belief—as the *Critique* shows—that truly universal notions about the universe are illusions. Once the objectivity of the universe is thus abandoned, so is abandoned the terrain of objective science, a point amply illustrated by Kant's *Opus postumum*, a classic morass of subjectivism imposed by the precepts of the *Critique*.

While a study of the history of science, and in particular of the history of Kant, the scientist, can be very helpful in perceiving this logic, it will help only those who already are convinced of a truth which Chesterton, not a scientist but an unusually penetrating observer of scientific reasoning,[39] gave a classic formulation. It is a rebuttal of "the modern idea . . . that cosmic truth is so unimportant that it cannot matter what any one says." But, as Chesterton declared in the same breath, "there are some people, nevertheless—and I am one of them—who think that the most practical and important thing about a man is still his view of the universe. We think that for a landlady considering a lodger, it is important to know his income, but still more important to know his philosophy. We think that for a general about to fight an enemy, it is important to know the enemy's numbers, but still more important to know the enemy's philosophy. We think the question is not whether the theory of the cosmos affects matters, but whether, in the long run, anything else affects them."[40]

The context of this passage, which William James quoted with glowing approval,[41] has for its target that self-defeating modern relativism, according to which the only right thing is the total lack of concern as to whether anything is truly right. To that relativism few gave so much impetus and so thick a veneer of rationality as Kant did, although his professed aim was the very opposite. In Kant's case too the force of inner logic prevailed. That logic was already in evidence in the subtly subjective attitude of the author of the *Allgemeine Naturgeschichte* toward the universe. It asserted itself in his effort to tell in a largely a priori fashion what the universe ought to be. Of course, there is always an a priori component in that bold imagination, extrapolation, and system-making which distinguish the creative scientist from the engineer, to say nothing of the mere compiler of facts and observations. Long before Kant the case of Descartes had already made it abundantly clear that bold, a priori imagination coupled with "qualitative" or rather facile and often arbitrary references to mechanical laws yields not cosmogony but only a novel about the cosmos.

This blunt appraisal by Huygens of Descartes' cosmogony[42] is wholly appropriate to the cosmogony of the *Allgemeine Naturgeschichte*. As in Descartes, in Kant's cosmogony too no part was played by such basic ingredients of true science, as the casting of theories into mathematically formulated laws and the testing of their predictions against observations in a rigorous quantitative manner. But how could one expect such a performance from a Kant who though not properly trained in mathematics and physics, looked upon himself as another Newton, who did in the physics of cosmology what Sir Isaac did in its mathematics? True, he claimed that the definitive working out of the physical part of cosmology was an easier task than doing the same for its mathematical part. But did he not also claim that one could present, if necessary, even that physical part with all the "parade" which mathematics can offer?[43]

Kant's parading in Sir Isaac's cloak was a shabby performance. Prior to the publication of the *Allgemeine Naturgeschichte*, in which elementary calculations are time and again erroneous, Kant had given evidence of his fumbling arithmetic as he calculated the retardation of the earth's rotation, a calculation which he apparently based, in part at least, on a theorem in the Second Book of Newton's *Principia*.[44] As one to whom much of the *Principia* was a closed book, Kant failed to see that he had derived far more from that theorem than it contained, and most important, that the amount he derived for the retardation could only make the experts smile. To be sure, had he made his calculation correctly, and had he referred to the theorem in question, competent scientists would have still remained unconvinced.[45] Kant's essay, written with an eye on the Prize set in 1752 by the Academy of Science in Berlin, was not only not submitted to that august body, but its author claimed, ironically enough, the very opposite of that which Paolo Frisi, professor at Pisa, set forth in his prize-winning essay, published in 1756.[46] Frisi discussed with great mathematical skill a number of factors which in his view could conceivably slow down the earth's rotation, but found them all wanting with the exception of the impact of the ether, an impact too small to be considered.[47] Among the factors Frisi found wanting were the tides, atmospheric and oceanic, which he discussed with reference to investigations by Euler and d'Alembert. It is not likely that Frisi had in mind Kant's essay, buried in the obscurity of the Königsberg weekly, as he declared: "These we have said in passing lest there should remain some doubt [suspicion] in anyone's mind that through the constant motion of air or water towards some shore there should arise against the rough surface of our earth such a friction which could accelerate or retard the diurnal motion."[48] The very few competent scientists, if there were any, who read Kant's essay, would have felt, rightly or wrongly, uneasiness on reading at its end that it was merely a small part of a much larger work which Kant was soon to publish under the title, "Cosmogony, or an Attempt to Deduce the Origin of the World-Edifice, the Formation of Celestial Bodies, and the Causes of Their Motion from the Universal Laws of the Motion of Matter according to the Theory of Newton,"[49] a work to which he finally gave the title, *Allgemeine Naturgeschichte*. In the long run Kant himself grew wary of it as a whole. But its true instructiveness lies in its entirety which is now offered to the English-speaking public in a new translation and evaluated in a historical perspective based on the scrutiny of original sources, particularly those used by Kant.

II. *Cosmogony before Kant*

By calling his cosmogony *Allgemeine Naturgeschichte* or *Universal Natural History* Kant clearly aimed at benefiting from the popularity of Buffon's *Histoire naturelle*. By 1755 five of its scores of volumes had already been published, and each was as much in demand as the first which contained a cosmogony restricted to the solar system and sold out in three weeks in August 1749. As will be seen, Kant's debt to Buffon's work, which began to be published in German translation the very next year, extended far beyond the choice of title. Had Kant chosen "Cosmogonie" for a title, as he originally intended to do, his cosmogony might have become the first book to be known by that word. A closely similar word, cosmologia, had graced by then the title pages of at least three works,[1] but in none of them was the world considered as something being generated or evolved.

The word cosmogony was also used in speculations about the genesis of the world, especially after Descartes gave them a new twist and impetus. The twist was certainly "scientific" when compared with the narration of those divines (and their number was legion in the seventeenth century), who simply recounted the "Mosaick cosmogony," an expression used by William Whiston,[2] himself the proponent of a "scientific" cosmogony. Cartesian cosmogony had for its rival the Epicurean vision of worlds emerging from chaotic whirls of atoms, a vision versified by Lucretius and restored to a new respectability by Gassendi around the middle of the seventeenth century. Not a few found at that time something worthwhile in that "most ancient, and in a manner universally received tradition amongst the Pagans . . . that the *cosmogonia*, or generation of the world, took its first beginning from a chaos." As a part of many similar phrases in Cudworth's famed work, *The True Intellectual System of the Universe*,[3] cosmogony and its derivatives could not fail to gain wide currency.

As already noted, bold as Descartes's cosmogony was, it was but a phantasy. Malebranche, the most articulate spokesman of Cartesian philosophy, was a rather lonely voice among Cartesians with his profuse praises for Descartes' cosmogony which, as he ruefully noted, was suspect for many because it was so clear that even women could understand it.[4] Cartesian physicists, such as Rohault, largely kept silent about the genesis of stars and planetary systems as proposed by Descartes.[5] The most appealing feature of that genesis was, of course, the vortex. It was already used by Epicurus, but Descartes was the first to claim for it, through a long-winded discourse, universal explanatory power concerning the physical realm. Wisely enough, he let the Creator give a circular twist to the prototypes of cosmic vortices, namely, to each celestial domain filled with three kinds of matter. Prior to that, Descartes let the Creator parcel into roughly equal domains the unlimited, if not infinite, extension, or basic form of physical reality, although he also suggested that all these "initial conditions," to use the modern jargon, were the only natural or reasonable ones to start with in cosmogony. In other words, Descartes, for all his genuine reverence for the Creator, was in the grip of the age-old temptation to tell a priori what the universe ought to look like.

As one could expect from an a priori cosmologist as Descartes, he hardly looked at the sky to see what the universe is really like. In the *Principes*, written more than thirty years after Galileo had reported that the telescope showed the Milky Way to be a host of small stars (an idea widely entertained for centuries before Galileo), Descartes simply ignored the Milky Way.[6] The reason for this seems to lie in his infatuation with homogeneous infinity, as the natural state of existence, of which the Milky Way was a palpable rebuttal. Had Descartes been less captive a mind, he would have pondered the shape and hue of the Milky Way and might have even reached the conclusion that the Milky Way was an all-encompassing vortex of stars. The universe would have then appeared not as a pale uniformity but a strikingly singular or specific entity which would have hardly encouraged the a priori assumption fatal to cosmology that the universe cannot be anything except what it actually is.

Cartesian cosmogony was a grandiose fancy. It stood in sharp contrast to that fixity which characterized the long-dominant world view, whether it was articulated by Plato, Aristotle, Ptolemy, Copernicus, or Kepler. Descartes conjured up the universe as a huge self-developing mechanism in all its parts, and especially in its principal parts, the domains of each star. From the mechanism of a domain there followed in its center the birth and even the eventual death of a star. If a dead or encrusted star, unable to maintain its own domain, was captured by a neighboring domain permanently, it became a planet there. A planetary system was therefore the successive floating of dead stars into the domain of a particularly active or strong star. The dynamics of capture could, however, also be such as to foreclose permanent capture, a case which Descartes took for the origin of comets. While all this could easily be brushed aside as mere fancy, the vortex, the all-purpose mechanism of Cartesian cosmogony, was not something to be taken lightly. The motion of planets around the sun strongly suggested a vortex mechanism even after Newton reached the pointed conclusion in the *Principia* that not only the comets did move in orbits (according to Descartes they moved from one stellar domain, or solar system, into another along sinuous paths), but that their highly eccentric orbits could not arise in a roughly circular vortex. Such a vortex still could seem to be instrumental in bringing about the almost circular orbits of planets. Huygens may have had this in mind as he penned in 1694, or seven years after the publication of the *Principia*, the cryptic note: "The vortices destroyed by Newton. Replaced by vortices of spherical movement."[7] Almost forty years later no less a physicist than Bernoulli still did his best to explain the motion of planets on the basis of vortex motion.[8]

It was another question whether the best that physics (Newtonian physics) could offer would account for the formation of vortices on a cosmic scale. Affirmative answer to that question was indispensable if one was to proceed to speculations about the formation of a planetary system from a whirling material. Newton would have been the logical choice to answer this question, but he published little that would qualify as cosmology and cosmogony, and he cared not to reconcile his various dicta. He believed in the existence of a continuous ethereal fluid no less firmly than he did in "hard, impenetrable . . . Particles," or atoms, created by God in the beginning.[9] He held that there was a basic difference between fiery and opaque matter, and entertained the idea of suns replenishing themselves by the fall of comets into them.[10] Apart from this, his world view was static, or uncosmogonical, corresponding to his conviction that the laws of mechanics were inadequate for producing the major features of the present system of the world.[11] By that system he largely meant the system of planets. He also believed that the placing of stars at roughly equal distances from one another was also the result of a direct intervention by God. Early in his career, Newton explicitly held that the world of stars was finite in infinite space,[12] a belief which he seemed to retain to the end. Otherwise Voltaire, who had spent three years in the aged Newton's entourage, would have hardly stated emphatically in his *Elémens de la philosophie de Neuton* that "according to Newton (and according to reason) the world is finite."[13]

The "Newtonian" reasons for the finiteness of the world had been first set forth by Richard Bentley a few years after the publication of the *Principia*. A classicist and a divine by training, Bentley did so in a series of sermons, the first Boyle lectures, which he devoted to the confutation of atheism.[14] The atheists in question were the Epicureans of his time, whom Bentley did not name, but whom he took to task for their view of the universe as a self-evolving mechanism, let alone as a product of fortuitous concurrence of atoms. Bentley also found in the *Principia* weapons which he believed could be effectively turned to support the thesis of his seventh sermon that particles originally dispersed in space "could never of themselves, by any kind of natural motion, whether called Fortuitous or Mechanical, have conven'd into this present or any other like Frame of Heaven and Earth."[15] Bentley first reminded his audience of the force of gravitation as being proportional to the mass and of the immensity of the ratio of space empty of matter to space actually filled with it. In other words, the original chaos had to be pictured as a space interspersed with particles (atoms) separated from one another by enormous stretches of void. Such particles could conceivably come together either by external impulsion or by gravitational attraction. As to impulsion, Bentley emphasized the enormous improbability of collisions between such particles; as to attraction, he distinguished between two cases: a finite and an infinite universe. If the universe was finite, then all matter would have long ago coalesced into one single body, provided that the cosmic past had been sufficiently vast, if not infinite. Bentley, for the sake of argument, allowed the formation of individual planets even in such a case. But then, he declared, "they could not possibly acquire such Revolutions in Circular Orbs, or . . . in Ellipses very little Eccentric."[16] For this to happen, Bentley argued, a planet must have been formed at a specific distance from the sun and be given there a transverse impulse to counter its being attracted toward the sun. The ether, Bentley noted, was too tenuous to propel a planet, freshly formed, into its proper position with respect to the sun. Bentley certainly did not entertain the possibility that the formation of planets and their moving into their proper orbits could be simultaneous processes. Nor did Bentley envisage the possibility that the stars might turn around a common center. His idol, Newton ("that very excellent and divine Theorist" as Bentley referred to him[17]), ignored the Milky Way[18] and Bentley was left to see in the apparent stable position of stars an evidence of divine intervention: "He that considers what a mathematical Center is, . . . will never be persuaded that such an Universal Equilibrium arising from the coincidence of Infinite Centers, can naturally be acquired or maintained."[19] The argument that such an equilibrium would naturally arise in an infinite homogeneous universe, Bentley brushed aside with the remark that such a universe would have been preceded by an infinite homogeneous chaos in which no agglomeration of particles would have ever taken place because gravitational attraction would have been equal at all points in all directions. Or as he put in a classically terse phrase the rebuttal of the idea of an infinite homogeneous universe: "An equal Attraction on all sides of all Matter is just equal to no Attraction at all."[20]

Bentley's series of sermons was the sensation of the closing years of the century. Its English editions rapidly followed one another.[21] A Latin translation was published as early as 1696 in Berlin,[22] and a German translation saw print in Hamburg in 1715.[23] While from the sermons Bentley's reliance on the *Principia* was very clear, a public though only generic endorsement by the *Principia's* author of the points made by Bentley came only in 1713 in the famous Scholium appended to the second edition of the *Principia*.[24] The very specific endorsement which Newton gave to Bentley in their correspondence between December 1692 and February 1693 concerning details of Bentley's utilization of the *Principia*, was not made public until 1756.[25] Little impact was made meanwhile by Halley's public airing in 1720 of two objections to the infinite homogeneous universe: Any form of physical infinity was to be reconciled with the problem of an actually realized infinite number, whereas a universe of homogeneously distributed stars seemed to involve the optical paradox of enormous if not infinite light-intensity at any point.[26] Halley considered in detail only the second objection and seemed to answer it by parting with the postulate of homogeneity. To counter the same objection Chéseaux proposed in 1744 the absorption of starlight in the ether.[27]

Neither Halley, nor Chéseaux made an impact on their contemporaries by their confident handling of some patent difficulties inherent in the idea of an infinite homogeneous universe. Attention remained riveted on the solar system and such was certainly the case with William Whiston and Buffon, whose cosmogonies were well known to Kant. In 1696 Whiston, Newton's successor in the Lucasian chair, argued that a comet passing close by the earth caused the deluge and changed at the same time the originally circular orbit of the earth into its present, slightly elliptical shape.[28] Such a near-collision was implicitly postulated by Whiston for the final shaping of the orbit and surface of each planet already in orbit around the sun and other stars. Whiston gave a glimpse of his more general cosmogonic ideas only in scattered remarks.[29] He seems to have believed that the creation of a fiery chaos out of nothing was followed by the formation (presumably through a direct action of God) of fiery and opaque globes, that is, stars and comets. Most of the latter were placed by God into highly eccentric orbits around the stars, but some comets became planets by being put in perfectly circular and concentric orbits. It was these planet-comets that were removed by a grazing collision with a highly eccentric comet from their perfectly circular orbits into slightly eccentric ones, a process which in the earth's case produced the deluge and the bending of its axis with respect to the ecliptic, the cause of four season. Such was Whiston's way of turning the "Mosaick history"[30] into a "scientific" account.

The close passing of a comet by the earth, or any other planet, bespoke for Whiston of a divine arrangement. Buffon too—a beautiful engraving in the first volume of his *Histoire naturelle* was the proof[31]— viewed his comet as having been hurled by God's omnipotent arm. But Buffon was highly original in arguing that several conspicuous uniformities of the solar system, such as the orbiting and rotating of planets and satellites in the same sense, the confinement of all members of the solar system (Buffon slighted the comets, and so did Kant) in the same plane, and the like, were indications of a single physical factor at work. In voicing almost verbatim the same, Kant should have acknowledged his indebtedness to Buffon whom he followed, ironically enough, in a calculation which was not only patently wrong but also explicitly ascribed by Buffon to Newton, a fallacy that should have been noticed by Kant, an allegedly serious student of the *Principia*. Kant, who also borrowed (again without acknowledgment) Buffon's polished though hollow protestations of diffidence, was not enough of an expert to note the basic fallacy in Buffon's theory. According to Buffon, the elongated material torn out of the sun by the grazing collision of a comet with it, first went into a highly elliptical orbit and then cooled gradually so as to permit the formation of a string of planets in it. The turning of this very elongated orbit touching at one point the sun's surface into half a dozen almost circular orbits was another matter. Buffon, not a student of celestial dynamics although a mathematician of some skill, gave only a qualitative and somewhat vague answer to this problem. He acknowledged that the torn-out material would have an orbit which included the point of grazing collision. A bullet shot with sufficient force from a musket at the top of a very high mountain would, he noted with a likely reliance on a diagram in a small and posthumous treatise of Newton,[32] return to the same point. But, Buffon argued, if instead of a bullet one would take a rocket which would continually accelerate itself, an orbit could be obtained whose "perigee would be all the more removed from the earth, the greater would have been the force of [its self-] acceleration and the more it would have changed the first [original] direction [of motion]."[33] Buffon then referred to the pulsating character of the eruption of a volcano, such as Vesuvius, to make it appear probable that in the flaming material torn out from the sun a similar process might have been operative.

Needless to say, Buffon had no right to assume the presence of a self-guiding propellant in the material torn out from the sun, a point rather elementary in our age of space shots, but also very obvious two hundred or so years ago. Kant's failure to note this basic defect in Buffon's theory is rather revealing and so is his failure to note that unlike his own theory, that of Buffon was anything but an endorsement of the principle of plenitude taken for an undisputed verity by most at that time. In Buffon's theory planetary systems must have appeared as extremely rare occurrences, unless one assumed that God let every star be grazed by a comet of carefully specified mass and orbit. As to the speculations of Burnet, Leibniz, and others[34] about the formation of the earth, their main merit was the strengthening of the cosmogonical perspective. They contained at most a hint about the formation of another planet, let alone about the formation of the planetary system, to say nothing of the realm of stars and the universe as such. Kant, who intently followed Swedenborg's publications, undoubtedly knew of the latter's cosmogony in which planets formed from rings detached from the sun, in a confused manner to be sure.[35] The cosmogonical ideas, which in the decades preceding Kant were most portentous for future speculations, were formulated by Maupertuis in his *Discours sur les différentes figures des astres*, first published in 1732 and ten years later in a considerably enlarged form, which was reprinted with minor modifications four times in the next dozen years.[36] Kant was certainly familiar with a review of the *Discours* as part of a collection of Maupertuis' works published in 1744 under the title, *Ouvrages divers de Mr. de Maupertuis*.[37] He may have read the *Discours* in the more complete editions of Maupertuis' works published in 1752 and 1753, especially as they were printed in Germany, in Dresden and Berlin, respectively.

What is certain is the fame which Maupertuis enjoyed in Germany after he became President of the Berlin Academy in 1746. The ensuing importation of French scientific and philosophical talent into Berlin was largely the work of Maupertuis, the first notable Newtonian in France.[38] Voltaire and Madame de Chatelet received from Maupertuis their initiation to Newtonianism. Maupertuis' work on the flattening of the earth, his journey to Lapland to measure there the length of a degree of an arc, his formulation of the law of least action, his studies on heredity, were his more memorable feats which made the study of his writings obligatory during the rest of the century. Laplace was certainly familiar with them and so was Kant, according to his own admission, with the *Discours* at least.

In the *Discours* the flattening of a celestial body owing to is rotation is an ever recurring theme. It was also the theme which·prompted Maupertuis to make some seminal utterances that are usually overlooked in histories of cosmogony, and especially in studies concerning the background of the theories of Kant and Laplace. The *Discours* started indeed with the question of whether or not the earth was a perfect sphere. That it could not be a perfect sphere was the unanimous verdict in the late seventeenth century, but opinions differed whether it was an elongated or a flattened sphere. Huygens and Newton were among those who advocated the latter view, although with different results because their theories of gravitation were somewhat different. This in turn gave Maupertuis the opportunity to discuss gravity itself as something intrinsic to matter in Newtonian theory and to see whether it could be reduced, as Descartes believed, to vortical motion. Maupertuis' arguments in support of Newton came to conclusion in a paragraph the cosmogonical ring of which was unmistakable and deserves to be quoted in full: "All preceding laws of gravity give the stars, which have a revolution around their axis, the figures of flattened spheroids: and although the planets which we know in our solar system approach sphericity, they were no less subject to [susceptible of assuming] very flattened figures. Only a gravity less great, or a revolution more rapid around their axis, was necessary for this [to happen]. And why should the kind of uniformity, which we see in a small number of planets, prevent us from suspecting at least the variety of the others which the immensity of the heavens hides from us? Relegated to a corner of the universe with weak organs [of perception] why should we limit things to the few which we perceive of them?"[39]

That celestial bodies did indeed display a large variety of flattening was the burden of the sixth chapter in the *Discours*, a chapter entitled, "Luminous Spots Discovered in the Sky." Masses of fluid matter, Maupertuis declared at the outset, "which have a movement of revolution around their center [axis], must form very flattened stars and [they do so] in the form of millstones which one can range in the class of suns or of planets according to whether the matter which forms them is luminous in itself or opaque and capable of reflecting light. Whether the matter of these millstones is throughout of the same nature, or whether it gravitates toward a star of different nature, it overflows it [the star] everywhere and forms around it a flattened spheroid which encloses the star." [40]

Maupertuis then recalled that as astronomical observations of these luminous spots or nebulous stars progressed they were not found to be congeries of stars—indeed they were found not even to enclose a star—but great oval spaces, of a hue somewhat clearer than the rest of the sky. Some of these luminous spots were observed and listed by Halley, [41] who believed them to be the light created before the creation of the sun. Derham saw in them openings into the empyrean heavens, [42] but their most convincing explanation lay, Maupertuis added, in gravity. Being flattened spheroids, those among these luminous masses "which approach sphericity will be seen," in accordance with the variety of their observed shapes, "as circular spots whatever is the angle which the axis of their revolution makes with the plane of the ecliptic; others, whose figures are flattened, must appear circular or oval spots, according to the manner in which the plane of their equator presents itself to the ecliptic." [43] The chapter came to a close with a survey of the perplexity concerning the estimates of the distance of these nebulous stars. Maupertuis, however, felt no perplexity whatever in respect to the sudden apparition and disappearance of some stars. If a star, especially a nebulous star, was flattened "infinitely" or at least very much by its rotation, it was not to be seen by us any longer if its plane of rotation happened to coincide with the plane of the ecliptic. On the other hand, if the position of a very flattened star was changed by the perturbation of its planets, then it could again become visible. [44] After all this, the last or concluding chapter of the *Discours*, a chapter on the ring of Saturn, would disappoint the modern reader. For all his insistence on the possibility of an endless variety of flattening in a rotating celestial body, Maupertuis attributed the ring of Saturn not so much to its rotation as to its capturing the tail of several comets. In a somewhat similar way Maupertuis tied the zodiacal light to the sun. Planets which captured only the tail of one comet or only a part of it, would have, so Maupertuis opined, but a very faint ring around them. At the same time he confidently warned that "one ought not to be astonished on seeing [in the future] planets surrounded by several rings similar to that of Saturn." [45] The recent discovery of rings around Neptune shows how reliable his confidence was, whatever our conviction about the unreliability of a comet to provide a planet with a ring. Rarely in the history of cosmogony was a good expectation mixed up with so poor an explanation.

The same is also true of Thomas Wright's speculations about the Milky Way contained in his *An Original Theory and New Hypothesis of the Universe* (1750)[46] which also exercised, though indirectly, a heavy influence on Kant. To be sure, in Wright's view the universe was ready-made and not-at-all evolutionary, and therefore his *Theory* was not a cosmogony. Still, Wright was the first to state in print an idea indispensable for any future cosmogonical theory. According to him the Milky Way's shape and hue were caused by the facts that an "infinite number of small Stars"[47] (the expression was not to be taken literally either with respect to infinity or to the smallness of the stars in question) was located within a vast layer and that the stars had within it an orbital motion. Wright thought that these two facts could simultaneously be satisfied in two frameworks or models for the Milky Way. One of the two models was a ring, the other was a spherical shell. Although analogy with the planetary system supported the ring model, Wright's own preference was for the spherical shell. Since he put a divine eye in the center of the system of stars, it was more appropriate that stars could be met in every direction by that omnipotent vision. Although Wright referred to nebulae or rather nebulous stars, they were not other Milky Ways to him. He saw in them relatively small clusters of stars.[48] This is not to suggest that he failed to conjure up many other Milky Ways, or galaxies, but he held most of them to be strictly invisible to us, whatever their infinite number.[49] Wright's vision of a universe of galaxies—he did not suggest that they formed ever more encompassing systems of galaxies—was theological, not scientific. He needed them as evidence of God's infinite plenitude and as abodes for all kinds of eternal retribution: awards as well as punishments. Herein may lie the explanation of the fact that Wright's attention to basic laws of physics was tenuous at best as he discussed at the end of the Ninth or concluding Letter of his work the properties of "the common centre of gravitation"[50] for all stars in that spherical shell, of which one segment appears to us as the Milky Way. About that center Wright admitted that unless all creation was ideal, that is, an exclusively spiritual reality, that center had to be of real matter. He did not profess to know whether it was "a globe of fire superior to the sun, or otherwise a vast terraqueous earth but more refined, transparent, and serene."[51] The last word indicated the ease with which the physical and the psychical mixed in Wright's vision of the cosmos: "The common centre of gravitation . . . may be supposed," he wrote, "to attract all virtues and repel all vice."[52] Such was hardly the perspective of scientific cosmogony.

The history of cosmogony before Kant includes an unjustly forgotten work, *Origine de l'univers, expliquée par un principe de la matière*, by Pierre Estève (1720–1790?), member of the Académie des Sciences in Montpellier since 1746.[53] That it was published (anonymously) in Berlin in 1748[54] raises the intriguing question of whether Kant knew of it at least indirectly. Although Kant was more conscientious than were many of his contemporaries in giving due credit where it belonged,[55] his acknowledgement of his indebtedness to others left much to be desired. Instancess of this, as the notes to the text will show, abound in the *Allgemeine Naturgeschichte*. More important than Kant's possible dependence on Estève should seem the fact that in the *Origine de l'univers* there is anticipated a pivotal and in a sense original point of the cosmogony of the *Allgemeine Naturgeschichte*, namely, the emergence of the unidirectional orbiting and rotating of planets from a small asymmetry in the motion of particles toward the center of the solar system. The lesson of this is rather similar to the one relating to the explanation of the Milky Way. In both cases the insight seems to have been so much in the air as to need no scientific genius for its articulation.

The *Origine de l'univers* is not Estève's best work.[56] It did not deserve the enthusiastic reaction of Friedrich K. Schumann, a privatdozent at the University of Tübingen. He had been for years in possession of a copy of that exceedingly rare work when he finally gave it a reading and found it so similar to the contents of the *Allgemeine Naturgeschichte* as to promise in 1923 in the pages of *Kantstudien* a long essay on his find,[57] a promise not fulfilled. But the *Origine de l'univers* deserves much more than the comments of Erich Adickes, who having been given access to Schumann's copy inserted a long footnote at the last minute to his monograph on Kant the scientist.[58] Adickes clearly missed the crucial point by stating that Estève anticipated Kant inasmuch as he traced the formation of the universe to the primordial homogeneous matter subject to the forces of attraction and elasticity. The crucial point was the slight asymmetry mentioned above. As to the rest of Adickes' comments, they showed him caught in inconsistencies owing to his bias for Kant. Clearly, a detailed comparison between Kant and Estève would have been in order if the *Origine de l'univers* showed its author as a "thinker, interesting in many ways, though never rising above the average." Adickes, for whom the chief instructiveness of Estève's book was that it served as a contrast to Kant's genius, failed to see the irony in the fact that the author of the *Allgemeine Naturgeschichte* perfectly fitted his description of Estève as a thinker who "on occasion hits upon a good idea but cannot do the right thing with it, because he is unable to give the new idea the necessary scientific form and foundation whereby it can obtain proper status and effectiveness."

Had Adickes shown for Estève the measure of objectivity proper for a historian, the *Origine de l'univers* would not have remained buried in oblivion for another half century, a period marked with a sudden rise of interest in the history of science and in its source materials. Part of that interest is the realization that Wright's, Lambert's and Kant's insights about the Milky Way retain their significance even though they were unknown to Herschel, the one who effectively put the Milky Way and nebulae on the map of science. Consequently, Estève's theory of the origin of the solar system has an interest of its own which should seem particularly relevant in connection with Kant. Even apart from Kant, the starting phrase of Estève's book "the revolution which took place in these last centuries in physics, has served to unveil the laws by which the universe maintains itself," will strike modern minds preoccupied with scientific revolutions as a gem of no small value.[58] For a student of the *Allgemeine Naturgeschichte* no less striking will appear Estève's preface, in which he speaks of the unalterable law (attraction) of matter of which all its forms are a consequence of that law, heaps encomiums on Newton, and comes to grip with the dilemma of Providence versus mechanism.

Estève's work ("of very low scientific, or rather unscientific level" in Adickes' estimate) was in at least one sense far more scientific than the *Allgemeine Naturgeschichte*. Unlike the latter, it did not come to a close with speculations on planetary denizens (a topic eschewed by Estève),[60] but by an appendix containing a mathematical analysis of the figure to be taken by a rotating fluid mass under the influence of gravitation. As in the *Allgemeine Naturgeschichte*, there is no mathematics in the three books comprising Estève's work, of which the first is devoted to attraction as a force inherent in matter as its principle of motion. The second book is devoted to the formation of worlds (planetary systems) in virtue of that principle, whereas the third deals with some peculiarities of such systems, and especially of ours. Printed in a format smaller than the *Allgemeine Naturgeschichte*, the 246 pages of Estève's work contain about one half as much text and are narrower in scope. Estève sees no system in the infinite expanse of the realm of stars, each of which he takes for a sun with planets around it. His sole reference to the Milky Way portrays it as a "swarm of stars very close to one another."[61] The large number of stars shown by telescope in the Pleiades does not move him to mention the nebulae, or rather nebulous stars. The universe of Estève is the solar system inasmuch as he fails to consider the effect of attraction among stars.[62] This is not to suggest that his statements about attraction are always trivial.

24

He supports, for instance, the corpuscular notion of light by attributing the bending (diffraction) of light rays around a column to the latter's attraction.[63] The idea that light rays may be bent when passing close by a star did not occur to him.

In the second book Estève starts with the question of the succession of forms, which he illustrates by the successive combination of letters into a large number of words.[64] His is, however, an ambivalent position concerning evolution: on the one hand he claims the fixity of germs both for living and non-living forms, on the other hand he asserts the formation of those germs from homogeneous matter under the impact of attraction. "The world could not be produced by one stroke such as it is. There was necessary a particular formation for each of the smallest particles which compose a celestial body."[65] These smallest particles compose the atoms, which are of the most diverse forms, but combine into pyramids[66] which, following their collision, rebound in all possible directions. There arise therefore small aggregations rushing in various directions, a result in which Estève sees the rudiments of projectile motion directed at an angle from the line leading to the center.[67]

This sidewise motion will be obtained, Estève warns, only by some particles. The rest will gather in the center, forming the sun. In the major centres of the matter orbiting around the sun there arise the planets and satellites, which, according to Estève, comprise 1/450th of the sun's mass.[68] His explanation of the sun's light is mechanical though tainted with recourse to Descartes' subtle matter. The formation of atmospheres is traced by Estève to the arrangement of lighter particles in layers according to their specific density.[69] Estève offers a special chapter on the rotation of celestial bodies which starts with the remark that by completing its orbit around the sun, a planet does in effect turn once around its axis. But what about, say, the 365 revolutions of the earth while going around the sun only once? According to Estève the light emanating from the sun makes the planet or rather its atmosphere, collide with the interplanetary material beyond its orbit and this collision accelerates its period of rotation which originally is as long as its period of orbiting.[70] Since this action of the sun's light is transmitted on the planet's body in proportion to the density of its atmosphere, a celestial body without atmosphere, like the moon, will not have its original rotation increased.[71] Another factor, which may cause the acceleration of a planet's rotation, is the tidal effect of its satellites on its atmosphere and ocean. Such is Estève's explanation of the relatively fast rotation of Jupiter with four satellites.

After discussing the physical evolution of the earth, Estève turns to the origin of the comets' tails and of nebulous stars. Concerning the former, he relies on their close approach to the sun. As to the latter, he takes them for suns with enormously thick atmosphere which dampens their light. He most emphatically discards the idea that they may be, as the Milky Way, a heap of small stars.[72] They are for him rather one single nebulous body. For Derham's view of nebulous stars as openings into the empyrean heavens, Estève has no sympathy whatever. The last chapter of the second book deals with the possibility of the collision of a comet with a planet, a process with various results, among them the turning of a planet into a comet. The same chapter also contains an endorsement of Maupertuis' explanation of Saturn's ring.[73] The conclusion of that chapter and of the second book is a statement that the theory given above explains the formation of the universe on the basis of the law of physics (attraction) and not by a recourse to a hand (God's) which either dispenses that law or interferes with it incessantly.[74] Such is an advance beyond the Newtonians who content themselves with explaining only the actual movements of the celestial bodies but not their formation. Not only does Estève find the idea of some Newtonians about the instantaneous creation of the universe in its present form to be incompatible with the law of gravitation, but he also holds high the notion of a Creator who chooses that law and lets its potentialities unfold gradually: "Such a Creative Being would act in the shortest, noblest, and most sublime manner."[75]

Philosophical reflections of this kind will recur at far greater lengths in the *Allgemeine Naturgeschichte*. Its author did not have to borrow them from the *Origine de l'univers*, tantalizing as this possibility may appear. Kant was certainly enough of a thinker to sense the currents along which ideas were to develop. He was more than receptive to a specific impulse. In metaphysics, his reading of Hume is a case in point. The rest was done by his irresistible bent on system making, a most needed, a most satisfying, but also a most dangerous enterprise. In science, or rather cosmogony, Kant's was a similar story. Estève may have been an impulse for Kant. Wright certainly was, and so were Maupertuis and Buffon. The rest was Kant's making and, for those who see beneath the glitter of sweeping systems, also the unmasking of his true mental physiognomy.

III. *Kant the Cosmogonist*

Wright's *Original Theory* was reviewed in 1752 in the prominent *Gentleman's Magazine* where it was pointed out that stars confined within a spherical shell would not produce the visual appearance of the Milky Way.[1] After that the silence on Wright's book was well-nigh complete in England for almost a century.[2] Its German summary, which appeared in 1751 in the *Freye Urtheile*, a Hamburg semiweekly,[3] struck, however, a resonating chord in one of its readers, Immanuel Kant, a native of Königsberg where he completed his university studies in 1744, at the age of twenty. During the next two years he worked on his first book, a discussion of kinetic forces,[4] but his father's death in 1746 forced him to earn his living as a family tutor for the next seven years. His third post was with the family of Count Kayserling near Königsberg. Both the Count and his wife were highly cultured and their company, together with their library, was undoubtedly helpful for Kant whose great ambition was the chair of philosophy at the University of Königsberg.

First, he had to become privatdozent, which he achieved by taking the degree of magister in July 1755 with a dissertation on the nature and properties of fire and by defending in September of the same year an essay, "A New Explanation of the First Principles of Metaphysical Knowledge."[5] But by then he had failed in the principal part of his strategy for a rapid rise on the academic ladder. No sooner had his *Allgemeine Naturgeschichte* been published anonymously in March than its publisher went bankrupt and all his holdings, including most copies of the *Allgemeine Naturgeschichte*, were impounded, as reported from a distance of half a century by Ludwig Ernst Borowski, one of Kant's first three biographers.[6] Only a few copies of the original edition[7] exist now and this has almost invariably been explained by that legal calamity.[8] But a year later the *Allgemeine Naturgeschichte* was put on sale in Königsberg by a local printer and with clear reference to its author's name.[9] The move could hardly secure wide distribution for the book, most copies of which seem to have been condemned to decay by mould, dust, and worms in the new owner's warehouse. Problems relating to ownership may have been a reason that in spite of his friends' urging Kant did not bring out the book in a new edition some years later.[10] Meanwhile Kant could only regret that Frederick the Great, to whom the book was dedicated, did not learn of it, as was dolefully recalled by Borowski[11] who did not consider the possibility that the king, perhaps on advice, did not find the book worthy of attention. At any rate, to continue with Borowski, Kant did not succeed in his strategy that "under the authority of the king closer investigation of his system would be done by the learned in [the Academy of] Berlin and in other places,"[12] in the hope of obtaining a suitable appointment at the university of his native town. When ten years later the Berlin authorities began to promote Kant at Königsberg no reference whatever was made to the *Allgemeine Naturgeschichte*.[13]

Whether such scientists as Maupertuis, Euler, and others in Berlin would have been impressed by the *Allgemeine Naturgeschichte* is another question. To be sure, both Maupertuis and Euler wrote cosmological treatises free of mathematics for the benefit of a general audience,[14] but behind these treatises lay their authors' mastery of Newtonian physics. Euler and others would have immediately recognized that Kant's overt claim of being the Newton of the physical part of cosmology was a hollow boast. That Kant had no mastery of some basic laws of Newtonian physics can, of course, but shock those who have taken for verity the long established cliché that Kant had been well instructed in Newton's *Principia*, and even in the Leibniz-Newton controversy, by Martin Knutzen and Johann Gottfried Teske, professors at Königsberg.[15]

The original version of that cliché was penned by Borowski, one of the first students who attached themselves to Kant when he started his lectures as privatdozent in his own lodgings. In 1782, after twenty years of absence, Borowski, then a high-ranking dignitary of the Lutheran Church, returned to Königsberg and resumed contacts with Kant. His admiration for his former teacher resulted in a brief biographical sketch of Kant, the manuscript of which was submitted to him for approval in 1792. To that sketch Borowski added after Kant's death another section which included a passage dealing with Kant's turning, early in his university studies, "from the flowering field of humanities to the dry steppes of philosophy." For this turn two professors, Knutzen and Teske, were, according to Borowski, responsible: "Their lectures in philosophy, physics, and mathematics, which were really excellent, stimulating for the genius, and very entertaining (there are still many fellow students of mine who gratefully remember Teske), attracted Kant very much. Knutzen, a good judge of brains, found in him excellent disposition, encouraged him in private conversations, lent him subsequently Newton's works in particular and, since Kant found them to his taste, everything else that he requested from his [teacher's] richly stacked library. Thus was Kant initiated into the study [of a subject] in which he soon surpassed his teacher. Knutzen lived to see that the young tree, which he had planted and gently attended, brought forth fruits which were to produce astonishment: already four years after [Kant's] entry to the university, our fully trained [Kant] began to work [on an essay] on the evaluation of living forces. One would read with profit for the illustration of what I said here the preface of the aforesaid writing. From now on [the study of] philosophy, mathematics, and especially astronomy, in which his hypotheses, already proposed [by him] in 1755, were confirmed by Herschel, were all his life always very close to his heart."[16]

The effusive tone of this passage and what follows it—an encomium of Kant's versatility in chemistry, anthropology, physical geography, political science, classical and modern literature—suggest that this is not a sober evaluation but a legendary account to which Kant himself contributed by an affectation of modesty which, revealingly enough, could not stand differences of opinion.[17] After his circle of admirers in Königsberg began to look on him as a prophetic forerunner of Herschel, he could easily qualify, for instance, his statement that his achievements and those of Newton were the same, by adding that the smallness of the former and the greatness of the latter ought not to be forgotten.[18] One wonders, however, whether Kant would have protested had he read Borowski's statement that "philosophy *and mathematics* were the two fields which provided the main readings" of Kant in his later years (italics added).[19] Typically, while Borowski mentioned Hume and Rousseau (no friends of mathematics) as Kant's favorite philosophical authors, he named no mathematicians. As to Knutzen, Borowski may have been right that he was an inspiring teacher, but whether he was an expert in physics and in Newton is another matter. Benno Erdmann, whose hundred-year-old but well-researched biography of Knutzen is still the principal source on him, felt impelled to speak of the "little competent" Borowski insofar as Kant's learning from Knutzen physics and mathematics was concerned.[20] Erdmann spared Borowski from a well-deserved stricture after providing evidence that Kant had, for good reasons, a very low opinion of Teske.[21] Knutzen, who died in 1751 at the age of thirty-eight, and was Kant's senior only by eleven years, was professor extraordinarius of logic and metaphysics. As was the general custom of those times, Knutzen too gave courses in many fields, a custom suggesting their superficiality. According to the catalogues of the university, between 1740, when Kant entered the university, and 1747, when Kant left Königsberg to serve as family tutor, Knutzen lectured—in addition of giving the regular philosophical curriculum—in rational psychology, natural philosophy, ethics, law, rhetoric, mnemonics, and "doctrine of errors."[22] He also gave courses in mathematics, algebra and analysis.[23] The low level of those courses may be surmised from the fact that in 1744, for instance, Knutzen's teaching load amounted to six hours a day.[24] The haphazard way in which mathematics and physics were taught in Königsberg even a quarter of a century later is suggested by the roundabout way in which Kant became professor of logic and metaphysics in 1770. The chair of mathematics having become vacant in that year, it was offered to Kant, but since F. J. Buck, professor of logic and metaphysics (and no more competent than Kant in mathematics), opted for it, Kant took Buck's chair.[25]

As to Knutzen, he may have been a polyhistorian genius, but his published works indicate that he was no mathematical physicist. Most of his publications were in ethics and metaphysics. Of his few scientific publications Erdmann found worthy of mention only a smallish treatise on the famed comet of 1743 with six tails, about which he pointedly noted that it contained no mathematical details, not even a computation of the orbit and period of the comet,[26] a very poor performance when judged in the light of the many truly scientific works that had been published since Newton's *Principia* on cometary orbits.[27] If one adds to this the repeated assertions of Adickes that science courses, which the university of Königsberg offered around the middle of the eighteenth century, did not exceed the level of courses in the upper classes of German gymnasia a hundred or so years later,[28] the true merits of the cliché originated by Borowski will be immediately apparent. It is indeed safer to say, especially if one keeps in mind the science of Kant's cosmogony, that what Kant learned from Knutzen was above all a carefully nurtured illusion that being enthusiastic about Newton's physics amounted to an expertise in it. Kant clearly was carried away by his enthusiasm as he declared at the outset that his account of the mechanism of the evolution of the system of planets could, if needed, be presented with all the pomp inherent in the mathematical method.[29] The declaration would certainly not prevent the reader from thinking that Kant himself could handle the task. But in matters of mathematical physics Kant had always been a mere dilettante, though his dilettantism did not lack the happy glimpses of a bold vision, a remark repeatedly made by Adickes.[30] Such a combination benefited cosmogony with a few fortunate though not always original insights and burdened it with a discourse which, apart from a few pages, was long-winded, repetitious, hastily composed, poorly documented, and most likely not proofread. Hardly an advantage was the book's pagination. The regularly numbered pages (1–200) were preceded by six pages marked in Roman numerals (I–VI) and these in turn by 58 pages incompletely marked by signatures, or a total of 264 pages.

Among Kant's happy insights was his explanation of the hue and shape of the Milky Way. The explanation followed naturally if the Milky Way was taken for a congeries of an enormous number of stars confined within a flat disk. Kant, in fact, found the explanation so natural that he marvelled why it had not been proposed long before,[31] that is, long before it was set forth in Wright's *Original Theory*. Its summary in the *Freye Urtheile*, he acknowledged, led him to regard the fixed stars as a system, and he also credited Wright with having made the first happy step toward seeing a systematic constitution in the universe. Yet, Kant also claimed to himself the glory of a co-discoverer, although he noted that he was unable to see the exact differences between his and Wright's notion of the Milky Way.[32] He certainly overlooked the fact that Wright, even according to the German summary of his work, proposed not only a disk theory but also a spherical shell theory of the Milky Way. Kant's confident assertion that nebulous stars, precisely because of the explanation by Maupertuis (whom he called a "philosopher of more enlightened views"[33]) of their varied shapes, were so many Milky Ways, was another fortunate insight of his. Unlike his notion of the Milky Way, it was still largely a guess,[34] and no different was the case with his claim, already voiced by Wright, that stars must be in orbital motion around the center of the Milky Way. In both cases Kant held out the hope of future observational verification.

Kant's insistence that natural philosophy must not cease searching for a scientific, that is, mechanistic explanation of all features of the physical universe was certainly commendable, but Descartes had long made that insistance a commonplace. Again, he was preceded by Buffon, to recall only the most prominent case, in courageously dissenting from the authority of Newton who attributed several features of the solar system and of the universe to God's direct intervention and hampered thereby the development of a scientific cosmogony. Rhetorics rather than ability marked his effort to restore respectability to the Cartesian motto, "Give me matter and I will construct the universe."[35] Wisely enough, Kant departed from Descartes, for whom animals were automata,[36] by noting that the realm of the living, be it a caterpillar or a blade of grass, was not yet a topic for mechanistic science.[37]

The insistance that scientific cosmology, or cosmogony, is to claim to itself all parts and features of the universe, is not enough to assure credibility to any specific cosmogonical theory. In spite of the enormous successes achieved in cosmogony during the last decades,[38] even the most modern and sophisticated theories of cosmogony are so many illustrations of this point. Kant's cosmogony had only a few apparent successes. No wonder. The tools which Kant used were either primitive or contrived. True, by the mid-eighteenth century reference to attraction or gravitation was far from being primitive, but the repulsive force, which Kant postulated to be universally active only in the primordial distribution of matter and the surviving evidences of which he saw "in the elasticity of vapours, the effluences of strongly smelling bodies, and the diffusion of all spirituous matter,"[39] was another question. There was something distinctly primitive in the manner in which Kant staked on the principle of least resistance two pivotal points of his cosmogony. One was the gradual transformation of the initially linear onrush of particles toward a center first into elliptical and later into circular motions and in much the same plane around that center. The other was the same direction of all these motions in complete analogy with the motion of planets around the sun.

Kant's derivation of systems of primordial linear motions is a little remembered but pivotal and certainly very contrived part of his cosmogony. It relates to his concept of the original distribution of matter at the moment of creation. He presented that distribution in almost quantitative specifics with respect to the solar system, but only in studied vagueness insofar as the whole universe was concerned. Matter, according to Kant, existed from the beginning in an unlimited number of kinds of elements, all atomistic in their constitution, but differing with respect to density. He seemed to believe (a belief related to the assumption of some form of primordial homogeneity) that all their kinds existed in the same amount.[40] This meant that particles or atoms or elements of greater density or specific weight were originally located much farther from one another than particles of elements of lesser specific weight. This was for him the original of "simplest state" of matter, or the "simplest chaos."[41] It was through that carefully contrived "simplicity" that he tried to avoid falling into the errors of Epicurean cosmogony. Already within the space occupied now by the solar system, that is, from the center of the sun to half of its distance to the neighboring stars, the density in question varied within enormous limits which Kant illustrated by the difference between the radius of the planetary system and the thousandth part of a line.[42]

It was this carefully contrived primordial arrangement of particles of greatly varying density which secured in Kant's eyes the immediate gravitation of all particles composing the future solar system toward the densest one located where the center of the sun was to be. This very arrangement of particles could easily appear to be equivalent to a distribution of matter, in which every particle was surrounded by the same amount of matter in every direction and had therefore to be in a gravitationally stable equilibrium. Kant did not consider this implication of his apparently non-homogeneous distribution of matter. Nor did he face up in this connection to the problems created by his emphatic assertions that the universe contained in its infinite expanse an infinite amount of matter hierarchically organized.[43] This hierarchical organization presupposed particles of incomparably higher density than the density of particles which served as the nuclei of stars. Kant not only spoke of an enormous fiery body in the center of the Milky Way, a body which he took for Sirius.[44] He also spoke of central bodies of systems more encompassing than the Milky Way, nay of the central body of the entire universe,[45] bodies needed to keep their systems in dynamical stability. In terms of the cosmogony of Kant, for whom the universe was infinite, the nucleus of the central body of the entire universe had to be of infinite density, or if not, it had to possess an infinite mass, points which Kant sidestepped with convenient recourse to the words enormous and immense.[46]

His few tentative encounters with the problems of an infinite universe were a distinct muddle. While he acknowledged that no central point could be specified in infinite homogeneous space, he suggested that the point, where the cosmic evolution started, could naturally be taken for such a point. The impossibility of a central point on the mathematical level of infinity was not a problem, he noted with affectation of profundity, on the physical level.[47] He derided those who opposed the notion of an infinite universe with reference to the impossibility of an actually realized infinite quantity.[48] He only exposed the shallowness of his reasoning with his two counter arguments. In one of them he took eternity (a presumed part of his opponents' religious belief) for a succession of an infinite number of instants, in the other he merely took refuge behind the protective cover of the jargon of mathematics. The cover was the expression "differential," that is, infinitesimal magnitude, with which he would, in due course, refute the alleged impossibility of an actually realized infinite number.[49] He never fulfilled that promise.

A careful look at the question of infinity could hardly be expected from Kant, who several years earlier insisted that God must realize universes not only with three dimensions but also with all other conceivable numbers of dimensions.[50] The insistance was not a brilliant anticipation of non-Euclidean geometries and worlds but a reflection on his rationalist theology and on his lack of rigor in reasoning. Now he was dictating to God to produce an infinite three-dimensional universe which, once created in its "simplest" condition, would turn into a spectacle of worlds rising, decaying, and rising anew for an infinite stretch of future aeons. This notion of the universe as a perpetuum mobile foreshadowed Kant's gradual shifting into pantheism,[51] and also illustrated the role which one's ultimate presuppositions (be it a professed agnosticism) play in theorizing about the cosmos. Kant's a priori postulating an infinite universe obviously had a role in trapping him in the inconsistency of assigning our position in the universe both somewhere near its center and somewhere in a ring of space with fully formed worlds located between two rings where everything was in a chaos, a place which could obviously be at any distance from that center.[52] The universe conjured up in the *Allgemeine*

Naturgeschichte could best be represented by a series of concentric waves or rings of which the "crests" were the regions of fully formed worlds, whereas its "troughs" were the regions of chaos, succeeding one another like a treadmill, hardly the symbol of perfection. Such was the Kantian result of the Kantian a priori precept that the infinite perfection of God must evidence itself in an infinite creation.

The precept was part of an inarticulate teleology which ran through the entire *Allgemeine Naturgeschichte*. On the one hand it forced Kant to populate all the planets with denizens appropriate to the physical characteristics of each planet, a task which Kant executed with unabashed relish. On the other hand it made him bog down in the process of substituting mere mechanism for the optimistic and anthropocentric teleology advocated by Leibniz and Wolff and the innumerable followers they had around the turn of the century. That teleology implied the idea of special arrangements throughout nature for the benefit of man, arrangements about which Kant could easily show either that they were not special at all from the viewpoint of mechanical science, or that the Leibnizians and Wolffians were still to explain why the same arrangements did not exist on other planets though they believed them to be as populated as was the earth.[53] The substitution by Kant of mechanism for teleology was part of his effort to explain everything mechanically. It also made him claim that the mechanistic formation of the universe was proved by its ubiquitous slight deviations from geometrical perfection, a perfection which would have been the necessary hallmark of the universe had God's hand been directly at work in all its details and not through the mediation of mechanical laws.[54] A naive distinction, to be sure, between "perfect" and "imperfect" geometrical configurations, which revealed Kant's inability to see that if Newtonian mechanics ruled in the universe, the interaction among any and all its parts must be perfectly exact. "Imperfect" configurations were not the result of the laws of mechanics. They could arise only if the elementary particles created by God were either asymmetrical or asymmetrically placed with respect to one another, a point which Kant failed to perceive as he mixed his theology with his science, both rather second-rate.

As to Kant's account of the mechanical explanation of the main parts and features of the planetary system, it certainly exemplifies the maxim that the more faulty is a theory, the more space is demanded by a critical survey of it. Such a survey is not necessary for those familiar with the still unsolved problems presented by our system of planets. Those unfamiliar with those problems and/or convinced of the greatness of Kant, the cosmogonist, will undoubtedly remain unconvinced by such a survey, however detailed. It is not for them that critical remarks about Kant's theory of the evolution of the system of planets are offered in the notes to the text. Unfortunately, the patently obscurantist pages of the *Opus postumum*[55] are not yet available for the English reader, although it is to be kept in mind that the various printings of the German original failed for the most part to open the eyes of latter-day Kantians. They usually excuse the *Opus postumum* with a reference to Kant's old age, although only in his last or eightieth year was Kant beset with a notable weakening of his physical and mental powers.[56] The excuse certainly fails to apply to the seventy-year-old Kant, who at the height of his fame, was still active in publishing. It was that Kant who produced in 1794 an essay on the influence of the moon on weather on the earth. The hairsplitting distinctions and the thesis-antithesis-synthesis structure that set the tone of this essay indicate the kind of science that was genuinely Kantian, that is, uncritical, his endless references to critical reasoning notwithstanding. For was there any trace of critical reason in Kant's asserting that epidemics in Bengal were evidently influenced by eclipses of the moon?[57]

The most telling indication of the basically unscientific character of Kant's cosmogony and in particular of his theory of the evolution of the planetary system, lies in the fact that it had been ignored by German scientists for a full century. This is all the more revealing as a summary by Kant of his cosmogony, which will be discussed below, had been made repeatedly available in print since 1763. Moreover, four editions of the *Allgemeine Naturgeschichte* saw print during his last ten years, the very years which echoed with news about Herschel's observations of thousands of nebulae and his study of the structure of the Milky Way. What is usually reported about those years in studies on Kant is the acclaim accorded to him as a forerunner of Herschel. In his philosophical "principate" he was certainly seen in that light. But even then there was another side to the story, part of a larger and mostly ignored story, the topic of the next section.

IV. A Century of Silence

Most copies of the *Allgemeine Naturgeschichte* were already in danger of never reaching the public when a review of it appeared in the July 15, 1755, issue of the *Freye Urtheile*, the journal which four years earlier sparked Kant's speculations in cosmology with its summary of Wright's *Original Theory*. The review started with the words: "The unknown learned author ventures into a field where, for good reasons, little can be proven, but where one must be satisfied with probabilities; and these he had certainly raised to the highest level. A few [ideas]

35

he has in common with his predecessors; but we must attribute to him most [of what he says]." In the review, special note was made of the fact that from Kant's hypothesis one could derive the period of the revolution of Saturn. The reviewer was astonished by Kant's claim that all stars moved around a central point, but apart from this he gave a matter-of-fact account of all major parts of the book, even of Kant's discourse on the denizens of planets. After noting that according to Kant the inhabitants of the earth and Mars were in the middle between two extremes—the utter stupidity of the denizens of the lower planets and the extreme ingenuity of those of the higher planets—the reviewer concluded: "The author proceeds everywhere very cautiously and never goes beyond the limits of hypotheses. He leaves everything to the judgment of the perceptive reader. In the preface he defends himself against the objections of clergymen: God [Kant argues] is no less admirable when he makes so perfect a matter which of its essence must produce such changes that are in harmony for a common purpose. The style is lively and spirited; and the author has the skill to present with ease the most difficult astronomical propositions. Therefore we recommend this book to all our readers who love ideas of this kind and are able to judge them."[1]

Since a copy of Kant's book reached the *Freye Urtheile*, it is most likely that another was at the same time also sent to the *Göttingische Anzeigen von gelehrten Sachen*, a biweekly of far greater importance, and even more devoted to a full coverage of the latest learned publications. No word came from Göttingen, or from Berlin for that matter. The silence on the *Allgemeine Naturgeschichte* had to be broken by Kant himself and in words which clearly showed his feelings about the lack of notice. In 1763 Kant published a critical investigation of the proofs of the existence of God under the title, *Der einzig mögliche Beweisgrund zu einer Demonstration des Daseyns Gottes*, or "the only possible argument for a demonstration of the existence of God."[2] There he rejected not only the cosmological argument but also the view which he had repeatedly and emphatically endorsed in the *Allgemeine Naturgeschichte*, namely, that the harmonious coordination of the various parts of the universe does prove the existence of God. If such was the case, then Kant should have spared the reader a relatively long section of his book,[3] an outline of the order of the universe arising from mechanistic processes. The outline was a summary of his *Allgemeine Naturgeschichte* which Kant clearly tried to rescue from oblivion in this roundabout way. That some such factors were at play transpires from the concluding paragraph of the preface and the long footnote appended to it. The footnote followed a sentence in which Kant made a pointed reference to the *Allgemeine Naturgeschichte* and to its "daring hypothesis," which, as he remarked, would not please those interested only in metaphysics. Clearly, Kant hoped to resuscitate at least in an indirect way the *Allgemeine Naturgeschichte* as can be further seen from the footnote itself in which he complained that the book obviously "had not even come to the knowledge of the famous Mr. J. H. Lambert, who six years afterwards, in 1761, proposed in his *Cosmologische Briefe* about the systematic conception of the universe at large, about the Milky Way, about the nebulae, exactly the same theory which can be found in my above-mentioned theory of the heavens ... The agreement of the ideas of that brilliant man with those which I had then proposed and which match even in smaller details, increases my confidence that this essay in the future will find further confirmation."[4]

Kant's complaint that not even "the famous Lambert" learned about the *Allgemeine Naturgeschichte* suggests that he was hardly comforted by what he saw in a book by Sebastian Friedrich Trescho, a young Lutheran minister, which was published almost exactly the same time, toward the end of 1762, as was Kant's book on the proofs of the existence of God, and by the same publisher. Trescho's book, a series of "amusements at the cost of nature in a few summer hours," was a conversational portrayal of nature's purposefulness as evidence of God's existence in that teleological framework which Kant had already disavowed in the *Allgemeine Naturgeschichte*. Kant's name was mentioned in the outline of the "hours" but not in connection with his speculations on the physical qualities of Jupiter's inhabitants, although they were reproduced almost verbatim in the fourth "hour" of Trescho's book. Those speculations, Trescho noted, departed from the opinion of Wolff and others who pictured Jupiter's inhabitants as so many giants of gross bodily composition. In the sixth "hour" Trescho elaborated the popular view that lately the weather had notably deteriorated, an indication, together with the more frequent occurrence of earthquakes and floods, that "the earth must gradually come to an end, just as an old lady ceases, in the course of years, to bear children." As a confirmation, Trescho recalled the portrayal by a "sound philosopher" (Kant) of the decay of celestial bodies and their systems.[5] Shortly afterwards, in early 1763, the publisher, who brought out Kant's work on the proofs of the existence of God, printed a criticism of it by Daniel Weymann, who had in 1759 obtained the degree of magister from the University of Königsberg with a dissertation against Leibnizian optimism. In his criticism Weymann did not refer to Kant's cosmogony at all, perhaps because he did not discuss Kant's work step by step. But a rejection of that cosmogony could seem implied in Weymann's insistence that the sole form, accepted by Kant, of demonstrating God's existence, led to the idea of a necessary eternal being not really different from Spinoza's eternal world or from Epicurus' eternal atoms.[6]

As to Lambert, he proposed a theory of the Milky Way, of nebulae, and of systems of Milky Ways, in a few respects very similar to the one in the *Allgemeine Naturgeschichte*, although years later Kant insisted, as will be seen shortly, that Lambert had no clear idea about the true nature of nebulous stars already observed. In many a respect the differences were substantial. Most importantly, Lambert's universe was strictly finite and non-evolutionary. Kant could not be unaware of this, but he must have before long felt that his effort to call attention to his stillborn *Allgemeine Naturgeschichte* was not entirely in vain. The one who took notice was none other than Lambert, yet even he did not go as far as to mention the *Allgemeine Naturgeschichte* in print, prolific author though he was. Lambert's comment on the *Allgemeine Naturgeschichte* was part of a letter of his to Kant, a letter which started a well-known correspondence between the two. Written on November 13, 1765, the letter was the result of Lambert's desire to get in touch with Kant ever since a copy of the *Einzig mögliche Beweisgrund* was shown to him in 1764 by J. G. Sulzer, one of the chief architects of the strategy aimed at overcoming Frederick the Great's reluctance to appoint Lambert a member of the Berlin Academy. A year later, when a certain "Professor and Preacher Reccard," whom Lambert described in the letter as one "who was born for astronomy and finds his satisfaction in the depths of the firmament," was to travel from Berlin to Königsberg, Lambert saw the proper moment to be at hand. The main part of his letter started as follows: "A few years ago Professor Sulzer showed me your *Einigen* [sic] *möglichen Beweis von der Existenz Gottes*. I found in it my thoughts and selection of materials and expressions, and reached in advance the conclusion that when my *Organon* should reach you, Sir, you would in a similar way find yourself expressed in most parts." After several paragraphs, partly devoted to the similarity between his and Kant's ideas, Lambert turned to the sensitive issue: "I can with assurance say to you, Sir, that your ideas about the world-edifice, which you mention in the preface of the *Einigen* [sic] *möglichen Beweis* etc., have not come to my notice until now [last year]. What is related in the *Cosmologische Briefe* on p. 149 goes back to the year 1749. Contrary to my habits then, I went into my room after the evening meal, and looked through the window at the stellar sky and especially at the Milky Way. The insight, which I had then, to see it as an ecliptic of the fixed stars, I wrote down on a quarto page and that was all that I had as a written note before me, in much the same way as I am writing this letter [on a quarto page]. In 1761 somebody from Nürnberg told me that a few years earlier an Englishman had put similar thoughts in print in form of letters to other Englishmen, but the time not being ripe, the translation begun in Nürnberg was not completed. I replied that the *Cosmologische Briefe* will make no impact until an astronomer shall discover something in the sky . . ."[7] This last remark was no less appropriate about the *Allgemeine Naturgeschichte*.

Strangely enough, the *Allgemeine Naturgeschichte* was not mentioned in Kant's reply to Lambert. Kant rather informed Lambert about his collecting material on the metaphysical bases of natural science, a book which became published only two decades later.[8] Lambert in turn did not ask Kant to send him a copy of the *Allgemeine Naturgeschichte*, although he tried to obtain one for himself. In his letter of October 1, 1768, to G. L. Le Sage, Lambert mentioned that he was unable to purchase through booksellers in Berlin a copy of the book which had already been shown to him.[9] A copy or two of the *Allgemeine Naturgeschichte* must have therefore reached Berlin several years earlier, but though it may have circulated among a few of the learned, it produced no comment. Neither in that letter to Le Sage, nor elsewhere did Lambert care to comment on the contents of the *Allgemeine Naturgeschichte*. That he found meritorious in it only the explanation of the Milky Way may be gathered from the brief reference to Kant in the third edition of a popular treatise on astronomy published in 1777 by Johann Elert Bode, Lambert's former assistant.[10] A year later a similar reference to Kant appeared in Bode's more technical treatise on astronomy.[11] The reference consisted in Bode's adding Kant's name to that of Lambert as the ones who wrote of the constitution of the universe with a sublimity worthy of the Creator's wisdom. The context was Bode's account of the realm of stars as confined within a lentil-shaped space. This reference to Kant reappeared in further editions of both works,[12] of which the popular treatise was the most widely read astronomical work in Germany until the middle of the nineteenth century. But Bode, who died in 1826, never cared to mention Kant's theory of the evolution of the solar system, of galaxies, supergalaxies and of the entire universe. He may have inherited from Lambert, to whom he owed his career, a distaste for evolutionary views, but he may just as well have been advised by Lambert about the amateurism of Kant's cosmogony.

Quite similar reasons may have been at play in *Anfangsgründe der Naturlehre*, a textbook on general science destined for wide use in Germany, which Johann Christoph Polykarp Erxleben, professor in Göttingen, first published in 1772. He justified with a reference to Wright's *Original Theory* the claim that all stars may be found equidistant from one another if seen from a proper vantage point.[13] Kant was not mentioned as Erxleben spoke of the Milky Way as a system of stars, about which he did not care to be as specific as to indicate its disk-shaped form. He, however, praised Lambert's grandiose ideas without specifying them.[14] The *Anfangsgründe der Naturlehre*, whose author died in 1777 at the age of thirty-three, was seen through six editions (from third to eighth between 1784 and 1796) by Georg Christoph Lichtenberg, also professor in Göttingen, but only from the fourth (1787) edition on did Lichtenberg care to refer briefly to the *Allgemeine Naturgeschichte* and only on a point about which until then only Wright's *Original Theory* was mentioned as a source.[15] In the sixth (1794) edition of the *Anfangsgründe* Kant's priority over Lambert concerning the Milky Way was acknowledged.[16] The reason for this seems to be the publication in 1791 in the *Astronomisches Jahrbuch* by Bode, its editor, of a letter which Kant wrote to Bode on September 2, 1790. The letter was occasioned by Kant's reading in a newspaper of Herschel's observation of the period of rotation of Saturn's ring. Kant called Bode's attention to p. 87 of the *Allgemeine Naturgeschichte* and added: "Even Mr. Herschel's way of presentation concerning the nebulous stars as systems in themselves matches favorably the one which I then put forward on pp. 14, 15 of the aforementioned work, and it must have been a slip of memory on the part of the late Erxleben that in his physics [*Anfangsgründe*] he ascribes that thought to the late Lambert as the one who first had it, although his *Cosmologische Briefe* came out 6 years later than my writing [*Allgemeine Naturgeschichte*], and that I cannot find myself [mentioned] after all search in [connection with] any such presentation."[17]

What makes this letter of Kant truly revealing is that he failed to complain to Bode that although in the numerous editions of Erxleben's work there was a detailed account of the cosmogonical theories of Descartes, Burnet, Whiston, Leibniz, Waller, de Luc, and even of some now completely forgotten authors, no reference to the cosmogony of the *Allgemeine Naturgeschichte* was ever made in the *Anfangsgründe* either by Erxleben or by Lichtenberg.[18] Actually, Kant was not entitled to complain on that score. No sooner had he been appointed a dozent in 1756 than he had announced a course in physical geography and by 1760 his lecture-notes reached a practically final form which he dictated to his class each year until 1795.[19] That he made relatively few annotations over three decades to those notes[20] attested the ever-present aprioristic strain in his thinking. Of course, it is true, as he insisted in the introductory chapters of his course, that ideas and general overviews are indispensable for a proper digesting and arranging of data.[21] But too much confidence in one's ideas could lead to affect adversely one's attitude toward data, a case tellingly illustrated by his stubborn refusal to accept some data about Bavaria that did not fit his preconceptions.[22] After predicting that Napoleon was, for geopolitical reasons, to land his troops in Portugal, he decried news about their landing in Egypt as a journalistic hoax.[23] For forty years he confidently lectured about distant lands, the depths of oceans, the heights of mountains and atmosphere, and even the art of seafaring,[24] without ever setting sail on the Baltic or travelling on land further than forty miles from Königsberg. Clearly, there was some inner guilt in his denouncing those who after visiting other continents felt entitled to write a book on physical geography.[25] Behind the facade of self-assurance there seemed to lie a sense of insecurity deeper than his reluctance to travel. He must have been afraid even of his own ideas about the genesis of our globe, the topic of the fourth section of the First Part of his lecture-notes. In that section he discussed in separate paragraphs the views of Burnet, Whiston, Leibniz, Buffon, and others[26] on the geological past of the earth, but kept entirely silent about the relevant parts of his own *Allgemeine Naturgeschichte*!

It seems that here too, as in other cases, Kant was a thinker afraid to keep calling attention to his most cherished ideas after they had either failed to elicit any response, or one which was adverse or threatening.[27] The almost complete silence that surrounded the *Critique* for several years after its publication was not broken by Kant, but by K. L. Reinhold who, from his chair in Jena, set the academic consensus.[28] That consensus quickly shifted from Kant to Fichte when Reinhold himself changed his predilection. There was no Reinhold to break the silence about the *Allgemeine Naturgeschichte*, or rather about the cosmogony it contained. A mere academic non entity in comparison with Reinhold, J. F. Goldbeck ignored that cosmogony in his spirited defense of Kant's priority over Lambert concerning the explanation of the Milky Way and of nebulous stars which he submitted in 1781 in his *Litterarische Nachrichten von Preussen* à propos his account of Kant's just published *Kritik der reinen Vernunft*.[29] Two years later F. E. Biester, in his recension of Goldbeck's book, attributed to Kant's modesty the latter's reluctance to vindicate his priority over Lambert, but once more the cosmogony of Kant was not mentioned.[30] That cosmogony did not create an echo among scholars even though its summary in the *Einzig mögliche Beweisgrund* saw print four times between 1763 and 1794 in the four editions of that work.[31] Nor did the world of science take heed when in 1784 there appeared Herder's famed philosophy of history although its first paragraph came to a close with the declaration: "The human intellect perhaps never attempted a longer flight and completed it successfully in part at least, than when through Copernicus, Kepler, Newton, Huygens, and Kant it perceived and laid down firmly the simple, eternal and perfect laws of the formation and motion of planets." [32]

Kant himself did not seem to be particularly combative about his cosmogony. In connection with Goldbeck's defense of his priority over Lambert, Kant made moves to forestall the possibility of appearing as a rival of Lambert, although the latter had died four years earlier. In a letter of June 8, 1781, he asked Biester to place a note in the next issue of the *Litterarische Nachrichten*. In that note, which was not printed, Kant described his *Allgemeine Naturgeschichte* as a "weak sketch" in comparison with Lambert's "masterly outline" of the cosmological system. The thrust of the note concerned not so much the priority of the *Allgemeine Naturgeschichte* over Lambert's *Cosmologische Briefe*, but Bode's failure to point out in his *Anleitung* the differences between Kant's and Lambert's interpretation of the Milky Way with respect to elliptical nebulous patches. "Their elliptical figure provides," wrote Kant in the note to his letter to Biester, "the essential basis for the conjecture which I dared to make about the Milky Way as a mere member of a still greater system of similar world-orders. Still the correcting of [one's] share in conjectures, which should always remain conjectures, is of small importance." [33] That the *Allgemeine Naturgeschichte* was an unabashed evolutionary treatment of the cosmos, or cosmogony in short, whereas Lambert's *Cosmologische Briefe* contained repeated rejections of evolutionary views, did not seem for Kant a point important to note.

Nor did he seem to be anxious to call attention to his system of cosmic evolution in a paper which he published in 1785 after he had spotted in *Gentleman's Magazine* an interpretation of Herschel's observation of a volcano on the moon on May 4, 1783. Such was a rather puzzling attitude on Kant's part, because, according to him, the interpretation in question (indirectly confirmed by Herschel's discovery) was "highly significant in respect of cosmogony, namely, that [all] celestial bodies obtained their first formation in a fairly similar manner." Kant then outlined in quick strokes the stages of that formation: the primordial stuff of all celestial bodies was originally spread out in a vaporous condition across the entire space, then there arose, first through chemical and afterwards through "cosmological attraction" (gravitation), rotating fluid bodies. Their respective temperatures were determined by the quantity of matter which included among all sorts of elements the element of heat as well. Consequently, the central bodies of each system had the larger a quantity of heat, the larger a system they ruled. Finally, there came the pointed remark that although it was impossible to explain the very first of all natural phenomena, the motion of atoms, all subsequent phases of natural processes ought to be explained through known laws and not by a doubtful recourse to "immediate divine arrangement."[34]

All this was, in a nutshell, the cosmogony and teleology of the *Allgemeine Naturgeschichte*, a work which Kant did not care to mention. His reticence was all the more curious as he also spoke of Saturn's ring (referring to Huygens but not to himself) and took issue with Buffon on the action of streaming seawater in the formation of the earth's surface. It seems that his former describing the *Allgemeine Naturgeschichte* as a "weak sketch" was more than a gesture of modesty. As the author of the *Kritik* Kant may have begun to develop an ambivalent attitude toward the *Allgemeine Naturgeschichte*. Even about its parts, such as the Milky Way and nebulae, in respect to which he wanted public recognition, he curiously passed up his own golden opportunities to call attention to the work of his youth. Thus in 1790, when he published the *Kritik*'s first sequel, a critical appraisal of the faculty of judgment, he did not mention the *Allgemeine Naturgeschichte* as he offered "examples of the mathematically sublime in nature" in the form of increasingly larger, naturally given, units of measurements: "The earth's diameter [would supply a unit] for the known planetary system; this again for the Milky Way; and [the latter for] the immeasurable number of Milky Way systems called nebulae, which presumably constitute a system of the same kind among themselves; let us expect no bounds here."[35]

Kant seems to have felt that since in the *Kritik* he most emphatically disputed the mind's ability to form a reliable notion about the totality of things insofar as they form a universe, the *Allgemeine Naturgeschichte*, which had for its foundation that very same ability, was to be left unmentioned. There were, of course, not a few details in the *Allgemeine Naturgeschichte* of which Kant, with his reputation as the embodiment of pure rationality being at its peak, could hardly be proud. Indeed, in 1797 he suggested to Johann Heinrich Tieftrunk, who planned a collected edition of Kant's early works, to ignore his publications antedating 1770![36] Several years earlier, in 1791, he had explicitly voiced his apprehension lest an "unbidden edition" of the *Allgemeine Naturgeschichte* might see print. The evidence is in Kant's letter of April 19 of that year to Johann Fredrich Gensichen,[37] a letter which survived only in English translation and to which Gensichen added a note. It contained information about "several inquiries, both public and private," expressing interest in making the work widely available through a new edition. To forestall that possibility, Kant availed himself of the good services of Gensichen, a trusted admirer of his, to help bring out a much curtailed and corrected version of the work. Kant listed the most important aspects of the *Allgemeine Natur-*

geschichte in four points of which the first concerned his priority by six years over Lambert's explanation of the Milky Way. The second related to nebulous stars as so many Milky Ways. Here Kant took to task Erxleben and Lichtenberg for their misrepresentations of Lambert's explanation of nebulous stars. As Kant correctly noted, Lambert "supposed them (at least one of them) to be obscure bodies illuminated by neighboring suns." The third point was Kant's specification of the axial rotation of Saturn and his theory of the formation of Saturn's ring. Cosmogony was the fourth and last point, but merely as an appendix to his remark about Saturn's ring. His explanation of it, Kant wrote, "is somewhat favorable to the theory of the production of the great globes themselves according to the same laws, except that their property of rotation is originally produced by the fall of this dispersed substance by the general gravity. It does so chiefly, if the later opinion, added as supplement to the theory of the heavens, which is approved by the important applause of Mr. Lichtenberg,[38] is connected with it, that: yon' prime matter, vaporously dispersed through the universe, which contained all stuffs of an innumerable variety in an elastic state, forming the globes, effected it only in this manner, that the matters of any chemical affinity, if in their course, they met together according to the laws of gravitation, destroyed mutually their elasticity, produced by it bodies and in them that heat, joined in the larger globes (the suns), externally with the illuminated property, in the smaller ones (the planets) with the interior heat." Kant's German wording may not have been any clearer.

Gensichen's excerpting from the *Allgemeine Naturgeschichte* appeared as an appendix to the German translation of three famed memoirs of Herschel on the construction of the heavens. The translator was G. M. Sommer, associate pastor at the Haberburger Church in Königsberg and assistant librarian at the Royal Schloszbibliothek. In his introduction to the translation Sommer justified the addition of excerpts from the *Allgemeine Naturgeschichte* on the ground that they were the theoretical explanation of what Herschel observed about the construction of the heavens.[39] Clearly, Sommer had in mind Kant's cosmogony. In his introduction to the excerpts Gensichen merely stated that they carried Kant's full approval.[40] Indeed, they embodied several corrections by Kant.[41] The excerpts contained nothing of the lengthy Preliminary Discourse and only a half of the First Part. The First and Second Sections of the Second Part were also reduced to about a half. The Third Section was completely omitted, while the Fourth Section was reduced to about one fourth and the Fifth Section, on Saturn's rotation, to about one third. Nothing was reported by Gensichen of the last hundred pages. He rather added four points. In the first he emphasized the superiority of Kant's idea of the Milky Way over that of Lambert. In the second he claimed that Lambert was uncertain about the true nature of nebulae and deplored Erxleben's and Lichtenberg's handling of Kant's priority. In the third he recalled Kant's computation of "more than thirty years" of the rotation of Saturn and its correspondence with Herschel's observations.[42] In the fourth he claimed that Kant's theory of the formation of the ring of Saturn was of great relevance for the understanding of the formation of celestial bodies. They were generated not by the rotation of their respective central body, but through the gravitational fall toward the center of the dispersed primordial stuff. The particles of that gaseous stuff annihilated their elastic forces as they came together through gravitation and formed either the externally hot bodies (suns), or bodies which were hot only internally (planets and moons). Clearly, Gensichen took to heart the four points listed by Kant in his letter to him. As to Gensichen's remark, approved by Kant, against the role of the axial rotation of the central body in producing its system of planets, it was unfortunately not recalled by those who more than half a century later created the myth of a Kant-Laplace theory, although Gensichen's excerpts of the *Allgemeine Naturgeschichte* could not be unknown to them.

Gensichen was hardly an impartial judge. In a long note he reconstructed the mathematics which he believed, perhaps on Kant's instruction, to lie behind the value given by Kant of the rotation period of Saturn.[43] The note contained the brief remark that in 1790 there appeared in the *Astronomisches Jahrbuch* for 1793 a calculation by "Professor Bugge of Copenhagen of the same period on the basis of a quite different method."[44] Indeed, Thomas Bugge, professor of astronomy and mathematics at the University of Copenhagen and director of the Observatory there, had to work with a different method in which no reference to Kant would have been appropriate. Had a reference to him been made by Bugge, it might have been more polite but undoubtedly just as devastating in substance as the one formulated by Johann Chr. Schwab, best remembered as a translator and commentator of Euclid. Being a collaborator of J. A. Eberhard, a resolute though outmoded Wolffian opponent of Kant's critical philosophy, Schwab could not achieve much with his two essays on Kant's theory of planetary evolution and on his explanation of the formation of Saturn's ring, published in 1792 and 1793 in Eberhard's short-lived anti-Kantian periodical.[45] Unable to obtain a copy of the *Allgemeine Naturgeschichte*, Schwab found nevertheless enough non sequiturs in the extracts published by Gensichen to reach the conclusion: "The Kantian hypothesis leads us into a chaos of whirls out of which we are no longer able to escape."[46] The most revealing remark of Schwab was his reference to someone "very strong in the mathematics of physical astronomy" whom Schwab consulted. He advised Schwab that "it did not follow from Kant's theory that in the planetary system all planets must move in much the same plane," but also urged him not to reveal his name.[47] The request well reflected that notorious feature of academic life in which dissent from the views of a suddenly acclaimed thinker provokes the fear of ostracism. Twenty years later Olbers, one of the leading German astronomers of the time, found a very, similar situation in Paris, which he pointedly reported in a letter to Bessel in Königsberg. No less men of science than Lagrange, Delambre, Poisson, Prony, Rossel, Arago, and Biot preferred not to criticize in public the theory of the evolution of the solar system which Laplace had already proposed in three "improved" forms, lest they should provoke his resentment.[48]

Kant did not reply to Schwab's criticism which hit his cosmogony especially hard at its detail most valuable in his eyes, the theory of the formation of Saturn's ring. Nor did Kant make an effort to engage on behalf of his cosmogony a physicist skilled in mathematics. As to the extracts, they could easily give the impression that the *Allgemeine Naturgeschichte* was a scientific treatise rather than a teleologico-philosophical essay ending in a flight of fancy. But no sooner had the extracts been published than the absence in them of certain parts of the original was pointedly noted. Ernst Gottfried Fischer, a mathematics teacher in a gymnasium in Berlin, asked in 1791 in the pages of the *Astronomisches Jahrbuch* whether the absence of those parts had for its cause Kant's diffidence in their reliability.[49] Fischer especially referred to the gradual decay of fully developed worlds into a chaos and its subsequent turning into new worlds, a perspective very much to his liking. In comparing Herschel's account of nebulae with Kant's theorizing, Fischer found them to be matching pieces inasmuch as Kant provided the system which tied together the specifics ascertained by Herschel.[50] The harmony of the two seemed to Fischer all the more remarkable, because Herschel "having left his Fatherland at an early age grew unfamiliar not only with its literature but also of its language [!] and therefore could not know anything of Kant's writing."[51] In Fischer's eyes, Kant and Lambert[52] were the classic cases in astronomy when the brilliance of mind anticipated the results of observations.[53] He also noted with much satisfaction that Herschel, whose observations made it possible to decide the truth of the theories of the former two, was also, at least by birth a German.[54]

Prior to Fischer's essay, Herschel's findings had been for years reported in the *Astronomisches Jahrbuch* though never with a reference to Kant.[55] Although closely tied to the German translation of Herschel's classic memoirs, the excerpts by Gensichen were passed over in silence when the translation was referred to by Johann Georg Soldner in the *Astronomischers Jahrbuch* in 1800. The occasion was Soldner's discussion of the question whether stars in the Milky Way were in motion around a physical or around a purely geometrical center. Soldner, who supported the latter case, noted though that the question arose following "Kant's and Lambert's deep investigations, admirably verified to a great extent by *our* Herschel"[56] (italics added). There was no reference whatever to Kant when the German translation of the first edition of Laplace's *Exposition du systeme du monde* (1796) was enthusiastically reviewed in 1798 in a Frankfurt magazine "for the latest developments in natural science."[57] True enough, the reviewer did not mention Laplace's own cosmogony, that is, his theory of the evolution of the solar system contained in a short chapter at the end of that work. Possibly, the reviewer did not sympathize with the evolutionary outlook, but this was certainly not the case with Olbers. Yet Olbers, who supported his belief in the infinity of the universe with a long quotation from the *Allgemeine Naturgeschichte* (which he did not name as if it had been all too well known among astronomers),[58] sought no support in it as he discussed in another context the evolution of celestial bodies.[59] Nor did other leading German astronomers care to comment on Kant's cosmogony, let alone to do what Kant hoped from them, namely, to evaluate it in terms of mathematical physics and astronomy. Particularly disappointing must have appeared to Kant the report of Schröter in 1803 on Saturn's rings, a report long on observational data, on Herschel, Laplace, and others, but void of any reference to the *Allgemeine Naturgeschichte*,[60] although its availability was much enhanced by three separate editions between 1797 and 1808 and by four editions of Kant's minor works during the same period.[61]

Certainly, Bessel, the first professor of astronomy at Königsberg and also the first director of the observatory there from 1810 until his death in 1846, could not be unfamiliar with Kant's cosmogony. He also had at least one signal opportunity to gratify the academics and the larger public of Kant's native town with at least a passing reference to Kant's ideas on the Milky Way, the nebulae, and the hierarchical structure of the universe. The opportunity was Bessel's public lecture on Herschel on February 10, 1843, to the Physical Society of Königsberg, the text of which was given in full in the *Königsberger Allgemeine Zeitung* immediately after its delivery.[62] In the lecture Bessel dealt with Herschel's contribution to topics, such as the cause of the whiteness of the Milky Way, the motion of stars as the cause of the stability of their system, other nebulae as stellar systems, the construction of the entire stellar realm, volcanos on the moon, and last but not least the rings of Saturn, all of which would have justified a reference to Kant. If there were any in Bessel's audience who looked for such a reference, they were sorely disappointed. Those among them who had already attended Bessel's lecture on the constitution of celestial bodies, especially of planets, on January 17, 1834, given to the same Society, may have suspected Bessel's reason for passing over Kant in silence. Bessel brought that lecture to a conclusion with a remark on the habitability of planets, a remark which could easily be taken for a scathing, though covert, indictment of Kant: "We must recognize, here too, as in general, a limit to our knowledge and admit that we can know something factual in nature only when it is either in the realm of the sensory perception or is connected with the evidence of the senses through inferences; the fruitless effort to transcend these limits—and this darkens with fantasies a science which is so rich in explorable phenomena—to bring in unexplorable ones, could only emanate from those who did not know how to open their way to the former. Such is the situation; indeed, I could prove this in each individual case, but fairness demands that we should not blame astronomy for something done against its laws." [63]

The sole reference to the *Allgemeine Naturgeschichte* in a cosmogonical work published in 1802 by the now deservedly forgotten K. W. and E. F. L. Marschall von Bieberstein,[64] was no dent on the icy silence which German astronomers kept on Kant's cosmogony. In all likelihood Kant did not learn of that work, but in the same year he received a complimentary copy of a booklet written by Johann A. H. Reimarus, physician in Hamburg.[65] The booklet was a criticism of Jean-André de Luc's effort to save the literal interpretation of Genesis in the teeth of science. In the accompanying letter Reimarus thanked Kant for the guidance he received from his "insightful explanation of the formation of the world." [66] Indeed, in the booklet passages of Kant were quoted verbatim on three different occasions, but they were from the cosmogonical section of Kant's article on volcanos on the moon.[67] To heighten the irony, another work of Kant, his *Critique of Judgment*, was also quoted, but not the *Allgemeine Naturgeschichte*. Whatever Kant's reaction to this, he must have known in his heart that silence on that work was, in no small extent, his own making.

Silence was the natural thing to expect abroad. In France, where Kant even as a metaphysician was but vaguely known until Victor Cousin commanded attention on him in the 1830s, the *Allgemeine Naturgeschichte* failed to receive mention even in Lalande's massive and meticulous bibliography of astronomical works.[68] It was equally ignored by those who promoted in France Lambert's cosmology.[69] The sole exception was d'Utenhove, astronomer of Utrecht, who exaggerated the renown of the *Allgemeine Naturgeschichte* as he remarked that the whole world knew its author, the famous Kant of Königsberg. The remark occurred in d'Utenhove's many notes to Darquier's translation into French of Lambert's *Cosmologische Briefe*, a translation which at long last saw print in 1801 through d'Utenhove's efforts.[70] In those notes there are more than a dozen invariably approving references to the *Allgemeine Naturgeschichte*,[71] which was presented by d'Utenhove (who had a copy of the original!) to his readers in the following words: "The system of Buffon is known for most of the French readers. At any rate different authors have given different systems of cosmogony. The best and the most plausible of them all seems to be enclosed in an excellent small anonymous work which has for title, *Allgemeine Naturgeschichte*, etc., that is, *Histoire naturelle et Théorie générale du ciel, ou essai sur la constitution et l'origine mécanique de l'Univers entier déduites des principes de la gravitation Newtonienne*, Königs. et Leips. 1755. This book (whose author the whole world knows in the famous Kant of Königsberg) has too much similarity with the work which we publish to be passed over in silence."[72]

D'Utenhove, who repeatedly insisted on Kant's anticipation of Lambert and Herschel's ideas, emphasized in the foregoing context that Lambert, a friend of Kant, would in no way have plagiarized from Kant's work, "of which its author let an extract be made in 1791, and in 1797 an anonymous author took the liberty to reprint it in its entirety with his own notes which he did not hesitate to call in the title corrections of the author himself. But we hope to see of it a new edition from the very hands of the author while he is still alive."[73] D'Utenhove was certainly well informed about the *Allgemeine Naturgeschichte*, but his glowing references to it were not effective in breaking the silence about it. The translation, which he saw through press with his valuable annotations, has become a work even rarer than the *Allgemeine Naturgeschichte*.[74]

In England, Herschel, for all his ties with Hannover, did not learn about Kant's cosmogony[75] in spite of an early publication in English translation of minor works of Kant, among them his essay on the moon's influence on the weather. The publication revealed both the lack of the anonymous translator's command of German and also his lack of proper grasp of science. His remark, that Kant could see with his mind's eyes what Herschel could see only with his giant telescopes,[76] echoed that confidence in the a priori approach which Kant's philosophy inspired and which set the tone of the evaluation of his cosmogony by his admiring friends in Königsberg such as

49

Sommer, Gensichen, Borowski, and others. They did not suspect that when almost half a century later Alexander Humboldt would at long last refer to the *Allgemeine Naturgeschichte* as an "excellent work" in the section of his famed *Kosmos* on the explanation of the universe, he would not only deplore in the same breath Kant's speculations on the denizens of other planets,[77] but keep an almost complete silence about its contents throughout his lengthy account of the stellar universe and the solar system.[78] Kant was not mentioned as Humboldt made a passing reference to the formation of celestial bodies from gaseous masses.[79] Nor was the *Allgemeine Naturgeschichte* referred to when Humboldt named Wright, Lambert, and Kant as the ones who formulated the notion about the structure of the universe which Herschel later confirmed with his observations.[80]

The situation was no different in the massive volumes of the second and much enlarged edition of Gehler's *Physikalisches Wörterbuch*, which engaged the collaboration of leading German professors of physics and astronomy as its twenty volumes went through print between 1825 and 1845.[81] The last volume contained a well over hundred-page-long article, "Weltall," written by J. J. Littrow, director of the Observatory in Vienna and famed for his books on astronomy.[82] Twenty pages in that article dealt with the origin and evolution of the universe, pages that informed in detail about Whiston, Leibniz, Buffon, Franklin, and Laplace, but which contained not a word on Kant.[83] In the same *Wörterbuch* Kant received praise only for his theory of the Milky Way,[84] whereas, he was wholly ignored in the article on planets.[85] The editorial board obviously knew the difference between science and Kantian speculation. Indeed, in the article on the history of physics Kant was described with tongue in cheek as "the great reformer of philosophy" who started the trend to discourse on matter through introspection.[86] The trend received detailed attention in the article on matter with copious references to Schelling, Oken, and Hegel, the champions of that Naturphilosophie[87] which German scientists detested and fought almost to a man.

Kant, of course, tried his best to dissociate himself from Schelling and the rest. Yet, the physics as given in his *Opus postumum* was sheer Naturphilosophie with its crass subjectivism.[88] One could, therefore, expect Schelling, Oken and Hegel, who offered astonishing dicta on the realm of planets,[89] to say something on the planetary cosmogony of Kant whose legitimate successors they claimed to be and indeed they were. Their silence on Kant's cosmogony was well-nigh complete. Hegel, for instance, had but a few words for Kant in his massive *Encyclopädie der Wissenschaften* in which Kant's (and Herschel's) presentation of the Milky Way as resembling a disk was brushed aside as "wholly indeterminate and general."[90] When silence was finally broken in the German philosophical realms about Kant's cosmogony, the break could easily be seen, from the scientific side at least, as a mere affrontery to science. The time was the midpoint of the nineteenth century, when German men of science were still keenly aware of the abuses heaped on them by the champions of Naturphilosophie in particular and by idealist philosophers in general.[91] The voice was that of Schopenhauer, a sharp critic of the latter, but his main criticism of them was in fact an urging that they should see themselves for what they really were: not as champions of the reason but as champions of the will. It was that will in which Schopenhauer saw the core of existence, cosmic and human, spiritual and material, and he urged a return to Kant as the one, who unlike his successors, did not conceal the primacy of will behind endless references to reason.

Schopenhauer certainly did not wish to be guilty of such tactics either in his major works or in his minor essays. One of the latter was a set of thoughts on philosophy and natural science, published in his *Parerga und Paralipomena* in 1851. The ten pages which Schopenhauer offered on Kant's "extremely ingenious cosmogony"[92] started with the remark that Kant first proposed it in 1755 in his *Allgemeine Naturgeschichte* "and then more completely [!] in the seventh chapter of his *Einzig mögliche Beweisgrund* in 1763," a remark which for a historian of science should already *prima facie* make suspect the rest of what Schopenhauer said on that cosmogony. As to men of science, the concluding sentence of those ten pages informed them that "what is moral, is the kernel or ground-bass [note] of matter, however little inclined are mere physicists to grasp this." They had every right not to grasp this or Schopenhauer's other dictum that "matter generally is the mere visibility of the will,"[93] which preceded his encomium of Kant's cosmogony. As far as German men of science, especially physicists, were concerned, they could take that encomium as a kiss of death given to Kant the cosmogonist. Strangely enough, it was their leader for the entire second half of the nineteenth century, who a few years later resurrected Kant the cosmogonist into glory.

V. *The Workshops of Glory*

Without the assumption, declared Hermann Helmholtz in a celebrated popular lecture given in Königsberg on February 7, 1854, that the planetary system "was once a connected mass with a uniform motion of rotation . . . it is impossible to explain why all the planets move in the same direction round the sun, why they all rotate in the same direction round their axes, why the planes of their orbits and those of their satellites and rings all nearly coincide, why all their orbits differ but little from circles, and much besides." The obvious meaning of this negative statement was positive, namely, that the assumption in question makes the explanation possible, although Helmholtz was quick to add that it must "from the nature of the case forever remain an hypothesis." An hypothesis of very special value it was, however, in Helmholtz's eyes. It served him with a grandiose illustration of the conservation, through their convertibility, of the various forces operating in nature, the topic of his lecture delivered under the title, "On the Interaction of Natural Forces."[1] According to that illustration the gravitational contraction of the solar nebula, or the original state of the planetary system, was converted into the heat of the sun, a point which, as Helmholtz admitted, had been entertained before him, but could quantitatively be evaluated only on the basis of his paper "On the Conservation of Force," which soon after its publication in 1847 established itself as a classic of science.[2]

It was in this context that Helmholtz introduced Kant as the one who first uttered that assumption "on our own homeground, within the walls of this town."[3] On the face of it Helmholtz's remark was an innocuous appeal to local patriotism. But in 1854, in Königsberg no less than in any other town of Prussia, the dominant feeling was a patriotism anchored in the belief of Prussia's destiny to bring about and lead a unified Germany. Such a patriotism eagerly imagined a glorious national past, political as well as scientific, and could serve as a most effective workshop for the glory of Kant the cosmogonist. What the astronomer, J. J. Littrow, could not achieve in 1842 with his vague reference to Kant's cosmogony that the "Fatherland can rightly be proud of him,"[4] was now done, as if by magic, by Helmholtz's declaration, which effectively broke in Germany the silence on Kant's cosmogony almost exactly a hundred years after its publication: "It was Kant who, feeling great interest in the physical description of the earth and the planetary system, undertook the labour of studying the works of Newton; and, as an evidence of the depth to which he had penetrated into the fundamental ideas of Newton, seized the notion that the same attractive force of all ponderable matter, which now supports the motion of the planets, must also aforetime have been able to form from matter loosely scattered in space the planetary system."[5]

Part of the magic was Helmholtz himself, whose destiny to scientific leadership was not difficult to guess in 1854. A generation later Helmholtz was spoken of as "Reichskanzler of German physics."[6] His dicta were carefully cultivated by anyone aspiring to advancement in the academic establishment ruled by him. Owing to his authority, it became a shibboleth throughout Germany that Kant was a profound scientist and expert on Newton. Forged in the workshop of patriotic fervor, the glory of Kant the scientist could only be hollow. There was no substance at all to Helmholtz's claims that following Kant "astronomers have shaped" the nebular hypothesis, and that Laplace, after having it enunciated independently of Kant, "introduced it among astronomers."[7] The latter must have known that prior to 1854 and even for some time afterwards few of them espoused, let alone developed Laplace's or Kant's theory.[8] But no astronomer protested. There were no historians of science around to take Helmholtz to task concerning his reading of the *Allgemeine Naturgeschichte*, a chore which the many professional readers of Kant the philosopher were, not surprisingly, unable to perform. Helmholtz simply ignored Kant's presumptuous strictures on Newton and his postulating a repulsive force on equal footing with the force of attraction. His praise of Kant, as an indefatigable student of Newton's writings, exemplified the proverbially cavalier handling by prominent scientists of the historical source materials of their topics. As to the science of cosmogony proper, Helmholtz was equally shortsighted. He failed to notice the most destructive aspect of Kant's as well as of Laplace's theory, namely, that according to both the sun's angular momentum should exceed in much the same lopsided ratio the total angular momentum of planets as the sun's mass exceeds their combined mass, whereas the very opposite is the fact. This should have already been noted by Laplace whose work on planetary perturbations largely rested on his exploitation of the principle of the conservation of angular momentum. When in 1860 the French physicist of optics fame, J. Babinet, found that defect in Laplace's theory (Babinet took no notice of Kant), he talked it away in the same breadth.[9] By 1884, when M. Fouché pointed out in an even more incisive way before the French Academy that the defect was fatal to Laplace's theory, patriotic feelings were too strong in France to let sober facts and calculations prevail.[10]

In Germany no prominent scientist was to criticize Kant's theory on account of that basic defect for a long time to come. Much less could one expect such a voice of criticism from German philosophers, an increasingly large number of whom saw in the motto, "return to Kant," a program for rescuing thought from the rank subjectivism of Hegelian idealism and Schellingian Naturphilosophie. Moving toward the objective meant also a move toward science, the reason why certain philosophers not entirely uncritical of Kant found Helmholtz's panegyrics of Kant the scientist a rather welcome assurance. Friedrich Überweg was certainly not unaware of Helmholtz's address of 1854, when eleven years later he delivered on April 22 (Kant's birthday) in the same aula magna of the University of Königsberg a festive address on Kant's *Allgemeine Naturgeschichte*.[11] In view of Überweg's philosophical convictions it is most likely that he chose for his topic Kant's cosmogony because Helmholtz's authority had already established its soundness from the scientific viewpoint. Überweg, who had no quarrel with Kant's pre-*Critique* works, first earned his reputation by creating quite a storm with his support of empiricism against idealism, including its Kantian brand. The latter was his major target when there appeared in 1865 the third or concluding volume of his famed history of philosophy, which largely because of its thoroughness became a universally acclaimed and often reprinted source book.[12]

In his address Überweg made no secret of his conviction that the epistemology of the *Critique* was irreconcilable with the kind of cosmological theorizing which Kant offered in the *Allgemeine Naturgeschichte*.[13] But he saw a way of reconciling the pre-critical Kant with the author of the *Critique* through Kant's notion of ethical duty elaborated in the *Critique of Practical Reason*. Thus Kant's pre-critical studies of natural science became for Überweg so many evidences of the sense of duty with which Kant thoroughly explored his scientific topics and fearlessly unfolded the logic of his presuppositions. Überweg did his best to play down Wright's influence on Kant concerning the explanation of the Milky Way. Wright pursued a "theologico-astronomical game with fantasies," whereas Kant did strictly scientific research.[14] Equally fantastic was in Überweg's eyes Buffon's theory of the origin of the planetary system. Kant's inferences to the existence and features of the inhabitants of other planets were not only not described by Überweg as fantastic: he did not as much as hint of them. What was truly fantastic was Überweg's matter-of-fact statement, that as "Kant proposed it," the mutual impacts arising among the particles falling toward the sun would issue in a tangential movement still in evidence in the orbital motion of planets. Although Überweg recognized that Kant did not work out mathematically this pivotal part of his cosmogony, it was one of his "anticipations of insights worthy of a genius" which called for references to Kant whenever the contributions of Herschel and Laplace were discussed. Those insights "occurred to Kant not through fortuitous chance; they are rather the result of the inner familiarity with nature of a deep and thorough investigator free of prejudices, with the essence of his topic of research, and with the broader relation of it to the entirety of all objects of scientific research in general."[15] The phrase had no more worth than similar products of philosophical rhetoric, but it certainly fitted the unveiling shortly beforehand of a statue of Kant in his town of birth. Unlike Überweg's statements in general, the foregoing phrase was not based on a thorough study of sources and on an impartial presentation of pros and cons. Being a candidate for full professorship in Königsberg, Überweg had to pay his due to the city's most famous son and he did so with a coin which contained none of the gold of science and of its history.

A glittering coin it certainly seemed to be. Otherwise the Kant-Society of Königsberg would not have asked a scientist, E. Hay, to give the commemorative address on Kant's birthday the following year. Hay chose for his topic "the now famous cosmogony of Kant," and assured his audience that Kant "was in full possession of the scientific knowledge of his time."[16] After giving a summary of Kant's cosmogony, he declared that it had a scientific value not "for want of a better one," but because "it agrees with the laws of physics thoroughly and explains physically as perfectly as possible the phenomena."[17] It was in this vein that Hay found much good with Kant's speculations on the inhabitants of other planets. True, Hay acknowledged that the probability of their existence was not great. But he saw Kant's speculations as an evidence of Kant's espousing a universal evolutionism. No wonder that Hay deplored the fact that Kant not only left undeveloped the thesis of the *Allgemeine Naturge-schichte*, the specification of all mental characteristics by the properties of matter, but that he had later abandoned it completely. Whether Kant's cosmogony was more germane to pantheism or to materialism was a question which Hay left for others to decide.

The logic which activated the workshops of glory for Kant the scientist was equally in evidence in the long article which K. G. Reuschle published in 1868 on Kant and the natural sciences, an article written according to its author with special reference to the "latest research."[18] In Reuschle's survey of all works of Kant relating to science, most of the factual and informative details, presented in a flood of generalities, were so many exposures of the basic shortcomings and naiveté of Kant the scientist, and they mostly referred to his cosmogony. As an introduction to it Reuschle reviewed in detail Kant's work on the retardation of the axial rotation of the earth and found basic theoretical and computational errors in it. He characterized as "very contrary to physics" Kant's theory of the formation of Saturn's ring.[19] He chided Gensichen for taking as a confirmation of Kant's theory the computation in it of the rotation period of the interior of Saturn's ring; it verified only the validity of Kepler's laws. In comparing Kant's theory with that of Laplace, Reuschle took the view that the latter stood as high above the former as did the *Exposition du système du monde* over the *Allgemeine Naturgeschichte*. In comparison with Laplace's wise postulating an original rotation for the sun, Kant's effort of deriving the same from the onrush of particles toward the center was, in Reuschle's eyes, "laborious enough,"—a most benevolent estimate. In spite of all this Reuschle's judgment was that "almost as brilliantly as Frederick the Great shines in the political sky of the preceding century, does the Sage of Königsberg, Immanuel Kant, shine in the philosophical, or more generally in the scientific sky of that century." Kant was one of those philosophers who "enriched all brances of knowledge and in such measure that he, the hero of German philosophy, emerges also as one of the scientific greats of the preceding century."[20] To make matters worse for careful readers of Humboldt's *Kosmos*, Reuschle added that Kant certainly appears a great scientist in the rich historical material of that work.

Even if Reuschle wanted to use his findings in the only proper sense, namely, to cast doubt on the blooming reputation of Kant the scientist, he was hardly an authority compared with Helmholtz who added a new and powerful support to Kant's cosmogony in a lecture on the origin of the planetary system which he delivered in 1871 in Heidelberg as well as in Köln. There he described "the hypothesis of Kant and Laplace" as "one of the happiest insights of science, which at first astounds us by its boldness, and then connects us in all directions with other discoveries, through which the conclusions are confirmed until we have confidence in them."[21] In that lecture Helmholtz claimed that only circumstances prevented Kant from becoming a great scentist and, as a proof of Kant's enduring scientific interest, he referred to the occasional papers on science which Kant produced in his later years and to his lecturing on physical geography. One wonders whether Helmholtz studied any of those papers, for instance the one on the influence of the moon on the weather, or whether he took note when in the 1880s the neo-Kantians learned with stunned disbelief about the existence of a lengthy manuscript of Kant, which upon its publication became known as the *Opus postumum*.

The patriotism, which blinded Helmholtz to the irremediable defects of Kant's cosmogony and to its essential differences from the one proposed by Laplace, had in 1865 prompted J. C. F. Zöllner, the first to occupy the newly created chair for astrophysics in Leipzig, to present Laplace as a plagiarizer of Kant. Zöllner did so in his studies on stellar photometry, where he offered in parallel columns passages from the *Allgemeine Naturgeschichte* and from the *Exposition du système du monde*.[22] Since the studies were written "with special reference to the composition of celestial bodies," a scrutiny of the relation between the two cosmogonies could not seem to be entirely out of place. Zöllner, however, gave himself away as he had his charges against Laplace reprinted in a much enlarged form six years later in a book which even in a non-scientist with a modest measure of criticial sense should have caused misgivings. The book was in part devoted to the contention that the tail of comets represented the primordial form of matter and that only a return to the philosophy of Kepler, a German open to the arcane if not mystical aspects of reality, could keep the progress of physics on the right track![23]

Interestingly enough, it was about the same time that a voice dissenting from that acclamation given in academic circles to Kant the cosmogonist came from the academia. Unfortunately, the voice was only that of a privatdozent, Emil A. Budde, and was hardly voluble if judged by the seventy pages of his brochure. The exalted position which professors, like Helmholtz and Zöllner, had with respect to mere privatdozents, to say nothing of students, may explain the fact that neither Helmholtz nor Zöllner dignified Budde's brochure with a reply. A revealing fact, as both Helmholtz and Budde were at the University of Bonn at that time and Budde's brochure was "on contemporary cosmology," with a special reference to Zöllner's book in its very title.[24]. Budde was the first in Germany to speak of Babinet's paper on the question of angular momentum, although he failed to see Babinet's self-defeating handling of it. Budde was also the first to break through the nebulous halo created by Helmholtz around Kant's theory by pointing out that at the basis of it there lay not a nebulous solar atmosphere but a carefully contrived arrangement of particles of different densities. This arrangement, Budde emphasized, was equivalent to presupposing what it was supposed to explain.

This obvious point wholly escaped T. H. Huxley, the first to introduce in glory Kant the cosmogonist in England. In this case the workshop of glory was that mechanistic evolutionism of which Huxley was a chief champion. Whereas in 1858 no reference to Kant, however brief, was visible in Herbert Spencer's lengthy account and accolade of Laplace's nebular hypothesis,[25] eleven years later the English speaking world was notified by Huxley from his chair as President of the Geological Society of London that long before Laplace, Kant had "developed a cosmogonical doctrine in all respects similar to the well-known nebular hypothesis of Laplace."[26] It shows something of Huxley's perspicacity and perspective that his summary of Kant's cosmogony was centered on the cyclical character of cosmic evolution, in which chaos gives rise to a cosmos which in turn ends in a chaos destined to develop into cosmos again: "thus the worlds that are, lie between the ruins of the worlds that have been and the chaotic materials of the worlds that shall be."[27]

A quarter of a century later Huxley stunned the public, which he had already swayed to the world view of mechanistic evolutionism, by conjuring up the specter of an organic evolution in reverse, in which higher organisms gradually turn into less and less developed forms until even the most primitive organisms disappear.[28] Huxley's perspicacity was clearly in evidence when he pointed out in the same context that such a world view was not Western but Oriental, and that it deprived traditional ethical views of all their meaning.[29] Such was indeed the implication of Kantian cosmogony and philosophy, but the septuagenarian Huxley no longer remembered Kant. Nor was Huxley aware, when in speaking of Kant's cosmogony in 1869, of the pitfalls which are in store for "scientific reasoning" when a particular scientific theory—let alone when the theory, as is the case with Kant's cosmogony, is only apparently scientific—is forced to support a Weltanschauung such as mechanistic evolutionism. The pitfalls are those of contradictions and clichés. For if it was true on the one hand that Kant's theory "accounts for the relation of the masses and densities of the planets to their distances from the sun, for the eccentricities of their orbits, for their rotations, for their satellites, for the general agreement in the direction of rotation among the celestial bodies, for Saturn's ring, and for the zodiacal light," how could it also be true that "it would be very easy to pick holes in the details of Kant's speculations whether cosmological or specially telluric in their application"?[30] Possibly it was this kind of reasoning which prompted Robert Louis Stevenson to muse about those who "swallow the universe like a pill."[31]

At any rate, if Kant's cosmogony suited mechanistic evolutionism, and it certainly did, then careful weighing of its proofs had to yield to the cliché that Kant was a "good mathematician and well versed in the physical science of his time,"[32] a cliché worthy of a Huxley unmindful of at least one specific aspect of the physics of his own day, an aspect steeped in that mathematics of which he could at times be slightly contemptuous. Indeed, the main target of Huxley's presidential address was Kelvin's three mathematically elaborated arguments which denied the amount of geological past required by Darwin's theory of natural selection. Kelvin quickly rose to the defense of his arguments, a defense which praised Kant's theory with reserve but unreservedly damned Huxley's appraisal of it. Kant's theory, Kelvin argued, could lead with the help of the research of Davy, Rumford, and Joule on the mechanical equivalent of heat (the first law of thermodynamics), to predicting the actual temperatures of the sun, the earth, and other celestial bodies. But what about Huxley's contention that Kant had anticipated Hutton in submitting the idea of a cosmos endowed with a "reproductive operation by which a ruined

constitution may be repaired"?[33] Had Kant been familiar with Car-
not's work, that is, with the second law of thermodynamics, he would,
Kelvin declared, never have submitted the "chimera of such a reproductive operation."[34] Huxley had, however, already stated that concerning Kelvin and mathematical physics, evolutionists were so many
"Gallios who care for none of these things."[35] The sudden popularity
of Kant's cosmogony owed much to the carefree manner in which
some evolutionists leaped from the evidence of evolution to equating
a particular explanation of it with intelligibility itself. The springboard
of that leap was a faith which, though unable to move mountains,
could make mountains of difficulties appear as if they were mere
molehills.

Such a faith was certainly at its most robust in the case of Ernst
Haeckel, Darwin's chief champion in Germany. He hardly wished to
sound convincing about the difficulties of Kant's cosmogony as he
declared both that "weighty considerations may be brought forward
against it," and that "it explains in an excellent manner . . . the whole
structure of all that is accessible to our observations, that is, the
anatomy of the solar systems, and especially of our planetary system."[36]
Apart from the fact that no other solar systems were observed in
Haeckel's time any more than in ours, the phrase was a classic in a
rhetoric with no real ties with science. For if it was also true, to quote
Haeckel, that the development of the solar system may have been
"altogether different from what Kant supposes,"[37] Kant's theory could
not possess the explanatory powers Haeckel accorded to it. Caught
in the inebriating vistas of cosmic evolution, Haeckel could deliver
himself of an appraisal of Kant's cosmogony which revealed its nullity
to anyone moderately familiar with Lamarck's theory of evolution.
"I will not deny," Haeckel wrote, "that Kant's grand cosmogeny [sic]
has some weak points, which prevent our placing the same *unconditional
confidence* in it as in Lamarck's Theory of Descent"[38] (italics added).
But, leaving aside Haeckel's stultifying appraisal of Lamarck, his
statement was not reconciled with his next dictum on Kant's theory,
which, according to Haeckel, had only one "great and unsolved
difficulty," namely, that it "furnishes no starting point at all in explanation of the first impulse which caused the rotary motion in the gas
filled universe." But how could this be a fault if, to quote Haeckel
again, "we can as little imagine a *first beginning* of the eternal phenomena
of the motion of the universe as its final end"?[39] Indeed, if Kant's
cosmogony was for Haeckel a "wonderful theory," it was because it
appeared to him "purely mechanical and monistic," excluding any
action on the part of a personal Creator,[40] an estimate worthy of one

for whom the law of conservation of force (energy) and matter proved that the universe was uncreated and eternal.[41]

Other believers in the dogma of purely mechanistic evolutions and devolutions in an eternal universe were equally delighted to learn of Kant the cosmogonist. In 1874 John Fiske, the chief spokesman of Herbert Spencer in America, praised Kant's "rare scientific acumen" for having first elaborated "the grand theory of nebular genesis." Its principal merit in Fiske's eyes was the perspective of "the stupendous rhythmical alternation between eras of Evolution and eras of Dissolution, succeeding each other without vestiges of a beginning and without prospect of an end."[42] About the same time, Engels registered similar appraisal of Kant in a manuscript which, when published posthumously in 1928, became known as *Dialektik der Natur*.[43] In its introduction Kant's cosmogony is presented as the chief starting point of the development which, in Engels' belief, proved beyond doubt that "the ultimate entity is the eternal cycle of matter in motion."[44] Engels therefore could only deplore the fact that eighteenth-century materialists, nay even most of their numbers during the nineteenth century, had remained unaware of that "epoch-making work." One wonders whether Kant—especially the post-*Critique* Kant—would have raised a firm caveat on finding Engels present the *Allgemeine Naturgeschichte* as a work in which "the question of the first impulse was abolished."[45] In the long chain of Engels' claims—"many years later [after the publication of Kant's work] Laplace and Herschel expounded its contents and gave them a deeper foundation, thereby gradually bringing the 'nebular hypothesis' into favour. Further discoveries finally brought it victory; the most important of these were: the proper motion of the fixed stars, the demonstration of a resistent medium in universal space, the proof furnished by spectral analysis of the chemical identity of the matter of the universe and the existence of such glowing nebular masses as Kant had postulated"[46]—a historian of science would find several links a fictional history, but he would waste his energy by trying to convince of the historical truth any prisoner of the dogmatic cliché about Engels' greatness as an interpreter of science and its history.

A historian of science cannot even hope to have his own field quickly cleared of clichés of far less dogmatic character. He should rather be amused by the fact that with his encomiums on Kant's cosmogony Engels aligned himself with a tradition in the making, although in the same context he noted with sneer that "tradition is a power not only in the Catholic Church but also in natural science."[47] Towards the end of the century it had indeed become a tradition to look upon the *Allgemeine Naturgeschichte* as a classic of science. No sooner had the famed series, *Klassiker der Exakten Wissenschaften*, been launched in 1888 by Wilhelm Ostwald, the future Nobel-laureate in chemistry, than a new edition of the *Allgemeine Naturgeschichte* found a place in it. The editor, H. Ebert, followed not so much the standards of historical accuracy as that revealing aspect of a tradition which imposed an attitude bordering on complacency with respect to the scientific defects of Kant's cosmogony. As a result, the text was drastically curtailed in the new edition. The long Opening Discourse was left out as being too philosophical and theological, which it certainly is. As to the Third Part, the one on the denizens of other planets, its omission was justified with the remark that its topic was too removed from cosmogony proper. This was sweetened with Ebert's apology (astonishing in itself, let alone in a series of scientific classics) that the Part in question was "very insightful in comparison with all that had been written on that topic."[48] The merits of the scientific parts were summarized by Ebert with no less bias. First, he emphasized that whereas Laplace started with an already developing sun, Kant's starting point was as encompassing as possible, namely, a most diluted state of matter—hardly an exact rendering of what Kant proposed. Second, although Ebert made much of the untenability of Laplace's derivation of planets from rings, he kept silent about the true merits of the corresponding mechanism proposed by Kant.

A curious tactic, but a piece with Ebert's claim that only the first two Parts of the *Allgemeine Naturgeschichte* were added in French translation by the astronomer, C. Wolf, to his book, *Les hypothèses cosmogoniques*.[49] Clearly, Ebert spoke on the basis of hearsay of Wolf's work. Had he studied it, he might have profited of such sound remarks in it as "the actual motions of revolution and rotation of the sun and planets can only be the equivalent, without any increase or decrease, of the rotational motion imparted to the [solar] nebula by an exterior cause." According to Wolf, the hypotheses of Kant and Laplace had only one common aspect, their point of departure, inasmuch as both saw the birth of the planetary system from a primitive solar nebula, whose motion determined the planetary motions and gave them that remarkable uniformity which shows their common origin. "In all justice," Wolf wrote, "the German philosopher must be accorded the glory of having first enunciated this grandiose idea." But, Wolf added in the same breath, not only there was no further similarity between the theories of Kant and Laplace, but "Kant's conceptions are often in formal contradiction with the laws of mechanics." His theory, was Wolf's final verdict, "has today but a purely historical interest."

Curiously, Wolf failed to note the basic conflict with the laws of mechanics in Kant's theory of the formation of Saturn's ring.[50] Rather, he commended Kant for his postulating the existence of concentric divisions within the ring at a time when even the existence of the great division of Cassini was entirely unknown to him.[51] This was one of Wolf's few dicta on the historical record and certainly showed that expertise in astronomy is not enough to secure reliability to one's statements about its history. The same was true of A. J. von Oettingen, professor of physics at the University of Dorpat and editor of the physics section of Ostwald's *Klassiker*, who prepared in 1898 an annotated edition of the full text of Kant's work, in an obvious effort to supplant the edition by Ebert.[52] Oettingen's first remarks gave the impression that the tradition of handling with complacency the scientific defects of the *Allgemeine Naturgeschichte* would be resisted. After a brief paragraph on Kant's life, Oettingen offered almost two pages on Kant's first publication, the essay of 1747 on "living forces," emphasizing its utter lack of scientific merit. According to Oettingen, Kant "stood far behind his predecessors and contemporaries in understanding the basic problems of rational dynamics." He had no qualification to understand "either Leibniz or Bernoulli, and sided with the Cartesians on the basis of patently impossible arguments." Worse, in his effort to mediate between the Cartesian and the Leibnizian viewpoints of force (*vis viva*) he tried to elaborate "the highly mystical concept of the 'vivificatio' of bodies in motion without adding the slightest mathematically formulated proof and the least experimental evidence on behalf of his alleged reformation of the foundations of dynamics."[53]

This sound criticism began to vanish in Oettingen's closing remarks on Kant's essay. He deplored Kant's failure to repudiate that essay when he published in 1786 his *Die metaphysischen Anfangsgründe der Naturwissenschaft*, in Oettingen's eyes an equally primitive work.[54] But the true failure of both works was, according to Oettingen, that neither of them foreshadowed or did justice to the "great philosopher."[55] With this revealing remark Oettingen turned to the *Allgemeine Naturgeschichte* and registered a pleasant surprise as if he were now addressing himself to a truly scientific work worthy of Kant. To be sure, it contained little exact science (mathematical physics), but this could not be taken for a shortcoming if it was also true that its subject matter demanded rather "a healthy comprehension and a fortunate intuitive presentation; indeed, a vivid phantasy was indispensable for conceiving the thought developed there."[56] That Oettingen was bowing to the tradition in question was equally clear in the rest of his remarks which, for instance, contained a pointed reference to the great difficulty, from the viewpoint "of the latest in science," of Laplace's ring theory, but not a word about the impossibility of Kant's derivation of the circular motion of planets and of their rotation, although Oettingen was aware of the fact that unlike Kant, Laplace started by postulating a rotating nebula.[57]

The edition by Johannes Rahts of the *Allgemeine Naturgeschichte* in the Akademie Ausgabe of Kant's works[58] also showed the impact of the tradition, although in more subtle ways. Its annotations, which were not always the epitome of scholarship, contained mathematical details which gave the impression that Kant used sound theorems.[59] Also, Rahts put no emphasis on the fact that the *Allgemeine Naturgeschichte* was not so much a treatise written in the spirit of Newton in particular and of science in general, but an effort to reformulate teleology. Oversight of this point had already been part of the enthusiastic appraisal of some earlier monographs on Kant the scientist[60] and was not dampened by G. Eberhard's meticulous mathematical analysis of Kant's cosmogony. Actually, Eberhard did his best to take the sting out of his findings by emphasizing the value of insightful ideas, however poorly elaborated, for science. Kant's theory, he wrote, "makes the impression of a grandiose phantasy, of a work of sheer prophecy, or unconscious anticipation of the future," and therefore the *Allgemeine Naturgeschichte* "will remain one of the milestones in the history of our knowledge of the system of the world and in the evolution of human thought in general."[61]

When at the meeting of German scientists in Munich in September 1899 it was declared in a festive oration that "the theory created by Kant and Laplace was ... still valid in its essential features,"[62] no one there present suspected that T. C. Chamberlin and F. R. Moulton (they spoke only of Laplace) had already completed their first papers in which a basic inadequacy of that theory was unhesitatingly laid bare.[63] Both were to be ignored for a long time by admirers of Kant's cosmogony, who at the Meran meeting of German scientists in 1905 wanted to make it a part of the curricula of secondary schools.[64] Against their campaign little if anything could be achieved by the declaration of G. Holzmüller, a not-at-all prominent physicist, according to whom "the theories by Kant and Laplace were impossible with respect to the past and improbable to the highest degree with respect to the future, ... and ought to be considered not as a contribution to exact science but much rather as incurably sick," although his declaration was part of a carefully argued criticism of those theories published by the prominent firm, Teubner in Leipzig. Those strictures went to the heart of the matter as Holzmüller minced no words in pointing out that the *Allgemeine Naturgeschichte* was entirely in the style of Naturphilosophie and steeped in teleology. It was a work in which "phantasy played the principal role. One is faced there with a philosophically colored poem, with an epos of nature which was inspiring in its way and around which there grew a large literature. Under the scalpel of the critic it collapses into its nothingness. Historically, the poem had its role, even scientific ideas were perhaps inspired by it. It does not, however, belong into the textbooks of science."[65] To be sure, a few other, and much more important, figures spoke in the same vein. Kant's theory was subjected to a sustained criticism in the scholarly monograph which F. Nölke published in 1908 on the problem of the evolution of the planetary system.[66] Svante Arrhenius' stinging appraisal of Kant's theory as "being based on a mass of fantastic assumptions which do not correspond to the factual situation," was read by many thousands in the several re-editions of the German translation of Arrhenius' *Varldarnas utveckling*.[67] The general consensus was, however, reflected by the dictum in a booklet on the evolution of the world according to myth and science by Max B. Weinstein, well known for his monographs on mathematical physics. According to him the *Allgemeine Naturgeschichte*, "whose extraordinary significance Humboldt was the first [!] to point out, is now a common treasure of science which though will be corrected in details, has not found yet its equal as a whole."[68] As one who was "at a loss to summarize the work because almost every sentence in it contains a new idea,"[69] Weinstein clearly could not have second thoughts on account of various shortcomings which he found in Kant's theory. Not surprisingly, he was just as unable to understand, and this was his concluding remark, "why Haeckel calls Kant's theory monistic . . . in view of the manner in which Haeckel himself explains monism."[70]

It says something of the sometimes bafflingly slow diffusion of scientific ideas even in modern times that in Weinstein's book, which aimed at giving a survey of all modern forms of cosmogony, there was no mention of Chamberlin and Moulton.[71] The diffusion in question can be impeded by factors acting like political borders, such as the subconscious desire to protect the stature of a national hero. This was obviously at play in Germany in connection with Kant the cosmogonist, but similar was the situation in France where a chauvinistic fondness for Laplace's theory seems to have been the principal cause of a chronic neglect of the cosmogonical publications of Chamberlin and Moulton.[72] That the work of the two Americans was further refined from 1916 on in England by J. Jeans and H. Jeffreys, both strong critics of the nebular hypothesis,[73] was overlooked in Adickes' monograph on Kant the scientist, published in 1924–25, a work whose real value is not commensurate with its massive format and many notes.[74] Adickes, who referred to Chamberlin and Moulton, failed to see that their planetesimal theory represented a cosmogony which was far more than a modification of the one in the *Allgemeine Naturgeschichte*.[75]

The quasi-collision between two stars, which was the starting point of the Chamberlin-Moulton theory and was further refined by Jeans and Jeffreys, was not mentioned by Otto Bück, editor of the most widely used printing of the *Allgemeine Naturgeschichte* during the first half of this century.[76] His oversight matched his failure to call attention to the basic inadequacies of the theories of Kant and Laplace. The chief merit of his edition, apart from its popular inexpensive form, was the careful listing at the bottom of each page of the many printing errors and grammatical obscurities that make the original a cumbersome reading. Of course, such defects cannot cast doubt on the intrinsic value of a book. But constant exposure of the reader to such aspects of the *Allgemeine Naturgeschichte* may help him see its hasty composition and conceptual weaknesses. This in turn may reveal something of the true nature of the glitter of the halo that had been accorded to Kant the cosmogonist.

Those dazzled by that halo could but remain insensitive to the blunt warning given by Charlier in 1925 about the *Allgemeine Naturgeschichte*.[77] Actually, recent developments concerning theories of the origin of the planetary system could even encourage them, though only for superficial reasons, in their admiration for Kant's cosmogony. The substance of these new developments is a reaction to the collisional theories that were in vogue during the first four decades of this century.[78] This reaction is best seen in the light of the fact that according to the collisional theories the solar system is a highly exceptional occurrence and not a regular feature in the stellar universe. The rarity of planetary systems implies in turn the well-nigh uniqueness of a planet, like the earth, as a suitable abode for life, a result hardly to the liking of supporters of evolutionary theories in which intelligent life is a natural and ubiquitous product of cosmic development. Thus when, following the finding by H. N. Russell of irremediable faults with collisional theories,[79] a return was made to the nebular hypothesis, or at least to some sophisticated versions of it, it was soon noted (and with relief) by the Astronomer Royal of England that in the new approach the number of planetary systems in the universe appeared again to be enormously large.[80] True, the originators of the new approach, Alfvén, Peek, and Weizsäcker, did not emphasize that implication.[81] Yet, unquestionably, it is that implication which works as a powerful motivation behind the various theories proposed during the past thirty or so years and serves as another workshop of the glory of Kant the cosmogonist.

As in the past, and this was already the case with Kant himself, a theory can easily be taken for something approaching fact. In the process caution is thrown to the wind, as can be seen in the vogue enjoyed by bold estimates of the number of earth-like planets in the Milky Way[82] and in the funding of expensive projects to find planetary systems and intelligent life elsewhere in the universe. The dead barrenness found on the surface of the moon and even of Mars (this much vaunted candidate as abode for life outside the earth)[83] did not surprise those who kept in mind the difference between obviously fragile theories and hard facts. Sanguine calculators of the number of planetary systems in the Milky Way (to say nothing of faraway galaxies) do not seem to belong to this class. They seem to be unable to bow before the devastating verdict served on their calculations by W. H. McCrea, himself a proponent of a dazzling but faulty theory which implies that planetary systems are regular occurrences. What he stated early in this decade still retains its full validity: "In modern times, there is a tendency to assert quite blithely that there must be millions of planetary systems throughout the Universe and that many of these must contain life like ours. But we have no grounds for such easy inference. We do not know how the solar system was formed and until we do we cannot infer how many other such systems there may be; and we cannot observe any others directly, although there is *some* observational evidence in a few cases. We do not know how life started and so even if we could infer something about other planetary systems we cannot infer how many may have produced life."[84]

Such was the voice of sound criticism which in matters relating to the history of scientific topics was still to assert itself, when half a century ago, the bicentenary of Kant's birth was celebrated. Historians of science had not yet formed a group which by its sizeable presence would impose respect for accuracy on other academics dealing with their subject matter. At any rate, not all commemorative volumes published in connection with that bicentenary contained an appraisal of Kant the scientist and/or cosmogonist.[85] When he was considered as such, the burden of an already hallowed, though hollow, appraisal was in evidence, an appraisal largely unconcerned for the actual record. Nor was myopia concerning purely scientific matters absent. Thus S. G. Martin, one of the eleven contributors to the symposium held in Kant's honor at Northwestern University in 1924, was aware of the irreconcilability with thermodynamics of Kant's vision of a universe continually reborn from its ashes, though not of the basic inadequacy of Kant's derivation of circular planetary orbits. His conclusion, "Kant's early scientific essays were surely sufficient to secure him a permanent place in the history of science—although, indeed, that might not mean that his name would be frequently heard at the present day," was relatively moderate.[86]

Quite different was, at a similar symposium held at Yale University, the performance of Harlow Shapley, a leading figure among American astronomers and the chief champion of the view that spiral nebulae were not galaxies independent of and comparable in size to our Milky Way. Shapley started with the declaration that Kant's treatise on cosmogony was "the finest objective synthesis of science up to that time," to which he later added that Kant was "equipped with practically all of the science of his day," and that, considering his aptitude and method, he was a "natural scientist of the highest order. He could undoubtedly have been in the direct line of cosmic immortals—Copernicus, Kepler, and Newton."[87]

Such a resounding claim of highest scientific glory was, as one may suspect, forged in a workshop which, as Shapley's specifics about Kant's cosmogony were to show, had for its chief trademark a woeful unfamiliarity with the history of science. Of the four points, which according to Shapley tied modern cosmogony to that of Kant, the first was "Kant's pregnant suggestion concerning the origin of planets," about which Shapley said that Kant's conception "is better able to withstand the criticism of modern astronomical research" than would Laplace's theory. The prime advantage of Kant's theory was "its meteoric character, which frees it from the supposition of a hot gas, rotating as a unit and casting off rings." This partly contradicted Shapley's next remark that Kant made an error by assuming that this primordial solar nebula was at rest and that "since some original condition must be assumed, it is simplest, as Laplace foresaw, to assume original rotation rather than rest."[88] Concerning the second point, the nebulae, Shapley, in clear evidence of his failure to consult the source material (unless Hastie's *Kant's Cosmogony* could be called such), claimed that unlike Kant most of his contemporaries, such as Wright and Lambert, "confined their speculations mainly to the Milky Way."[89] About the Milky Way Shapley praised Kant for following "his speculations concerning galactic structure . . . with precise logic and inspired literary expression,"[90] a worse than hollow rhetoric. One can only gasp in disbelief on finding Shapley declare that Kant's arguments on behalf of the extragalactic status of most nebulae are "practically the same as those used by modern proponents of the theory that celestial spirals are other galaxies like our own."[91] The third point concerned the center of the universe. Here Shapley should have laid bare Kant's naive assertion of an absolute physical center in an infinite Euclidean universe. He merely referred to the untenability of seeing, with Kant, in Sirius the center of the Milky Way.[92]

The fourth point was the "shortening of the day."[93] Shapley, who praised Kant's originality of postulating on account of tidal friction a retardation of the earth's axial rotation, should have obviously spoken of "lengthening." His sole excuse for the minor and major blunders of his lecture was his reference to "the hurried and harrassed scientists of the present day," who overburdened by their own research, ignore Kant as well as his predecessors.[94] Understandable enough, but then they should not take it upon themselves to pontificate on topics relating to the history of science, not least on topics of their own special field, if they have no time to research the source material and even lack willingness to consult a historian.

The same holds true of philosophers riveting their speculations on science. Their number is steadily growing ever since quantum theory and relativity have occupied the center stage. From the 1920s on they repeatedly made the glory of Kant the scientist more resplendent with catchy phrases notable for their prominent context and for their failure to evidence familiarity with the source material. Millions were told in A. N. Whitehead's famed *Science and the Modern World*, first published in 1926, that Kant not only had the potentiality of becoming one of the greatest scientists, but was in fact a scientist.[95] A decade or so later, F. S. C. Northrop credited Kant with the explanation of the eccentricity of planetary and cometary orbits and celebrated the *Allgemeine Naturgeschichte* as "one of the greatest achievements in the history of science" owing to its "brilliance of imaginative conception combined with the rigor prescribed by restriction to the principles of Newtonian mechanics."[96] In the 1960s G. Buchdahl presented Kant as "the philosopher of science par excellence" without appraising his competence in matters scientific.[97] Such confidence may have been considerably strengthened by the fact that on the one-hundred-and-fiftieth anniversary of Kant's death, K. Popper celebrated him to millions of listeners of BBC as one of the greatest cosmologists.[98]

On the bicentenary of the publication of the *Critique of Pure Reason* many philosophers, and especially philosophers of science, will do their best to keep active with similar rhetoric that workshop in which the halo around Kant the cosmogonist-scientist has been forged for over a century. The forgery done by them will not lack some justification, and even an appealing one on a cursory look. Long gone are the days when it was fashionable to speak of science as a concern for facts of observation, for data of experiments, and for these alone. Ours are actually the days when something has already been perceived of the fallacy of the opposite extreme, so fashionable in recent years, that in science all great breakthroughs—revolutions, according to the still largely unsuspected jargon—are breakthroughs of ideas. It is in such a perspective that the *Allgemeine Naturgeschichte* may appear as a breakthrough, a great scientific first. Kant was certainly one of the first to propose the correct idea of the Milky Way, and the very first to claim that nebulous stars or nebulae are so many stellar systems similar to our own galaxy. Although some before him went on record as supporters of a mechanical explanation of the universe, and Descartes even gave an ambitious account of it, it was in the *Allgemeine Naturgeschichte* that there appeared in print for the first time a mechanical genesis of the entire universe with an unmistakably modern ring and sweep.

Does the *Allgemeine Naturgeschichte* qualify therefore as a great scientific classic and its author as a budding scientific genius? Those who see things in this way do so not without a plausibility which is subtly intangible and therefore irrefutable in the strict sense. Against their view it would be in vain to try to settle in a precise way the just measure of recognition due to the anticipation of a great scientific idea. While the history of ideas is a laboratory, it is not a place of quantitative evaluations. Yet it is precisely in that latter connection that scientific ideas have a special status. Unless tested against experimental and quantitative standards, they remain but ideas severed from reality and of little help for man to master it. There were at least a few before Copernicus who took the idea of heliocentrism seriously, though not to the extent of casting it, as Copernicus did, into a quantitatively elaborated system that could be tested. It was that aspect of Copernicus' work which turned it into a great scientific classic and not his faith in heliocentrism, important as it was. Scientific history from Copernicus to Kepler and beyond is much too clear on this point. No different is the case in connection with the step that carried science from the stars to their systems. Kant's discourse on the Milky Way and nebulae—and the matching dicta of Lambert and of Wright—made no impact precisely because they were not supported by observational evidence which came only with Herschel's telescopes. Incredible as it may seem, a full generation after those three had gone on record with their ideas, Herschel still could submit a very similar idea as if it were original. Most importantly, his discourse was not merely a happy speculation, but steeped in an amazing wealth of data relevant to it. It was equally important for Herschel's success that what he said on the Milky Way and galaxies was not made part of a fanciful portrayal of the entire universe, which plagued alike the *Allgemeine Naturgeschichte*, the *Cosmologische Briefe*, and the *Original Theory*. This is why the small valuable part in them remained a barren seed.

The case for viewing the cosmogonical part of the *Allgemeine Naturgeschichte*, namely, its theory of the evolution of the planetary system, as a great classic of science, is even weaker. Well trained physicists could only smile at the incompetent self-confidence with which Kant handled "Newtonian principles" (leaving largely alone Newtonian physics) and reached a few faulty quantitative conclusions. At any rate, neither in his time, nor a century or two later, had the *Allgemeine Naturgeschichte* an influence on scientists. That influence was exercised by Laplace, not by Kant. That the latter is remembered admiringly in modern cosmogonical works is a hollow cliché. For their fondly parroting that cliché philosophers[99] are less guilty than those men of science with whom it has become, for the past century or so, a fashion to claim that science has solved the problem of the formation of the solar system—and essentially along lines proposed by Kant (or by Laplace).

Philosophical, as other (including scientific) fashions, can at best be exposed for what they are, but not overcome, by arguments. The bicentenary of the *Critique* will revitalize a certain fashion in thinking which is typical of anyone saddled with an a priori bent of mind and with a reluctance to surrender to reality. Perhaps this translation will be helpful in showing that the apriorism (and subjectivism) of the *Critique* is already raising its bewitching head in the *Allgemeine Naturgeschichte*. For a historian of science it ought to seem particularly telling that, for all his criticism of Kant's cosmogony, a most competent cosmogonist like Nölke could in 1908 bring his book on the problem of the evolution of our planetary system to a conclusion with the following statement:

"We are of the conviction that the evolution, which man sees and which he formulates in his thought, would be wrongly taken for something absolute, independent of his thinking. When we recognize the idealistic character of our entire cognition and of its objects, to which as perceptions belong all—the earth, the sun, and the infinity of the stellar realm—, when we explain to ourselves that all these things have an existence only in our intellect, and when we finally perceive with our great philosopher, Kant, that the infinite space in which they are all ordered, and the infinite time through which we follow their evolution backward and forward, are nothing else but the forms of perception of the animal knowledge, then we will no longer ask toward what all these things are developing, once after the cooling of the sun there will be on the earth no living beings in whose mind such an evolution finds a representation. For with the death of the last intelligent being, space and time and with them all suns and worlds sink together into themselves, and nothing else remains than that which is eternal, the timeless and spaceless primordial being, which carries us in itself and through us the entire world, and which can issue itself in other modes of perception and worlds, once the evolutionary possibilities of this world have exhausted themselves."[100]

By 1908 enough was worked out in quantum theory and in relativity to make it clear (except for a diehard Kantian) that Kant's doctrine of time and space was useless for science. But Nölke's passage has a deeper significance than merely showing the delay with which the philosophical implications of new scientific breakthroughs make their impact. The significance lies in the fact that the world view of the passage is the one proclaimed in the *Allgemeine Naturgeschichte*, whereas its philosophy is a genuine echo of the *Critique*. That the two could come together in one passage in an able cosmogonical work will appear a coincidence only to those unmindful of the same inner logic which works everywhere where reason is at work. Historians of philosophy and philosophically sensitive historians of science know of many instances of this. Thus, when the prime objective of reason is no longer the universe but reason itself, the universe disappears and science itself becomes a struggle with mere concepts, nay the struggle of the concepts themselves for survival, an enterprise with dubious ties to reality. For a historian and philosopher of science, and especially of cosmology, the coming bicentenary of the *Critique* will therefore appear an event rich in illustrations of the working of that inner logic. Its inescapability is evidenced by that bondage in which modern philosophy and especially its most avidly cultivated branch, philosophy of science, is with respect to Kant. Instead of being a respectable indebtedness, the bondage in question is an imprisonment into that subtle anthropocentrism where Kant trapped philosophy. The Copernican turn, which Kant believed to have achieved in philosophy, is a far cry from the one connected with the name of Copernicus, whose faith in the fully objective rationality of the universe opened the road toward increasingly less subjective and therefore more scientific views of the cosmos.[101] Whatever Kant's intentions, his "critical" work inevitably leads to the most uncritical philosophical stance: subjective idealism, if not plain solipsism. The reason for this is that apriorism which is the dominating note not only of the *Critique* but already of the *Allgemeine Naturgeschichte*. The two have also another common trait, a cumbersome and often unclear phraseology, the cause of no small travail for the translator.

VI. *Translator's Travails*

German language and obscure style are often taken to be synonymous, and not without reason. Yet, plain lucid diction can be achieved in German no less readily than in any major language. Christian Gellert, one of the two German literary figures mentioned in the *Allgemeine Naturgeschichte*, achieved fame partly because his style was plain and unaffected. There were others too in that still heavily baroque Germany of the mid-eighteenth century who would not bend their knees to the fashion of lengthy convolutions. Kant was not one of them and yet his style was reputedly clearer than the style of many of contemporary German authors. Short phrases occur but rarely in the *Allgemeine Naturgeschichte* and hardly ever in succession. More often Kant's phrases girate for over twenty lines and on occasion stretch to thirty. One indeed wonders why Heine singled out that work as an evidence of the "excellent and witty style" which Kant was able to produce before he was engulfed in the writing of the *Critique*.[1] The *Allgemeine Naturgeschichte* contains not a few pages that would have justified Heine's judgment of the *Critique* as a work of "grey, dry, wrapping-paper style."[2]

What Kant, in Heine's opinion, could not achieve in the *Critique*, namely, the marshalling of new words for new thoughts,[3] was also true of the *Allgemeine Naturgeschichte*, a work whose author certainly aimed at being original. Whatever originality was there, it was often cast in long phrases, which—Cicero is the classic example—are not necessarily detrimental to clarity. But in Kant's case length proved to be a harbinger of stylistic perculiarities, the list of which was recited somewhat dolefully by Norman Kemp Smith, renowned for his translation of the *Critique*, in a phrase that can hardly be improved upon. Kant, he noted, "crowds so much into each sentence, that he is constrained to make undue use of parentheses, and, what is still more troublesome to the reader, to rely upon particles, pronouns and genders to indicate the connections between the parts of the sentence. Sometimes, when our main clue is a gender, we find more than one preceding substantive with which it may agree."[4] Although, unlike in the *Critique*, no key word is used in the *Allgemeine Naturgeschichte* now with one, now with another gender, the length of its phrases remains a challenge for the translator. Many of them could be broken into shorter sentences, an obvious advantage if the reader's comfort is the translation's main objective. The procedure may even bring out that clarity which Kant's thought may have possessed, but which he was unable to convey time and again. Smith certainly provided a text which is clearer in English than in the original and certainly helps the reader against becoming unduly discouraged by an exposition already obstruse on account of its subject matter. But if the translation's aim is to give an impression as close as possible to the one which is conveyed by the original, then even its punctuation ought to be retained to a fair degree. This translation certainly does not have for its aim that plastic surgery which amounts to making the dark plain, the crooked straight, and the rough smooth, a performance for which Hastie's translation was given so fervent an accolade.[5] Of course, in places (mostly short phrases and scientific expressions), which imposed on Hastie a close rendering of the original, no differences between his and this translation will be noticeable. As to the long sentences, their breaking into short ones is a risk even when length has not been to the detriment of clarity, as nuances and emphases are easily lost in the process. As a rule, long sentences and obscurity go hand in hand and reflect the author's inability to organize his train of thought.

Indeed, it was the author of a work on Kant's criticism of metaphysics, a criticism usually taken for the epitome of pure reason, who spoke of "dubious grammar, gratuitously ugly expressions and relative pronouns with ambiguous antecedents" as so many factors that have no right to be in a book just because it is on philosophy. To be sure, the author in question did not explicitly say that these features characterize Kant's style. He merely suggested that had Kant's manuscripts been in the care of such a firm-handed editor as was the case with his own work, there would have been "no occasion for a book" on Kant's criticism of metaphysics.[6] It seems that dubious grammar, relative pronouns with ambiguous antecedents, and the like embellishing the style of some great philosophers can help perpetuate scholarly interest in their thought. Whatever the added measure of profundity that may have on this account devolved on the *Critique*,[7] a work of hasty composition and faulty grammar,[8] the *Allgemeine Naturgeschichte* reveals no profundity even on that score. Its often imperfect phraseology, and the obscurity of thought which it carries, would therefore be remedied in an English translation only for reasons that have at most tenuous ties with scholarship.

Admiration for a philosopher may have various scholarly grounds, but these were notably absent in the case of Hastie as a translator into English of the *Allgemeine Naturgeschichte*. The reasons Hastie gave for his admiration of Kant the philosopher are shallow at best. It is such admiration that prompted him to overlook the obvious and declare: Kant's style in the *Allgemeine Naturgeschichte* is "clear, forcible, nervous throughout, and often raises in its physical descriptions to the picturesque and sublime."[9] A brave declaration, which should have made any perceptive reader of Hastie's translation somewhat nervous, as in Hastie's own admission the French translator, Charles Wolf, felt rather differently.[10] Although Hastie gave only a partial glimpse of what Wolf had said in this connection, he revealed enough of Wolf's apprehension. Wolf begged his reader not to impute to him "the obscurities which he finds on occasion. They really exist, I believe, in Kant's work."[11] The latter was rendered all too often in paraphrase by Wolf who, however, claimed that he refrained from ever substituting a paraphrase "to the sometimes vague and ill-defined expression of his [Kant's] thought" lest to risk a betrayal of it, and insisted that his translation was a rendering "word for word as much as possible of the original."[12] Even in paraphrase the work could prove rough going for many a reader, whom Wolf begged to have the patience to follow to the very end the author's "sometimes long and embarrassed developments" in order to be recompensed "by some truly eloquent pages full of philosophical depth."[13]

Hastie's ability to see clarity everywhere in the *Allgemeine Naturgeschichte* contrasts not only with the difficulties experienced by the French translator but also with the exasperation voiced, only two years before Hastie brought out his translation, by A. J. von Oettingen, an editor of the German original. In facing up to a relatively not too long (only eighteen lines) phrase, Oettingen exclaimed: "The entire sentence belongs among the most confused and poorly stylised sentences of the entire treatise." Moreover, the phrase in question was, by Oettingen's admission, of pivotal importance for the science of Kant's cosmogony.[14]

Apart from difficulties posed by an often convoluted, at times incomplete and confusing syntax, the translator of the *Allgemeine Naturgeschichte* will find enough problems with its vocabulary. In line with the Germanistic trend gaining strength in his time Kant often prefers the German equivalents of standard Latin words. Thus, although he does not disdain the word "Universum," he clearly prefers "Weltbau" and "Weltgebäude," both of which contain a nuance that can be saved only by translating them as "world-edifice." "Zentrifugalkfraft" (centrifugal force) is a rare occurrence in the *Allgemeine Naturgeschichte* and so is "Gravitation." Concerning the latter, Kant uses two German equivalents, "Fall" and "Senkungskraft," and does so, apparently, not only for the sake of variety but also because often the context itself indicates a motion which is sinking rather than falling. Hence the difference between "force of fall" and "force of sinking." Again, Kant is not reluctant to use words such as "zirkelrundig" (circularly round) which must have been an irritating pleonasm even in his late-baroque times. Although he never writes "Planetensystem" (system of planets), he uses on occasion the expression "planetarische System" (planetary system). Thus his "Sonnenwelt" calls for "solar world" rather than solar system. Again, the English "stuff" may not be a stylish rendering of Kant's "Stoff," but since he used "Materie" just as often, he supposedly meant something different, however slightly, by the two. While "Kugel" rendered as "globe" would not raise eyebrows, "Klumpen" may reveal itself as one of those "gratuitously ugly expressions" when rendered, as it ought to be, as "lumps" however celestial, such as "Sonnenklumpen" or "solar lumps."

Certain German words have, as one could expect, no strict and convenient English equivalents. Unfortunately, two of them, "Bestimmung" (determination in the sense of being specified) and "Entfernung" (being distant) together with its verb and past participle forms, appear all too often in the text to leave the translator free of headaches for at least a few moments. Headache comes even with such picturesque words as "Federkraft" (springforce), when it has to be rendered as plain elasticity. The greatest difficulty was caused by two words, which have no English equivalents and are yet of crucial importance in the physics of Kant's solution of the most enduring problem of cosmogony. The two words are "Schwung" and "Schwungskraft" (circularly or rather tangentially directed impulse and force). Rendering them as centrifugal force, if there is one, would be clearly a glossing over of the difficulty which Newton felt insuperable, namely, the derivation of a thrust-like impulse or force directed at a right angle to the fall toward the center of attraction.

If these difficulties were not enough, there is, for a translator intent on providing as faithful a rendering of the original as possible, the problem of Kant's quoting Pope's *Essay on Man* time and again. Its lines are ingrained so much in English memory as to make it a most reluctant decision not to quote them as they are in the original, but to give instead an English translation of a pedestrian paraphrase of Pope's classic by the German baroque poet, B. H. Brockes, hardly renowned even in his own time and now completely forgotten, whose translation was used by Kant.[15] Since Brockes' translation of Pope was printed with the English original facing the German text, Kant could have guessed the atrocious character of Brockes' performance. Worse, Kant was not even careful with Brockes' lines which, presumably, were not the only German translation of Pope available for him. That Pope could be done far better justice in German and even by one not remembered as an outstanding poet, Heinrich Christian Kretsch, was already demonstrated four short years after the publication of the *Allgemeine Naturgeschichte*.[16] So much in justification of a decision to put Pope's name under English lines which, rendering as they do Brockes, are a far cry from the beauty and conciseness of what Pope said. Fortunately, unlike Kant's lampooning of Swedenborg in 1766, the *Allgemeine Naturgeschichte* contains no words which prompted the former work's Victorian translator to cover up the disgrace with dots.[17] The disgrace of the *Allgemeine Naturgeschichte* is rather that boastful attitude in the face of grave scientific and philosophical difficulties, which at times did not even take cover under protestations of diffidence and modesty, unless an unclear style, no small problem for the translator, was the cover itself.

Allgemeine
Naturgeschichte
und
Theorie des Himmels,
oder

Versuch

von der Verfassung und dem mechanischen Ursprunge

des ganzen Weltgebäudes

nach

Newtonischen Grundsätzen

abgehandelt.

* * * * * * * * * * * * * * *

Königsberg und Leipzig,

bey Johann Friederich Petersen, 1755.

Universal

NATURAL HISTORY

and

THEORY OF THE HEAVENS,

or

An Essay
on the Constitution and Mechanical
Origin
OF THE ENTIRE WORLD-EDIFICE

treated

according to Newtonian Principles,

Königsberg and Leipzig
at Johann Friederich Petersen, 1755

[a2r]

TO THE MOST SERENE, MOST POWERFUL KING AND LORD

SIR

FREDERICK,

King of Prussia,

Margrave of Brandenburg, High Chancellor and Elector of the Holy Roman Empire, Sovereign and Arch-Duke of Silesia, etc. etc. etc

TO MY MOST GRACIOUS KING AND LORD

[a3r]

MOST SERENE,

MOST POWERFUL KING,

Most Gracious

KING AND LORD!

The feeling of personal unworthiness and the radiance of the throne cannot make my timidity too fainthearted as the kindness, [a3v]which the most gracious monarch extends over all his subjects with equal magnanimity instills in me the hope that the boldness in which I get involved will not be viewed with ungracious eyes. Herewith I lay with the most submissive reverence at the feet of your Royal Majesty one of the most trifling specimens of that zeal with which the Academies of your Royal Highness are animated [a4r] under the encouragement and protection of their enlightened Sovereign to the emulation of other nations in the sciences.[1] How contented would I be, if the present essay should succeed in obtaining its monarch's supreme approval of the efforts whereby the humblest and most respectful subject is invariably anxious to make himself useful [a4v] to his Fatherland.

With the deepest devotion till death

Your ROYAL MAJESTY'S

most humble servant,

Königsberg
March 14, 1755.

The Author[2]

80

Opening Discourse

I have chosen a topic which is capable [of instilling] right at the outset a large portion of readers with unfavorable prejudice from the side of its intrinsic difficulty as well as in respect to religion. To discover the systematic factor which ties together the great members of the created realm in the whole extent of infinity, to derive through mechanical laws the formation of the celestial bodies themselves and the origin of their motions; such ideas seem to surpass very far the forces of human reason. On the other hand, religion threatens with a solemn accusation against the temerity [a5v] with which one emboldens to assign to a nature left to itself such processes in which one rightly perceived the immediate hand of the Supreme Being and is anxious to find a defense of atheists[3] in the inquisitiveness of such considerations. I see well all these difficulties and yet I will not be dispirited. I sense the entire strength of obstacles which arise in opposition and yet I do not despair. I have ventured, on the basis of a slight conjecture, to undertake a dangerous journey and I already see the promontories of new lands. On these, [those] who have the courage to continue the investigation will set foot and will have the satisfaction of designating with their own names the same [lands].

I did not decide on starting this undertaking until I have seen with security in respect to the duties of religion. My [a6r] zeal was redoubled when at each step I saw the clouds, which seemed to hide a monstrosity behind their darkness, dissipate, and after their dispersion the splendour of the Highest Being break forth with the most vivid brilliance. Since I know that these efforts are free of all reproach, I will confidently present that which well-meaning or even weak minds would find objectionable in my plan and I am ready to submit it to the sternness of orthodox areopagus[4] with a candor which is the mark of an upright mentality. The attorney of the creed may therefore be allowed to let first his reasons be heard.

If the world-edifice with all [its] order and beauty is only the effect of a matter abandoned to its universal laws of motion, if the blind mechanism of the forces of nature knows how to develop itself

81

so splendidly from the chaos [a6v] and to reach by itself such a perfection, then the demonstration of [the existence] of a divine Author, which one derives from the consideration of the beauty of the world-edifice, is wholly invalidated, nature is sufficient to herself, the divine government is unnecessary, Epicurus[5] lives again in the midst of Christendom, and an unholy philosophy tramples underfoot the faith which provides for it a clear light to enlighten philosophy itself.

Even if I found this objection well grounded, the conviction which I have about the infallibility of divine truths is so strong that I would hold all that contradicts them sufficiently refuted and would reject it all.[6] But precisely the harmony which I find between my system and [the truth of] religion heightens my confidence with respect to all difficulties [a7r] to an unfrightened abandon.

I recognize the whole value of those proofs which one derives from the beauty and perfect disposition [ordering] of the world-edifice for a confirmation [of the existence] of the most wise Author. If one does not resolutely resist all persuading, one must be won over to such incontrovertible reasons [proofs]. But I assert: that by making use of these proofs in a wrong way the defenders of religion perpetuate the conflict with naturalists[7] inasmuch as they present without need a weak side.

One is wont to notice and point out the harmonies, the beauty, the purpose and a perfect relation of means to these [same purposes] in nature.[8] But while one extols nature in this regard, [a7v] in other respect one seeks to slight nature again. This suitable disposition, it is said, is foreign to her; were she to be abandoned to her universal laws, she would not produce but disorder. The harmonies show an alien hand which knew how to force into a wise plan a matter deserted by all regularity. But I answer: if the universal laws of matter are similarly a consequence from the highest plan, then presumably they can have no other destinations than the ones which themselves aim at fulfilling the plan which the highest Wisdom has set to Itself; or if this is not so, should not one be lured into the temptation of believing that at least matter and its universal laws were independent and that the wisest Power, which knew how to make use of them so splendidly, is though great, yet not infinite, [a8r] though powerful, yet not all-sufficient?

The defender of religion is worried that these harmonies, which can be explained from a natural disposition of matter, should prove the independence of nature from divine providence. He admits very plainly that if one can discover for all order in the world-edifice natural grounds, which can produce all that order from the most universal and essential properties of matter, then it becomes unnecessary to appeal to a highest government. The naturalist finds his calculation fulfilled by not disputing this presupposition. Rather, he adduces examples which demonstrate the fruitfulness of universal natural laws in perfectly beautiful results and exposes the true believer to danger through such reasonings which in his hands [a8v] could [should have] become invincible weapons. I will adduce examples. It has already been several times put forward as one of the most evident proofs of a benevolent Providence, which watches over man, that in the hottest regions of the earth the seawinds sweep over the land, as if they were called just at such a time when the heated land most needs their cooling, and refresh it. For example, in the island of Jamaica,[9] as soon as the sun rises so high that it throws the maximum of bearable heat on the earth, shortly after 9 o'clock in the morning, a wind begins to rise from the sea which blows from every direction over the land; its strength increases in the measure in which the elevation of the sun increases. About 1 o'clock in the afternoon, when it is naturally hottest, the wind is most violent and subsides again gradually with the setting of the sun, so that towards evening [b1r] the same stillness rules as at sunrise. Without this desirable arrangement the island would be uninhabitable. All coastal lands, which lie in that zone, enjoy this same benefit. It is most necessary for them because they, being the lowest regions of dry land, suffer the greatest heat; for the higher regions of the land, where this sea wind does not reach, are less in need of it, because their higher site places them into a cooler region of the air. Is not all this most beautiful, are not [here indeed in view] visible goals which are implemented through wisely applied means? But, on the contrary, the naturalist must find natural causes of all this in the general properties of air without [claiming] the right to assume special dispositions [made for that purpose]. He rightly observes that even if no man lived on such an island [b1v] these sea-winds must display periodic motions and through no other property than that of the air, namely, through elasticity and gravitation, and with no regard to that purpose, be it merely the indispensable necessity [of such a cooling] for the growth of plants. The heat of the sun removes the equilibrium of the air, inasmuch as it rarifies the air which is over the land and thereby prompts the cooler sea-air to rise from its place and take the place of land-air.[10]

What useful advantages do not [indeed] the winds generally have for the earth[11] and what use is not made of them by the cleverness of man [!]; nevertheless, to produce these advantages no other arrangements were needed than these same universal properties of air and heat which regardless of these aims must be available on the earth.

[b2r] Admit, the freethinker says here, that if useful and goal-

directed arrangements can be deduced from the most universal and simplest laws of nature, then there is no need for a special government of a supreme Wisdom and thus you are faced here with proofs which will catch you according to your own very thinking. The entire and especially the unorganized [inorganic] nature is full of such proofs which help [one] to recognize that matter, though operating through the mechanism of its forces, has a certain correctness in its results and does justice with no [external] compulsion to the rules of adaptedness. Should a well-intentioned [believer] challenge, in order to save the good cause of religion, this capacity of the universal natural laws, he will put himself in an embarrassing predicament and, through a poor defense, provide to unbelief occasion for triumph.

[b2v] But let us see how these reasons, which in the hands of the opponents frighten one as harmful, are rather strong weapons to challenge them. Matter, which operates according to its most universal laws, brings forth through its natural disposition, or if one is to call it such, through a blind mechanism appropriate results which appear to be the design of a highest Wisdom. Air, water, heat generate, when considered as left to themselves, winds, clouds, rain, storms, which moisten the land, and all useful results without which nature ought to remain sad, desolate, and unfruitful. They, however, bring forth [these] results not by sheer accident or chance which could have just as easily become harmful, but one can also see that they are through their natural laws limited to work in no other [b3r] than in this manner. What should one think of that harmony? How would it be possible that things of different natures[12] should have, in connection with one another, seemingly worked for such excellent co-ordination and beauties, nay for the purpose of such beings which in a sense find themselves outside the realm of dead matter, namely for the profit of men and animals, if they did not bespeak a common origin, namely, an infinite intellect in which all things were designed in respect of essential properties? If their natures were in themselves and independently of one another necessary,[13] what an astonishing accident, or rather what an impossibility would it be that they should have matched one another in their natural tendencies [b3v] so closely as if a superior wise choice might have have co-ordinated them [?].

Now, I confidently apply this [reasoning] to my present undertaking. I assume the matter of the entire world to be universally scattered and I make a perfect chaos out of it.[14] I see, in accordance with the established laws of attraction, the stuff forming itself and through repulsion modify its motion. I enjoy the satisfaction of seeing, without the aid of arbitrary notions, a well-ordered whole arise under the direction of established laws, a whole so similar to that world system which we have before our very eyes that I cannot prevent myself from holding it to be the same. This unexpected unfolding at large of the orderliness of nature will be at first suspect to me, because so composite a correctness [b4r] rests thereby on such a poor and simple foundation. I finally instruct myself from the previously given consideration: that such an unfolding of nature is to her not something unheard of but that her essential striving necessarily implies it and that this is the most splendid indication of her dependence[15] on that primary Being which is the source of [all] beings and has in itself their first laws of operation. This insight redoubles my trust in the plan which I have laid out. The confidence increases with every step which I make as I further proceed and my pusillanimity vanishes.

But the defence of my system, one will say, is equally a defense of Epicurus' opinions which have the greatest similarity to it. I will not wholly disclaim all agreement with him. [b4v] Many have become atheists through the appearance of such reasons which on more exact weighing could have most strongly convinced them about the certainty [of the existence] of the highest Being.[16] The consequences, which a perverted mind draws from irreproachable principles, are often very objectionable and such were the conclusions of Epicurus, although his conception was characteristic of the penetration of a great mind.

I will not deny either that the theory of Lucretius[17] or of his precursors, Epicurus, Leucippus, and Democritus,[18] have much similarity with mine. I set the first state of matter, as do those philosophers, in the universal dispersion of the basic stuff, or of atoms as they are called by them, of all celestial bodies. Epicurus posited a gravity, which drove these elementary particles to sink, and this [b5r] seems not to be very different from the Newtonian attraction which I assume; he also gave them a certain deviation from the rectilinear motion of fall, although he had absurd notions concerning its cause and consequences;[19] this deviation, which we deduce from the repulsive forces of the particles, corresponds in a sense to the alteration of the rectilinear fall; finally, the vortices, which arose from the confused motion of atoms, were a chief point in the doctrine of Leucippus and Democritus, and one will encounter them also in ours.[20] So much affinity with a doctrine, which was the true theory of atheism in antiquity, will not draw mine into the company of its errors. Even in the most senseless opinions which [b5v] can acquire approval among men, one can at times notice something true. A false basic proposition or a few unproven connecting propositions lead men from the footpath of truth through hidden detours into the precipice. Still, there remains, regardless of the similarity indicated, an essential difference between the old cosmogony and the present, so that quite opposite conclusions may be drawn from it.

The aforementioned teachers of the mechanical origination of the world-edifice derived all order, that can be ascertained in it, from the accidental chance which makes the atoms collide so felicitously that they form a well-ordered whole. Epicurus himself was in fact so impudent that he demanded that the atoms should deviate without any cause from their straight motion in order that they [b6r] could meet with one another. All [those teachers] together pushed this absurdity so far that they placed the origin of all living creatures in that very blind concourse and actually derived reason from unreason. However, in my doctrine I find matter tied to certain necessary laws.[21] I see in its complete dissolution and dispersion a beautiful and orderly whole to develop quite naturally. This does not happen through accident and from imprecision, but, so it will be noted, that the natural properties bring this about also necessarily. Should not one thereby be prompted to ask: why should matter have precisely such laws which aim at order and harmony? Was it indeed possible that many things, each of which has a nature independent from the others, should be disposed by [b6v] themselves exactly in such a way that a well-ordered whole should thereby arise, and when they do this, is not on hand an undeniable proof of the common nature of their first origin which ought to be an all-sufficient highest Reason in which the natures of things had been designed for united purposes?

Matter, which is the original stuff of all things, is also bound to certain laws and, if freely abandoned to them, must necessarily produce beautiful connections. Matter has no freedom to deviate from the plan of perfection. As it also finds itself subject to an upmost wise purpose, it must necessarily be directed into such harmonious relations through a First Cause dominating it, *and there is a God precisely because nature can proceed even in* [b7r] *chaos in no other way than regularly and orderly.*[22]

I have so high an opinion of the correct mentality of those who do honor to this plan by testing it that I feel assured that the reasons as indicated will, even where they cannot remove all concern about harmful conclusions from my system, at least place the purity of my aim beyond doubt. If nevertheless there are ill-meaning zealots, who hold it to be the proper duty of their holy calling to graft sinister interpretation to the most innocent views,[23] then I am reassured that their judgment will have exactly the opposite effect among reasonable men. One will not at any rate berob me of the right which Cartesius, when he dared to explain the formation of celestial bodies from purely mechanical laws, enjoyed on the part of equitable judges [b7v] of those times.[24] I will therefore quote the author of the universal World

86

History: "However, we cannot but think [of] the essay of that phil-osopher, who endeavored to account for the formation of the world in a certain time from a rude matter, by the sole continuation of a motion once impressed, and reduced to a few simple and general laws; or of others, *who have since attempted the same, with more applause, from the original properties of matter, with which it was indued at its creation*, is so far from being criminal or injurious to GOD, as some have imagined, that it is rather giving a more sublime idea of its infinite wisdom."*[25]

I have sought to remove the difficulties which seem to threaten my propositions from the side of religion. [b8r] There are a few no smaller difficulties with respect to the topic itself. Even though it be true, people will say, that God has deposited in the forces of nature a certain secret art so that it may develop by itself from the chaos into a perfect world system, will man's mind, which is inept in the smallest matters, be capable of fathoming recondite properties in so great a subject? Such an undertaking means as much as when one said, *Give me only matter and I will build you a world out of it.*[26] Cannot the weakness of your insights, which fails in the smallest things that present them-selves to your sense daily and at close range, teach you that it is in vain [to try] to discover the immeasurable and that which took place in nature before there was a [fully developed] world? I annihilate this difficulty inasmuch as I clearly show that [b8v] precisely this inves-tigation among all those that may arise in the study of nature, is the one in which one can reach the origin in the easiest and safest manner. Just as among all tasks of the study of nature none can be solved with more correctness and certainty than the true structure of the world-edifice at large, [together with] the laws of the motion and the inner driving mechanism of the orbiting of all planets where the Newtonian philosophy can provide such insights the like of which cannot be found in any part of natural philosophy;[27] in the same way, I assert, among all things of nature whose first cause one investigates the origin of the world system and the formation of celestial bodies together with the causes of their motions is the one which one may hope to grasp first in a fundamental and satisfactory way. The reason can here easily be seen. The [c1r] celestial bodies are round masses and of the simplest structure which a body, whose origin one seeks, can ever have. Their motions are similarly unmixed. They are nothing else but a free continuation of an impulse once impressed which, in connection with the attraction of the body in the center, become circular in form. In addition, the space in which they move is empty, the intermediate spaces which separate one from the other are quite unusually great,

---

* Part I, §88.

87

and all is most evidently arranged both for an undisturbed motion and for its evident display. It seems to me that one can here say in a sense without presumption: *Give me matter, I will build a world out of it!*, that is, give me matter, I will show you how a world must arise from it. For if there is matter available which is endowed with an essential [c1v] attractive force,[28] then it is not difficult to determine those causes which can contribute to the arrangement of the world system, considered at large. One knows what it takes that a body may reach the figure of a round globe; one understands what is required that freely floating globes should display a circular motion around the center toward which they are drawn. The respective position of orbits, the agreement of direction, the eccentricity, all can be brought to the simplest mechanical causes and one can confidently hope to discover them because they are based on the easiest and most evident grounds. But can one boast of such advantages concerning the smallest plants or insect[s]? Is one in the position to say: *Give me matter [and] I will show you how a* [c2r] *caterpillar can be generated?* Does one not remain here stuck with the first step owing to the ignorance of the true disposition of the object and of the development of the manifoldness present in it? One must not therefore take it as strange if I am ready to say: that the formation of all celestial bodies, the cause of their motions, in brief, the origin of the whole present arrangement of the world-edifice, will sooner be understood than the production of a single herb or of a caterpillar will become evidently and completely clarified from mechanical reasons.[29]

These are the causes upon which I base my expectation that the physical part of cosmology may hopefully achieve in the future the perfection to which Newton has raised its mathematical half. [c2v] Next to the laws, according to which the world-edifice exists in the form in which it is, perhaps no other laws in the whole study of nature are [more] capable of such mathematical determination than are those according to which it arose, and without doubt here the hands of the experienced surveyor would cultivate no unproductive fields.

Now that I had the occasion to recommend for a favorable acceptance the plan of my theory, one will allow me to clarify briefly the manner in which I handle it. The First Part deals with a new system of the world-edifice at large. Mr. Wright of Durham,[30] whose essay[31] became known to me from the *Freye Urtheile* of Hamburg from 1751,[32] gave me first the prompting to look upon the fixed stars not as a scattered swarming with no visible [c3r] order, but as a system which has the greatest similarity with a planetary system, so that just as in this [system] the planets find themselves very close to a common plane, the fixed stars too are in their position related as closely as possible to a certain plane which must be conceived as drawn across the whole sky and, through their thickest crowding toward it, represent that bright streak which is called the Milky Way. I have become convinced that because this zone, which is illuminated by uncounted suns, has very nearly the direction of a great circle, our sun must find itself very close to that great plane of reference. While I was pursuing the cause of this arrangement,[33] I have found it very probable that the so-called fixed stars, or stationary stars, can very well be the [c3v] slowly wandering stars of a higher order [system]. In confirmation of what one will find at its proper place about this idea, I will here adduce but one passage from Mr. Bradley's paper[34] on the motion of fixed stars: "If a Judgment may be formed, ⟨with Regard to this Matter,⟩ from the Result of the Comparison of our best modern Observations, with such as were formerly made with any tolerable Degree of Exactness; there appears to have been a real Change in the Position of some of the fixed Stars, with respect to each other; and such, as seems independent of any Motion in our own System, and can only be referred to some Motion in the Stars themselves. Arcturus affords a strong Proof of this: for if its present [c4r] Declination be compared with its Place, as determined either by Tycho[35] or Flamsteed;[36] the Difference will be found to be much greater than what can be suspected to arise from the Uncertainty of their Observations. It is reasonable to expect that other Instances of the like kind must also occur among the great Number of visible Stars; because their relative Positions may be altered by various means. For if our own Solar System be conceived to change its Place with respect to Absolute Space,[37] this might, in Process of Time, occasion an apparent Change in the angular Distances of the fixed Stars; and in such a Case, the Places of the nearest Stars being more affected, than [c4v] of those that are very remote; their relative Positions might seem to alter; tho' the Stars themselves were really immoveable. And on the other Hand, if our own System be at Rest and any of the Stars really in Motion, this might likewise vary their apparent Positions; and the more so, the nearer they are to us, ⟨or the swifter their Motions are,⟩[38] or the more proper the Direction of the Motion is, to be rendered perceptible by us. Since then the ⟨Relative⟩ Places of the stars may be changed from such a Variety of Causes, considering the amazing Distances at which it is certain that some of them are placed, it may require the Observations of many Ages, to determine the Laws of the apparent Changes, even of a single Star; much [c5r] more difficult therefore must it be, to settle the Laws relating to all the most remarkable Stars."

I cannot exactly determine the borderline which lies between Mr.

Wright's system and my own and in what pieces have I simply copied or further developed his sketch. Yet afterwards, worthy reasons occurred to me to expand it considerably in one respect. I considered the kind of nebulous stars, of which Mr. *de Maupertuis* speculates in his *Treatise on the Figure of Stars** [39] and which show [c5v] the figure of more or less [round] ellipses, and I have readily convinced myself [c6r] that they may be nothing else than a swarm of many fixed stars. The invariably [c6v] precise roundish shape [ovalness] of these figures thought me that here an inconceivably numerous host of stars had to be co-ordinated around a common center, because otherwise their free positions respective to one another would present rather irregular shapes and not exact figures. I have also realized that they must be mainly confined to a plane in that system in which they are united, because they form not circular but elliptical figures [40] and that because of their pale light they are inconceivably far removed from us. What I have concluded from these analogies will the discussion of them present to the scrutiny of the unprejudiced reader.

In the Second Part, which contains the proposition most specific to this essay, I endeavor to develop [c7r] the constitution of the world-

---

* As I do not have on hand the treatise just mentioned, here I will insert what pertains [to the topic] from the report about the *Ouvrages diverses* [sic] de Mr. de Maupertuis in the *Actis. Erud*, 1745.[a] The first phenomena[b] are those luminous spots in the sky which are called Nebulous stars and are held to be a swarm of small fixed stars. [c5v] But by excellent telescopes the astronomers have found them only as great elongated round spots which were somewhat more luminous than the remaining part of the sky. Hugen[c] [sic] has first found such spots in Orion; Halley recalls in the *Anglical. Trans.*[d] six such spots: 1. in the sword of Orion, 2. in the Archer, 3. in Centaurus, 4. in front of the foot of Antinous, 5. in Hercules, 6. in the belt of Andromeda. When these are viewed through a reflecting telescope of 8 feet, one sees that only one-fourth part of them can be taken for a swarm of stars; the remainder present only whitish spots without any special difference apart from the one that one spot comes closer to a circular rounding, whereas another is more elongated. It also seems that in the former the small stars visible through the telescope cannot cause its whitish glimmer. Halley believes that "from these appearances one can explain what occurs in the beginning of the Mosaic history of creation, namely, that the light has been created before the sun.[e] Derham[f] compares them to openings through which another immeasurable region and perhaps [c6r] the celestial fire[g] itself transpires. He thinks that he has been able to notice that the stars observable next to these spots are much closer to us than these luminous stars. To these the author adds from Hevelius[h] a list of nebulous stars. He holds these phenomena to be great luminous masses[i] which became flattened through enormous rotation.[j] The matter, which they consist of, if it had an illuminating force equal to the other stars, would have to be of enormous size, so that, seen from a much greater distance than that of the stars, they could appear to [through] the telescope under distinct shape and size.[k] If, however, they are equal about in size to other fixed stars, they should be not only very much closer to us but should also have a much weaker light, because [l] with such a proximity and with such an apparent size they still display so pale a glow. It would be worth the effort to [try to] discover their parallax if they have one. Because those who deny this to them, concluded perhaps from a few [cases] to all. The small stars which occur in these spots, as in Orion (or still better in the one in front of the right foot of Antinous which does not appear other than a fixed star which is surrounded by a cloud),[m] would, if they were closer, be seen[n] either [as superimposed] on them, according to the art of projection, or would appear through those [luminous] masses just as [they do] through the tails of comets."

edifice from the simplest state of nature through mechanical laws alone. If I am allowed to propose to those, who feel uneasy because of the boldness of this undertaking, a certain order concerning the scrutiny with which they honor my thoughts, I would like to ask that they first read the *Eighth Section* [of the Second Part] which, I hope, can predispose their judgment to a proper insight.[41] If I meanwhile invite the kindly reader to scrutinize my opinions, I am rightly concerned by the fact that since hypotheses of this sort are usually in no higher regard than are philosophical dreams, it may become a sour pleasure for a reader to resolve himself to [make] a careful investigation of histories of nature conceived by [the author] himself and follow the author patiently through all the windings along which he comes [c7v] around the difficulties which encounter him so as perhaps in the end to laugh, as do the spectators of the announcer of the London Marketplace,* at his own credulity. Meanwhile I confidently promise that if hopefully the reader would be persuaded by the indicated preparatory Section to dare risk on the basis of so probable opinions such a physical adventure, he will find on the continuation of his journey not so many crooked bypaths and impassable barriers as he was concerned about at the outset.

I have in fact decided with the greatest caution to forego all arbitrary speculation, I have, after I have set the world in the simplest chaos, applied no other forces than the forces of attraction and repulsion [c8r] for the development of the great order of nature, two forces which both are equally certain, equally simple, and also equally primary and universal. Both are borrowed from the Newtonian philosophy of nature.[43] The former is now a law of nature set beyond doubt. The second, to which the natural science of Newton cannot secure so much evidence as to the former, I assume here only in that understanding which is denied by nobody, namely, in connection with the finest dissolution of matter, as for example in vapours. From these so simple reasons I have derived the following system in an uncomplicated manner without thinking of other inferences such as the ones upon which the attention of the reader must fall quite by itself.

May I be allowed finally to give a brief clarification concerning the validity and the presumed value of [c8v] those propositions which will come along in the following theory and which I wish to be tested by equitable judges. One judges fairly the author according to the stamp which he impresses upon his wares; therefore I hope that in the various parts of this essay no stricter accountability will be made of my opinions than [the one] conforming to the specification of value

---

* See Gellert's tale, "Hans Nord."[42]

which I myself give of them.[44] In general, the greatest geometrical precision and mathematical infallibility can never be demanded from an essay of this sort.[45] When the system is based on analogies and correspondences, according to the rules of credibility and correct reasoning, then it has satisfied all the demands of its objective. I think I have achieved this degree of competency in some parts [d1r] of this essay such as in the theory of fixed star systems, in the hypothesis about the constitution of nebulous stars, in the general plan about the mechanical origination of the world-edifice, in the theory of Saturn's ring, and in some others. Somewhat less conviction will be secured by some particular parts of the development, as for example, the determination of the relations of eccentricity, the comparison of the masses of the planets, the various inclinations of comets, and a few others.

If, therefore, captivated by the fruitfulness of the system and the agreeableness of the greatest and most admirable subject which one can think of, I set forth in the Seventh Section [of the Second Part] the consequences of the doctrine as broadly as possible, although always along the guideline of analogy and of rational credibility, yet with a certain boldness; [d1v] if I present to the imaginative power the infinity of the entire creation, the formation of new worlds and the decay of old worlds, the unlimited space of chaos, I hope that one will grant so much consideration to the stirring agreeableness of the topic and to the pleasure which one has in seeing the harmonies of a theory in its greatest extent, so as not to judge it according to the greatest mathematical rigor[46] which anyhow in this kind of considerations cannot be had. I expect precisely this fairness in respect to the Third Part. One will invariably find there something more than [what is] purely arbitrary, although always something less than what is undoubted.

CONTENTS OF THE ENTIRE WORK

First Part

Summary of a general systematic constitution among the fixed stars derived from the phenomena of the Milky Way. The similarity of this system of fixed stars with the system of planets. Discovery of many such systems which appear in the shape of elliptical figures in the expanse of the heavens. A new notion about the systematic constitution of the whole creation.

Conclusion. Probable conjecture [about the existence] of several planets beyond Saturn from the law according to which the eccentricity of planets increases with distance.

Second Part

First Section

Reasons for the doctrine of a mechanical origination of the world. Counter reasons. The only concept among all possible concepts to satisfy both [viewpoints]. First state of nature. Dispersion of elements of all matter through the whole cosmic space. First stirring through attraction. Beginning of the formation of a [celestial] body at the point of strongest attraction. General sinking of elements towards this central body. Repulsive force of the finest particles into which matter is dissolved. Altered [d2v] direction of the sinking motion through the combination of this [repulsive] force with the former. Uniform motion of all these motions in the same direction. Striving of all particles to press toward a common plane and to pile up there. Diminution of the velocity of their motion toward an equilibrium with the gravity of the distance of their [original] place. Free orbiting of all particles around the central body in circles. Formation of the planets from these moving elements. Free motion of planets composed of those elements in the same direction in a common plane, in circles near the center and farther from it with increasing degrees of eccentricity.

Second Section

Treats of the different densities of planets and of the correlation of their masses. Cause why the near[er] planets are of a denser kind than the more distant ones. Insufficiency of Newton's explanation. Why the central body is of lighter kind [of matter] than the globes orbiting nearest to it. Correlation of the masses of planets according to the proportion of the distances. Cause [deduced] from the manner of formation why the central body has the largest mass. Computation of the dilutedness in which all elements of the world-material were dispersed. Probability and necessity of this dilution. Important proof of the manner of the formation of celestial bodies from a remarkable analogy of Mr. Buffon.

Third Section

About the eccentricity of planetary orbits and of the origin of comets. The eccentricity increases [d3r] gradually with distances from the sun. Cause of this law from cosmogony. Why the cometary orbits freely stray from the plane of the ecliptic. Proof that the comets are formed from the lightest kind of matter. Incidental remarks about the Northern Light.

Fourth Section

Of the origin of the moon and of the motion of planets around their axes. The material [needed] for the generation of the moon was contained in the sphere from which the planet gathered the parts of its formation. Cause of the motion of these moons with all [its] specifications. Why only the great planets have moons. Of the axial rotation of planets. Whether the moon had previously a faster [rotation]. Whether the velocity of the rotation of the earth decreases. Of the position of the axes of planets with respect to the plane of their orbits. Displacement of their axes.

Fifth Section

Of the origin of the ring of Saturn and of the computation of its daily rotation from its relations. First state of Saturn compared with the condition of a comet. Formation of a ring from the particles of its [planet's] atmosphere by means of motions impressed [upon them] by its rotation. Determination of the time of its axial rotation according to this hypothesis. Consideration of the shape of Saturn. Of the spheroidal flattening of celestial bodies in general. Closer determination of the condition of this ring. Probable expectation of new discoveries. Whether the earth had not a ring before the deluge? [d3v]

Sixth Section

Of the zodiacal light.

Seventh Section

Of creation in the entire extent of its infinity, both according to space and time. Origin of a great system of fixed stars. Central body in the center of the star system. Infinity of creation. Universal systematic connection in its entire being. Central body of the entire nature. Successive propagation of creation in the entire infinity of times and spaces, through endless formation of new worlds. Consideration of the chaos of unformed nature. Gradual collapse and demise of the world-edifice. Appropriateness of such a notion. Rejuvenation of the collapsed nature.

Addition to the Seventh Section

Universal theory and [natural] history of the sun in general. Why is the central body of a world system a fiery body. Closer consideration of its nature. Thoughts of the changes of the air surrounding it. Extinction of the suns [sun]. Closer look at its shape. Idea of Mr. Wright of the central body of the entire nature. An improvement of it.

Eighth Section

General proof of the correctness of a mechanical doctrine of the arrangement of the world-edifice [d4r] in general, and of the certainty of the present doctrine in particular. The essential ability of the nature of things to raise themselves to order and perfection is the most beautiful proof of the existence of God. Defense [of this thesis] against the charge of naturalism.

The constitution of the world-edifice is simple and is not above the forces of nature. Analogies which verify with certainty the mechanical origin of the world. The adducing of an immediate divine ordering does not do justice to these questions. Difficulty which prompted Newton to give up the mechanistic doctrine. Solution of this difficulty. The proposed system is the only means among all possible to do justice to the reasons [marshalled] on both sides. Further demonstration of this through the relation of the density of planets, of their masses, of the spaces between their distances [from the sun], and of the gradual connection of their determinations [specificities]. The motives of God's choice do not determine immediately these circumstances. Justification in respect of religion. Difficulties which arise in the doctrine about an immediate divine ordering.

Third Part

Contains a comparison between the inhabitants of the stars. Whether all planets are inhabited. Causes for doubting this. Basis of physical relationships between the inhabitants of different planets. Consideration about man. Causes of the imperfection of [d4v] his nature. Natural relationship of the bodily properties of living creatures according to their different distances from the sun. Consequences of this relationship for their spiritual capacities. Comparison of thinking natures [beings] [living] on different celestial bodies. Confirmation [of this comparison] from certain characteristics of their abodes. Further proof from the dispositions of divine providence which are made to their very best. Brief digression.

Conclusion

The conditions of man in the future life.

UNIVERSAL

NATURAL HISTORY

and

THEORY OF THE HEAVENS.

FIRST PART,

Sketch of a systematic constitution among the fixed stars,
and also
of the multitude of such fixed-star systems.

Behold that great wonder-chain which all parts of this world
Unites and draws together; and which contains the great whole.

Pope[1]

[I]

Brief Sketch
of the most necessary basic notions
of

NEWTONIAN SCIENCE*

which will be required
for the understanding of what follows.

Six planets, of which three have companions, Mercury, Venus, the Earth with its Moon, Mars, Jupiter with four and Saturn with five trabants, which describe circles around the sun as a center, besides the comets which do this on every side and in very long circles, form a system which is called the solar system or also the planetary world-edifice. The motion of all these bodies, because it is circular and re-entrant into itself, presupposes two [II] forces which are equally necessary in such kind of a doctrine, namely, a *tossing force* by which they would continue in the straight direction at every point of the curvilinear course and would recede [from it] into the infinite if another *force*, whatever it may be, would not always necessitate them to abandon that straight direction and to move in a curving track which encloses the sun as the center. This second force, as the geometry of it undoubtedly shows, aims everywhere at the sun and will therefore be called the sinking, the centripetal force, or also gravity.

If the orbits of celestial bodies were exactly a circle, then the most simple analysis of the composition of curvilinear motions would show that a constant trend toward the center would be required to it; but although those orbits are for all planets, as well as for comets, ellipses in whose common focus the sun is located, the higher geometry[2] with the help of the Keplerian analogy (according to which the radius

---

*I would like first to present this brief introduction, which perhaps in respect to most readers may be superfluous, to those who are not sufficiently familiar with the Newtonian principles for a preparation of the[ir] insight into the following theory.

vector, or the line drawn from the planets to the sun, always cuts from the elliptical paths such areas which are proportional to the times)[3] shows with infallible certainty that a force must relentlessly drive the planet during its entire orbit toward the center of the sun. This sinking force, which rules throughout the entire space of the planetary system [III] and aims at the sun, is also a well-proven phenomenon of nature and just as reliably is also demonstrated the law according to which this force stretches from the center to the distant reaches. It always decreases inversely as the squares of distances increase from the center. This rule flows also in an equally infallible manner from the time which the planets in different distances need for their orbitings. These times are always as the square root of the cube of their average distance from the sun,[4] from which it is deduced that the force which drives these celestial bodies to the center of their orbiting must decrease in inverse ratio of the square of distance.

The very same law which prevails among the planets inasmuch as they move around the sun, obtains also in the smaller systems, namely, in those which the moons form while moving around their planets. Their orbital periods are also proportional to the distances and demonstrate the same relation of the sinking force towards the planets as does the one to which the planet is subject with respect to the sun. All this is placed forever beyond contradiction through the infallible geometry,[5] by means of indisputable observations. Here also belongs the idea that this force of sinking is the very same impulse which on the surface of planets is called heaviness and that it diminishes from there gradually with distance [IV] according to the law indicated. This is seen from the comparison of the quantity of heaviness on the surface of the earth with the force which drives the moon to the center of its orbit, which again is as the attraction in the entire world-edifice, namely, in inverse proportion of the square of distances. This is the reason why the often mentioned central force is also called gravity.

Because, in addition, it is also probable in the highest degree that, if an effect takes place only in the present [presence] and according to the proportion of the approach to a certain body, [and] the direction of that effect too is bearing exactly on this body, it is to be believed that this body, in whatever way this should be, is the cause of that effect: thus one, for that reason, thinks to have enough [reason] to ascribe this general sinking of planets towards the sun to a force of attraction of the latter and to attribute this capacity of attraction to all celestial bodies.

If a body is freely left to that impulse which drives it to sinking toward the sun or towards any planet, it will fall toward it in steadily accelerated motion and shortly unite itself with the mass of it. If, however, that body receives a push from the side, it will, when this push is not so strong as to pose a counterbalance to the pressure of sinking, sink toward the central body [V] in a bent motion, and when the push which was impressed on it was at least so strong as to remove it, before it touched the surface of that planet, from the vertical line by the half thickness[6] of the body in the center, then it will not touch the surface of that planet, but after it had swung tightly around, it would raise itself, through the velocity gained from the fall, as high as it had fallen, in order to continue its orbiting in steady circular motion.

The difference between the orbits of comets and planets consists also in the deviation of the sidewise motion against the pressure which drives them to fall; which two forces, the closer they come to equality the more similar the orbit becomes to a circle, and the more unequal they are, the weaker is the tossing force with respect to the central force, [and] the more elongated is the circle, or as it is called, the more eccentric it is, because the celestial body approaches the sun more in one part of its path than in the other.

Because nothing is in nature weighed in the most exact way, no planet has a quite circular motion; but comets deviate from it most because the thrust, which was impressed to them sidewise, was in the least proportional to the central force of their first [original] distance [from the sun].

I will in the [this] essay very often avail myself of the expression of *a systematic* [VI] *constitution of the world-edifice.* In order that one may have no difficulty in picturing clearly what it ought to mean, I will explain myself briefly about it. Truly, all planets and comets, which belong to our world-edifice, already form a system in that they revolve around a common central body. I take, however, this designation in a still narrower sense inasmuch as I look at the exact specifications which made their connection with one another regular and similar. The orbits of planets relate as closely as possible to a common plane, namely to the extended equatorial plane of the sun; the deviation from this rule occurs only at the outermost border of the system where all motions cease gradually. If therefore a certain number of celestial bodies, which are ordered around a common center and move around it, are simultaneously so confined to a certain plane that they have the freedom to deviate from it on both sides as little as possible; if the deviation takes place gradually only with those which are most distant from the central point and therefore had less share in correlations than the others; then I say that these bodies find themselves tied together in a *systematic constitution.*[7]

Universal

NATURAL HISTORY

and

THEORY OF THE HEAVENS.

FIRST PART,

of the
systematic constitution among the fixed stars.

The doctrine of the universal constitution of the world-edifice has since Huygens' time gained no notable increase. At this time one still does not know more than what was already known then, namely, that the six planets with ten companions,[8] which all have the circle of their orbiting directed nearly at one plane, and the eternal[9] cometary globes, which freely stray on all sides, [2] constitute a system whose center is the sun, toward which all sinks, around which their motions proceed, and from which they all are illuminated, heated, and vivified; that finally the fixed stars, as so many suns, are centers of similar systems in which all may be arranged just as greatly and orderly as in ours, and that the infinite cosmic space swarms with world-edifices whose number and excellence has a relation to the inexhaustibility of their Creator.

The systematic element, which was found in the connection of planets that speed around the sun, vanished here in the multitude of fixed stars and it seemed as if the regular correlation, which occurs in the small [scale], does not rule among the members of the universe at large; the fixed stars obtained no law by which their position with respect to one another had been limited and one saw them fill the heavens and all the heavens of heavens without order and purpose.

Since man's thirst for knowledge has set for itself these limits,[10] nothing further has been done than to infer and admire the greatness of the One who has revealed himself in so inconceivably great works.

It was reserved to Mr. Wright of Durham, an Englishman, to make a happy step toward an observation [idea] which seems to have not been used [3] by him for proper purpose and the useful application of which he has not sufficiently considered.[11] He viewed the fixed stars not as a swarm, disordered and scattered without purpose, but he found a systematic constitution in the whole and a universal relation of these stars towards a main plane of the space which they fill.

We want to improve the thought which he had set forth, and to seek to impart to it that application by which it can be fruitful in important consequences, whose full verification is reserved for future times.

Anyone who views the starry heavens in a clear night will note that luminous streak which, through the mass of stars that are piled up there more than elsewhere and through their recognizability vanishing into great distances, represents a uniform light that has been called the Milky Way. It is surprising that the observers of the sky had not been long ago moved by the characteristics of this zone clearly distinguishable in the sky to deduce from it specific determinations concerning the position of the fixed stars.[12] For one sees it [that streak] taking the direction of a great circle and doing so in an uninterrupted connection around the entire heavens, two conditions which carry such an exact determination and a mark so clearly distinguishable from the unspecified more-or-less that [4] attentive students of stars should have naturally been prompted by it to examine with attention the explanation of such an appearance.

As the stars are not placed on the apparently hollow sphere of the heavens but, one being more removed than the others from our vantage point, they lose themselves in the depths of heaven, it follows from this appearance that in the distances at which they are from us behind one another they are not found in an equal dispersion on all sides but they must be related especially to a certain plane which goes through our vantage point and to which they are set to be found as close as possible.

This relation is such an indubitable phenomenon that even the remaining stars which are not comprised in the whitish streak of the Milky Way, are still seen all the more crowded and dense [-ly packed], the closer are their places [positions] to the circle of the Milky Way, so that of the 2000 stars,[13] which the naked eye discovers in the sky, the greatest part will be found in a not-too-wide zone whose middle [-band] is occupied by the Milky Way.

If now we draw in thought a plane through the starry sky into unlimited distances and assume that all fixed stars and [star] systems have a general correlation of their positions to that plane in order to find [5] themselves closer to it than to other regions, then the eye, which is located in that plane of reference, will spot on its look into the field of stars on the hollow spherical surface of the firmament this thickest crowding of stars in the direction of such a drawn plane in the form of a zone illuminated by more light. This bright streak will stretch in the direction of a great circle, because the position of the onlooker is in the plane itself. In that zone there will swarm stars which, because of the indistinguishable smallness of bright points which individually escape observation and, because of their apparent density [of crowding], will make apparent a uniformly whitish glimmer, in one word, a Milky Way. The remaining heavenly host, whose relation more and more decreases towards the drawn plane or which are also closer to the position of the observer, will [appear to] be more scattered even though their crowding would be seen related towards that plane. It finally follows from this that our solar world, because from it this system of fixed stars is seen in the direction of a great circle, is set to be found in that very same large plane and makes one system with the rest [of such worlds].

We [now] want, in order to penetrate better into the consitution of the universal connection which dominates in the world-edifice, to seek to discover the cause which made the positions of the fixed stars [6] related also [to] a common plane.

The sun does not confine the extent of its attractive force to the narrow district of the planetary edifice. In all appearance it extends itself into the infinite. The comets, which soar very far beyond the orbit of Saturn, are necessitated by the sun's attraction to return again and move in circles [orbits]. Whether it is also more proper to the nature of a force, which appears to be incorporated into the essence of matter, to be unlimited and [which] is also recognized to be such by those who assume Newton's propositions, we only want it to be admitted that this attraction of the sun should reach to about the nearest fixed star and that the fixed stars as so many suns should be effective around themselves to a similar extent, [and] consequently, that the entire host of them would be driven to approach one another through the [that] attraction; thus all world-systems are through the mutual approach, which is uninterrupted and unimpeded by nothing, in the condition of falling together sooner or later into one lump, unless they were prevented from that ruination, as is the case with the globes of our planetary system, through the forces fleeing from the center which, while they deviate the celestial bodies from straight fall, produce in connection with the forces of attraction the eternal orbital motions whereby the edifice of creation [7] is secured from collapse and made fit for an imperishable duration.[14]

Thus all the suns of the firmament have orbital motions either around one universal center or around many. One, however, can everywhere avail himself of the analogy which will be noticed in the orbits of our solar world: that, namely, just as the very same cause, which has imparted to the planets the centrifugal force,[15] through which they perform their orbitings, has also directed their orbits so that they are all related to one plane, the cause too, whatever it may be, which gave to the suns of the superior world, as well as to the wandering stars [planets] of higher world-orders, the force[16] of orbiting, has also brought their orbits as much as possible toward a plane and [caused] the deviations from it to tend to be limited.

According to this presentation one can to some extent picture the system of fixed stars through [analogy with] the planetary system, if one enlarges this infinitely. For if we assume instead of 6 planets with their 10 companions so many thousands of them, and instead of 28 or 30 comets[17] which have been observed, their hundred- and thousandfolds, but if we think of these bodies as self-luminous, then to the onlooker's eye which views them from the earth, there will arise that very shine as it does from the fixed stars of the Milky Way. For the imaginary planets would, through their closeness [8] to the common plane of their relation in which we find ourselves, represent a zone densely illuminated by innumerable stars whose direction goes along a great circle; these bright streaks would everywhere be sufficiently occupied by stars although, according to the hypothesis, as wandering stars they are not hoisted to one place; for there would always be enough stars on one side through their [continual] transfer, although others have [already] changed [moved away from] that locality [side].

The width of that illuminated zone, which represents a kind of a zodiac, will be determined by the various degrees of the deviation of said erring stars from the plane of their reference and by the inclination of their orbits against this plane; and because most of them are so close to that plane, their count will appear more scattered from that plane in the measure of their distance; the comets, however, which take on all areas [directions] without any distinction, will cover the field of the heavens from both sides.

The shape of the heavens of the fixed stars has, just as [is the case with] similar sytematic constitution, no other cause than does the planetary world-edifice in small, inasmuch as all suns form a system whose universal plane of reference is the Milky Way; those least related to that plane are seen on the side, they are, however, therefore far less [9] crowded and more rare. They are the so-called comets among the suns.[18]

This new doctrine assigns, however, to the suns a forward motion[19] and yet everybody views them as unmoved and hoisted to their places from the beginning. The designation, which the fixed stars have thus obtained, seems to be confirmed through the observation of all centuries and to be indubitable. This difficulty, were it well-founded, would annihilate the proposed doctrine. But in all evidence this lack of motion is only something apparent. It is only either an exceptional slowness, which is caused by the great distance from the center of their orbit, or an unobservability caused by the distance from the place of observation. Let us estimate the probability of this notion through the computation of motion which a fixed star close to our sun would have if we posited that our sun was the center of its orbit. If its distance, according to Huygens, were to be taken 21000 times greater than the distance of the sun from the earth,[20] then, according to the established laws of periods which stand in the relation of the square root to the cube of distances from the center, the time, which the fixed star [in question] must take to traverse its orbit once around the sun, [would be] more than a million and a half years and this would [10] make in 4000 years a shift of only one degree of [in] its position.[21] Since, however, only very few stars are perhaps so close to the sun as Huygens conjectured the Sirius to be, [and] since the distance of the rest of the celestial host perhaps unusually exceeds that of the latter, and [therefore] also uncommonly longer times would be required for their periodic orbiting, [and since] in addition it is also more likely that the motion of the suns of the starry sky goes around a common center whose distance is uncommonly great and the advance of stars would therefore be exceedingly slow; therefore it can from this be assumed with probability that the entire time, [which has elapsed] since man has instituted observations of the sky, is perhaps not yet sufficient to notice the change which had occurred in their positions. The hope must not yet, however, be given up to discover this change too with time. It will take subtle and careful observers, inasmuch as a comparison of observations very distant from one another[22] is required for it. These observations should preferably be directed at the stars of the Milky Way* which is the chief plane of all motions. Mr Bradley has [11] observed almost unnoticeable displacements of stars.[23] The ancients have noticed stars

---

* In particular at those clusters of stars of which there are many near one another in a small space, as for instance, the Pleiades, which perhaps form among them a small system within the larger one.

at certain places of the sky and we see new ones at other places. Who knows whether these are not the former which have only changed position.[24] The excellence of instruments and the perfection of astronomy give us well founded hope for the discovery of so extraordinary things worthy of attention.* The credibility of the subject [coming as it does] from the principles of nature and from analogy support[s] this hope so well that it can stimulate the attention of the investigators of nature in order to bring it to fulfillment.

The Milky Way is, so to speak, also the zodiac of new stars, which hardly in any other celestial region as in this alternately let themselves be seen and disappear.[25] If this change of their visibility derives from their periodic receding [from us] and approaching to us, then it appears well from the proposed systematic constitution of stars that such a phenomenon should be seen mostly in the district of the Milky Way. For, since there are stars which move in very oblong circles around other fixed stars [12] as trabants do around their planets, it is required by the analogy with our planetary world-edifice, in which only the celestial bodies close to the common plane of motions have companions moving around them, that also only the stars which are in the Milky Way would have suns moving around them.

I [now] come to the part of the proposed doctrine which makes it most appealing through the lofty presentation which it gives about the plan of creation. The series of thoughts which have led me to it is brief and uncomplicated; it consists in the following. If a system of fixed stars, which in their positions relate to a common plane, just as we have the Milky Way laid out, is so distant from us that all recognizability of the single stars of which it consists, is not possible even for the telescopes; if its distance has to the distance of stars of the Milky Way the same relation as this has to the distance of the sun from us; in brief, if such a world of fixed stars is viewed from such an immeasureable distance from the eye of the observer who finds himself outside it, then it will appear under a small angle as a small space illuminated by weak light, [a space] whose figure will be circular when its plane presents itself directly [perpendicularly] to the eye, and elliptical when it is seen from the side.[27] The [13] weakness of light, the figure and the knowable magnitude of the diameter [of that space] will be such a phenomenon when it is possible to distinguish it clearly from all stars that are seen individually.

One need not search for long for this phenomenon among the observations of astronomers. It was clearly perceived by various

---

* De la Hire remarks in the *Mémoires* of the Academy in Paris from the year 1693 that he had ascertained both from his own observations as well as from their comparison with those of Riccioli, a strong alteration in the positions of the stars of Pleiades.[26]

observers. They were wondering about its peculiarity; they speculated [about it] and [it] meanwhile gave rise at times to miraculous conceptions, at other times to probable notions, which latter were, however, just as unfounded as were the former.[28] The nebulous stars are the ones we have in mind, or rather a species of theirs which Mr. de Maupertuis thus describes: "*That they are small places illuminated somewhat more than the darkness of the empty celestial space which [and] all have this in common that they present more or less open ellipses whose light is, however, weaker than of anything which one notices in the sky.*" * The author of *Astrotheology*[30] imagined that they were openings in the firmament through which he believed to see the heavenly fire. A philosopher of enlightened insights, the already mentioned Mr de Maupertuis, holds them, in view of their figure and apparent diameter, to be astonishingly [14] large celestial bodies which, when seen from the side, present elliptical figures because of their great flattening caused by the thrust of rotation.[31]

One will easily be convinced that this latter explanation similarly cannot occur [be the case]. As this kind of nebulous stars must be beyond doubt at least as distant from us as the remaining fixed stars, not only their size would be astonishing by which they should exceed many thousand times even the largest stars, but it would be utterly most peculiar that with such an extraordinary size they should show, self-illuminating bodies and suns as they are, [only] the faintest and weakest light.[32]

Far more natural and comprehensible is [the view] that they are not single great stars, but systems of them whose distance present them in so narrow a space that the light, which is unnoticeable from each individually, issues in their immeasurable multitude into one uniform faint glimmer. The analogy with the system of stars, in which we find ourselves, their shape, which is exactly as it should be according to our doctrine, the weakness of light which requires a presumably infinite distance.[,] All [all] this agrees [so] perfectly [that] we should [be entitled to] hold these elliptical figures for just such [15] world-orders and, so to speak, for Milky Ways, whose constitution we have just unfolded; and if conjectures, in which analogy and observations agree perfectly to support one another, have the same dignity as formal proofs, one must hold the certainty of these systems to be demonstrated.[33]

At this stage the attention of the observer of the sky has enough motives to occupy himself with this project. The fixed stars, which we know, all relate to one common plane and make thereby a co-ordinated

---

* Treatise of the Figure of Stars.[29]

whole which is a world among worlds. One sees that in immeasurable distances there are more such star systems and that the creation in the entire infinite extent of its magnitude is everywhere systematic and mutually related.[34]

One could still conjecture that even these higher world-orders are not without relation to one another and through this mutual relation they again constitute a still more immeasurable system. In fact, one sees that the elliptical figures of these kinds of nebulous stars, which Mr de Maupertuis adduces, have a very close relation to the plane of the Milky Way.[35] [16] Here lies a wide field open for discoveries to which observation must give the key.[36] The nebulous stars properly so-called and the ones, about which one is uncertain to call them so, ought to be investigated and demonstrated according to the guidance of this doctrine. If one considers the parts of nature according to purposes and an unfolded plan, then certain features come to light which otherwise are overlooked and remain hidden if observation is scattered without guidance over all objects.

The doctrine, which we have proposed, opens for us an outlook into the infinite field of creation and offers a picture of God's work which is appropriate to the infinity of the Great Artificer. If the greatness of a planetary world-edifice, in which the earth as a grain of sand is hardly noticed, moves the intellect into admiration, with what astonishment will one be enchanted if one considers the infinite amount of worlds and systems which fill the totality of the Milky Way; but how this astonishment increases when one realized that all these immeasurable star-orders again form the unit of a number whose end we do not know and which perhaps just as the former is inconceivably great and yet again is only the unit of a new number system. We see the first members of a progressive relation of [17] worlds and systems, and the first part of this infinite progression makes already known what one must conjecture about the whole. There is no end here but an abyss of a true immeasurability in which all ability of human concepts sinks even when it is elevated by the help of the science of numbers. The Wisdom, the Goodness, the Power, which reveals itself, is infinite and is fruitful and operative in the same measure; the plan of its revelation must therefore, just as it is, be infinite and without limits.

But not only on the level of the large are important discoveries to be made which [would] serve to enlarge the notion one can form about the greatness of creation. On the level of the small there is no less to be discovered and we see even in our solar world the members of a system which stand immensely apart from one another and between which one has not yet discovered the intervening parts.

Should there be between Saturn, the outermost of planets which we know, and the least eccentric comet which descends to us from perhaps a distance 10 and more times greater, no more planet whose motion would come closer to the cometary motion than that [of Saturn] and should not still there be others [so that] through a gradation of their constitution by a series of intermediary members the planets gradually turn into comets and [18] connect this latter species with the former?

The law, according to which the eccentricity of planetary orbits stands in opposite relation to their distance from the sun, supports this conjecture. The eccentricity in the motions of planets increases with their distances from the sun and therefore the [more] distant planets come closer to the specification of comets. It can be also surmised that there are still other planets beyond Saturn which are still more eccentric and thereby also more related to them, [a circumstance which, as if] by means of a continuous ladder, makes the planets finally [turn] into comets. The eccentricity for Venus is 1/126 of the semiaxis of its elliptical orbit; for the earth 1/58, for Jupiter 1/20, for Saturn 1/17 of the same [semiaxis]; it visibly increases with distance.[37] It is true, Mercury and Mars form an exception to this law through their much greater eccentricity[38] than the measure of their distance from the sun allows it; but we shall learn in the following that the very same cause through which some planets were given a smaller mass in their formation [implies] also the default of the thrust required for the circular orbit, [and] consequently the eccentricity which goes with it, [and] consequently left them imperfect in both respects.

[19] Is it consequently not probable that the decrease [increase] of eccentricity would be about as appropriate to the celestial bodies immediately beyond Saturn as to those below it and that the planets are related to the species of comets with less sudden a gap?[39] For it is certain that this eccentricity makes the essential difference between comets and planets and [that] the tails and vaporous globes of the former are only the consequences of it;[40] similarly, that even the cause, whatever it may be, which has imparted to the celestial bodies their circular motion, became not only weaker at greater distances to make the rotational thrust equal to the force of sinking, and left thereby the motions eccentric, but that it therefore became less capable of bringing the orbits of these globes to a common plane on which the lower globes move and allowed thereby for the deviation of comets in all areas.

One would, therefore, according to this conjecture hope perhaps for the discovery of new planets beyond Saturn which would be more eccentric than this and also be closer to the cometary feature; but precisely because of this one would have a glimpse of them only for a brief time, namely, at the time of their [being in the] vicinity of the sun,[41] which circumstance, together with the smaller measure of approach [20] and the weakness of light have impeded so far their discovery and must make it difficult even in the future. The last planet and first comet might, if one so preferred, be called the one whose eccentricity were so great that in its vicinity to the sun would cut across the orbit of the planet near to it, perhaps also that of Saturn.[42]

UNIVERSAL

NATURAL HISTORY

and

THEORY OF THE HEAVENS.

SECOND PART,
of the
first state of nature, of the formation
of celestial bodies, of the causes of their motion, and of their
systematic relation in the planetary edifice as well as in respect
to the entire creation.

Watch the developing nature move toward her great goal,
Each sundust particle resonate to another sundust particle,
Each, which is attracted, attracts the other to itself,
The next again trying to envelope, to form it,
Watch matter in thousand ways and forms
Tend to the universal center.
                    Pope[1]

UNIVERSAL

NATURAL HISTORY

and

THEORY OF THE HEAVENS.

SECOND PART,
FIRST SECTION,
of the
Origin of the Planetary World-Edifice in general
and of the causes of its motions.

The consideration of the world-edifice shows, in respect to mutual relations which its parts have among one another and by which they point at the cause from which they derive, two sides, both of which are equally probable and worthy of acceptance. If on the one hand [24] one considers that 6 planets with 9 companions,[2] which describe circles around the sun as their center, all move from one side [in one direction] and, to wit, in that direction in which rotates the sun itself, which directs all their orbiting through the force of attraction, that their orbits do not deviate much from a common plane, namely, from the extended equatorial plane of the sun, that in the case of the most distant celestial body still belonging to the solar world, where the cause of motion presumably has not been as strong as in the vicinity of the center, [such] deviations from the exactness of this determination took place which have a sufficient [appropriate] relation to the default of the impressed motion, if one, I say, considers all this connection, then one will be moved to believe that a cause, whatever it may be, had a thoroughgoing influence in the entire space of the system and that the uniformity in the direction and position of planetary orbits is a consequence of the connection which they must have had with that material cause by which they were set in motion.[3]

If on the other hand we consider the space, in which the planets of our system move around, it is [now] completely empty* and bereft [25] of all matter which could have exerted a community of influence on these celestial bodies and could have entailed a harmony among their motions. This circumstance is established with more perfect certainty and exceeds, wherever possible, the former probability.[4] Newton, prompted by this reason, could not assign any material cause which through its spreading in the space of the planetary edifice should have maintained the community of motions. He asserted that the direct hand of God[5] has arranged this order without the application of the forces of nature.

It is seen through impartial consideration that here the reasons on both sides are equally strong and that both are to be valued [as] equal to complete certainty. But it is just as clear that there must be a notion in which these reasons apparently conflicting with one another may and should be united and that the true system ought to be looked for in that notion. We wish to indicate it in brief words. In the present constitution of space, in which the planets orbit, there is no material [26] cause present which could impart or direct their motions. That space is perfectly empty, or at least practically empty; it also had once to be constituted differently and be filled with a material sufficiently capable of transferring motion upon all celestial bodies found in it, and of making them consonant with its motion [and] consequently with one another's motions, and once the [force of] attraction has cleared the space in question and gathered all spread-out matter in special lumps, the planets, owing to the imparted motions, now have to continue their orbiting freely and unchanged in a non-resisting space. The reasons of the first-mentioned probability[6] obviously require this notion and because between the two cases a third is not possible,[7] this case can be considered with a considerable manner [measure] of approval which raises it above the probability of a hypothesis.[8] One could, if one were to go into details, finally arrive, through a series of conclusions drawn from one another according to the manner of a mathematical method with all the pomp which it entails and with a greater probability than what its application in physical topics commonly appears to be,[9] at the very plan which I will lay out about the origin of the world-edifice, but I prefer to present my views in the form of a hypothesis and leave it to the insight of the

---

* I do not investigate here whether this space can be called empty [25] in the most special sense. For here it is enough to note that all matter which may be found in that space is much too impotent that it could exert some effect in respect to the moving masses in question.

reader to scrutinize their merit rather than to make suspect their [27] validity through the appearance of a pretentious demonstration[10] and [thus] while I gain the ignorant, I would lose the approval of the well-informed.

I assume that all [forms of] matter, of which the globes that belong to our solar world, [that is], all the planets and comets consist, have filled, [inasmuch as they were] diluted into their elementary substance at the origination of all things, the entire space of the world-edifice wherein now these [fully] formed bodies are orbiting. This condition of nature, even if one considers it in and by itself with no reference to a system, seems to be the only simplest one that can succeed to the [mere] nothing.[11] Nothing was yet developing at the time. The coalescence of celestial bodies separate from one another, their separation proportionate to the [mutual] attractions, their shape which arises from the balance of the aggregated material, are a later condition. Nature, which bordered immediately on [the act of] creation, was as raw, [and] as unformed as possible. But even in the essential properties of the elements, which constitute the chaos, one can notice the hallmark of that perfection which they have from their origin on, insofar as their essence is a consequence of the eternal idea of the divine mind.[12] The simplest, the most universal properties which seem to have been planned without intent, the [very] matter, which seems to be purely passive and in need of forms and arrangements, has in its simplest [28] state a tendency to develop through natural development into a perfect constitution. But the *difference of the* [various] *kinds of elements*[13] [which] tends to the stirring of nature and to the shaping of the chaos, [is] the chief factor whereby the standstill, that would dominate in a universal balance among the dispersed elements, is removed and [thus] the chaos begins its development at the point of the more strongly attracting particles. The kinds of that elementary matter are without doubt infinitely various[14] according to the inexhaustibility which nature shows in every respect.[15] Those of greater specific density and attractive force, which in and by themselves take up lesser space and are also rarer, become, owing to the equal distribution [of matter] in space, more dispersed than those of the lighter kind. Elements of 1000 times greater specific weight are a thousand, perhaps even a million times[16] more dispersed than those which are lighter in that proportion. And since these differences ought to be thought of as [being as] infinite as possible,[17] it will happen that just as there may exist bodily constituent parts of a kind which exceeds another in the scale of density as does a globe, which is drawn with the radius of the planetary-edifice, another which has the diameter of the thousandth of a line,[18] [in the same way] also those [heavier] kinds of scattered elements are at so greater a distance from one another as [than] are these [of much lighter kind].

[29] In a space filled in such a manner the universal standstill lasts only for an instant. The elements have essential forces[19] to set each other in motion and are themselves a source of life. Matter is immediately in the tendency to develop itself. The scattered elements of heavier kind gather, through attraction, from a sphere around [them] all matter of lesser specific weight;[20] they themselves, together with the material with which they have been united, gather into points where particles of even denser kind are found, these in turn [gather] in a similar way to still denser particles and so forth. Inasmuch as one follows in thought this self-developing nature through the entire realm of chaos, one easily perceives that all results of this process would in the end consist in the putting together of various lumps [of matter] which, after the completion of their formation, would be at rest and forever unmoved.[21]

But nature has still other forces in store which especially evidence themselves when matter is diluted into fine particles, whereby they repulse one another and through their conflict with [the force of] attraction produce that motion which is, so to speak, an enduring life of nature. Through this repulsive force, which reveals itself in the elasticity of vapors in the strongly smelling bodies and in the expansion of all spirituous matter and which is [30] an indisputable phenomenon of nature,[22] the elements sinking toward their points of attraction become directed sidewise in all sorts of ways and the perpendicular fall issues in circular motions which surround the center of sinking. We want, in order to grasp clearly the formation of the world-edifice, to confine our consideration from an infinite essence of nature to a specific system, the one belonging to our sun. After we have considered its generation, we shall proceed in a similar way to the origin of higher world-orders and be able to sum up in a single doctrine the infinity of the entire creation.[23]

If, accordingly, there is in a very large space a point where the attraction of elements, [which are] found there, works stronger than anywhere else, then the basic material of elementary particles spread-out in the entire extent [of that space] will sink toward that point. The first effect of that universal sinking is the formation of a body in that center of attraction which grows, so to speak, from an infinitely small seed in quick steps, but in the measure in which that mass increases it moves the surrounding parts with ever stronger force to unite with it. When the mass of this central body is grown so far that the velocity, with which it draws toward itself [31] the particles from the great distances through the weak degree of repulsiveness whereby they hinder one another, is being bent sidewise [and thus] issues in side-motions, which, by means of the centrifugal force,[24] are capable of surrounding the central body in a circle, there arise great vortices of particles, each of which describes curved lines through the composition of the attractive [force] and of the sidewise-directed turning force;[25] these kinds of circles [orbits] all cut through one another, [a result] for which their great scattering in that place leaves [sufficient] place. Meanwhile, these motions conflicting with one another in various ways are naturally driven to bring each other into equilibrium, that is, into a state in which one motion is opposed to another as little as possible.[26] This happens, first, inasmuch as that the particles confine one another's motion as long as all continue in one direction; second, that the particles limit their vertical motion, by which they approach the center of attraction so long until they, all being moved in horizontal, that is, parallel-running orbits around the sun as their center, no longer cross one another and, through the equality of the orbital force with the sinking force, they always maintain themselves in free circular courses at the height at which they float; so that finally only those particles remain floating in the extent of space which through their fall acquire a [certain] velocity and through the resistance of others a [certain] direction, [32] whereby they can continue in *free circular motion*. In this state, since all particles move in one direction and in parallel-running circles, namely, in free circular motions, through the required orbital forces around the sun, the conflict and collision of the elements is removed and all is in the state of the smallest reciprocal action.[27] This is the natural result in which a material, which is caught in conflicting motions, always settles.[28] It is also clear that a large amount of the dispersed amount of particles must reach, through the resistance whereby they seek to bring one another to that state, such exactness of conditions;[29] although a still larger amount does not reach it[30] and only serves to increase the lump of the central body into which they sink, inasmuch as they cannot freely maintain themselves in the height [distance] in which they float, but cross the orbits of those below and finally lose all motion through resistance.[31] This body in the center of attraction, which consequently becomes through the amount of its collected material the chief piece of planetary edifice, is the sun, although it does not have yet that burning glow which it produces on its surface after its complete development.

It is still to be noted that, inasmuch as all elements of the self-forming nature move, [33] as was shown, in one direction around the center of the sun in such revolutions directed along a single region [direction] which also happen to be on [around] a common axis, the rotation of the fine matter cannot maintain itself in such a way;

because according to the laws of the central motion [force] all revolutions must intersect the center of attraction with the plane of their orbits, but among all these orbits running in one direction around one common axis there is only one which cuts through the center of the sun, [and] therefore all matter rushes from both sides [halves] of this axis drawn in thought toward that orbit which goes through the axis of rotation straight in the center of the common sinking.[32] Which [said] orbit is the plane of attraction of all elements floating around, around [in the nearness of] which [orbit] they pile up as much as possible and, on the contrary, they leave empty the regions distant from that plane; because those elements, which cannot come so close to that plane to which all tends cannot maintain themselves in the places where they float, but inasmuch as they collide with the elements floating around, they occasion their ultimate fall into the sun.

If one also considers this basic stuff of world-matter floating around in such a condition in which it arranges itself through the [force of] attraction and through a mechanical result of the universal laws of resistance, then we see a [34] space included between two planes not too distant from one another, in whose middle is the universal plane of attraction [and which] extends from the center of the sun into unknown reaches, in which all conceivable particles perform in free rotations, which correspond to the measure of their height [distance] and attraction which dominates there, exact circular motions and, therefore, inasmuch as in such a condition they hinder one another as little as possible, they must forever remain there, if the mutual attraction of these particles of the basic stuff would not start doing its effect and produce thereby new formations which are the seeds of planets that ought to arise. For inasmuch as the elements, which at not-too-greatly differing distances move around the sun, are through the equality of parallel motions[s] in an almost mutually relative rest, then the pull of the elements found there exerts here too, through the overwhelming specific attraction, a considerable effect* to start the gathering [35] of the nearest particles for the formation of a body which, according to the growth of its lump, extends farther its attraction and moves the elements to its composition from a wide range.

The formation of planets in this system has this advantage over

---

* The beginning of self-forming planets is not to be looked for only in the Newtonian attraction. This would be too slow and weak in a particle of exceptional fineness.[33] One would rather say that in this space the first formation happens through the concourse of a few elements which unite [35] through the customary laws of coherence[34] until those lumps, which whereby arise, gradually increase so far that the Newtonian force of attraction becomes capable of always enlarging them through its action-at-a-distance.[35]

any [other] possible theory[36] that the origin of the masses represents simultaneously [both] the origin of motions and the position of orbits at the very same moment; indeed, that both the deviations from the greatest exactness in these determinations as well as their harmonies become clear at a glance. The planets form themselves from particles which at the height [distance] where they float have exact motions in circular orbits; *so that the masses composed of them maintain the very same motions in the same measure along the very same direction.* This is enough to comprehend why the motion of planets is also circular and [why] their orbits are in one plane. They would be quite exact circles,* were [36] the reaches from which they gather the elements for their formation, very small, and [were so] also the difference[s] among their motions. But since a farther region is needed to form the thick lump of a planet from the fine basic stuff[38] which in the celestial space is very much scattered, the difference of distances which these elements have from the sun, and withal also the difference of their velocities, is no longer negligible; consequently, it would be necessary that for the planet to maintain in this difference of motions the equality of central forces and the circular [orbital] velocity, the particles, which from various heights [distances] with various motions come together on it [the planet], would exactly offset the deficiency of one another, which [outcome], whether this happens in fact fairly exactly,* nevertheless, since something always lacks in that perfect compensation, entails the deviation concerning the circular motion and the eccentricity.[39] It becomes clarified with the same ease that although the circles [orbits] of all planets ought to be at [in] fairly one plane, nevertheless even in this point a small deviation[40] ought to occur, because, as already mentioned, the elementary particles, though they find themselves as close as possible to the universal plane of condition[41] [reference] of their motions, nevertheless they enclose a certain space on both sides of it; so that it would be quite a lucky coincidence if all planets were to start their formation quite exactly in the plane of reference in the middle between these two sides, which circumstance would already occasion a certain inclination of their orbits toward one another,

---

* This exact circular motion concerns [36] properly only the planets near the sun; because concerning the great distances, where the farthest planets or even the comets have been formed, it is easy to guess that, because the sinking motion of the basic stuff is much weaker there, the expanse of space which is spread out there is also greater, the elements in and by themselves already deviate from the motion similar to a circle and thus they must become the origin of bodies built from them.[37]

* [This is so] because the particles from the region nearer the sun, which have a greater orbital velocity [37] than is required for circular motion in the plane where they gather on the planet, compensate that motion which is lacking in the velocity in those particles farther from the sun which incorporate themselves into the same body [planet], so that they may move circularly at the distance of the planet.

though the tendency of particles from both sides would confine this deviation as much as possible allowing to it but narrow limits. It is not to be wondered at that here too the greatest exactness of determinations will occur as little as in all things of nature, because in general the multiplicity of circumstances, which take part in each natural condition, does not allow an exact regularity.[42] [38]

SECOND SECTION

of the various density of planets
and of the relation of their masses.

We have shown[1] that the particles of the elementary basic stuff, as in and by themselves they were equally spread out in the cosmic space,[2] through their sinking down toward the sun remained floating in places where their velocity acquired through [their] fall offered exactly the balance against the attraction, and their direction, as this ought to be in circular motion, became bent vertically against the circle-ray [radius]. If, however, we now think of particles of various specific densities at equal distance from the sun, then the ones with greater specific weight tend deeper across the resistance of others toward the sun and will not be bent so soon from their way as the lighter ones, therefore, their motion will be circular only at a greater approach to the sun. On the contrary, the elements of the lighter kind, bent away from the straight linear fall, will issue in circular motion before they are driven too deep toward the center, and will also remain floating at greater distances, also they cannot penetrate so deep through the full space of elements [39] without their motion becoming weakened through their resistance and they cannot acquire the great degree of velocity which is required for orbiting closer to the center; so that, according to the required equality of motions, the specifically lighter particles will orbit in greater distances from the sun, the heavier ones, however, will occur in the closer [distances], and the planets, which are formed from them, become therefore of the heavier kind, [that is, those planets] which form themselves from the concurrence of these atoms closer to the sun than the ones farther from it.

It is also a kind of statical law[3] which determines for the material of the cosmic space its height [distance] according to the inverse proportion of density. Similarly, it is just as easy to understand that a given height [distance] will not be occupied by particles of similar specific density. Of these particles of certain specific kind those will remain floating at a greater distance from the sun and those acquire at a greater distance the proper measure of their fall demanded by the stable circular motion, which have sunk downward toward the sun from greater distances; whereas, those whose original place at the general distribution of matter in the chaos was closer to the sun could, regardless of their not greater density, come to their circle of orbiting closer to the sun. And then also the places of materials become determined [40], in respect to the center of their sinking, not only by their specific weight, but also through their original place in the first [primordial] rest of nature, so that it is easy to understand that their very different kinds will come together at each distance from the sun to remain hanging [floating] around it, but that in general the denser materials more frequently will occur nearer the center than farther from it and that also, regardless [of the fact that] the planets become a mixture of very different materials, nevertheless their masses ought to be heavier in the measure in which they are closer to the sun, and of lesser density insofar as their distance is greater.[4]

Our system shows in respect to this law of density ruling among the planets a notable perfection above all [any] other notion which has already been formed or still can be formed about their cause.[5] Newton, who had determined the density of each planet through calculation,[6] believed to have found the cause of their distance-determined relation in the appropriateness of God's choice and in the motivation of his purpose, because the planets closer to the sun must withstand more heat from it and the more distant ones must do with less degrees of heat;[7] which may not seem to be possible if the planets close[r] to the sun were not of denser kind [41] and the more distant ones were not put together of lighter material. But the insufficiency of such an explanation does not require much reflection. A planet, our earth for instance, is composed of many kinds of matter different from one another; among these it was only necessary that the lighter ones, which through an equal effect of the sun whose composition has a relation to the heat by which its rays are working, are more penetrated and moved, be spread out on the surface; but that the mixture of the remaining matter in the entirety of the lump should have this relation is not thereby clarified, because the sun has no effect whatever on the interior of the planet. Newton worried that were the earth to sink to the vicinity of Mercury into the sun's rays, it ought to burn as a comet and that its matter had not sufficient fire-resistance so as not to be dispersed through that glow.[8] But how much more should the sun's own material itself, which is still four times lighter than the one of which the earth consists, be destroyed by that glow; or why is the moon twice as dense as the earth,[9] although it floats with that at the very same distance from the sun? Also, one cannot ascribe the proportional densities to the relation respecting the sun's heat without becoming embroiled in the greatest contradictions.[10] One rather sees a cause, which apportions the places of the planets [42] according to the density of their lumps, [and which] ought to have a relation to the interior and not to their surface; it should, regardless of that consequence which it has determined, still allow for a diversity of matter in those very same celestial bodies and to establish this relation of density only in the wholeness of the composition; to which all whether some static law other than the one which is presented in our theory can [really] do justice, I leave it to the insight of the reader to judge.

The relation among the densities of planets entails still another circumstance which through a full harmony with the theory as presented above verifies the correctness of our theory. The celestial body, which stands in the center of other globes moving around it, is usually of lighter kind than the body which orbits nearest around it. The earth with respect to the moon and the sun with respect to the earth show such relation of their densities.[11] According to the plan which we have presented, such a state of affairs is necessary. For then the lower planets are mostly built from the remainder of elementary materials which through the advantage of their density could penetrate to such a vicinity of the center with the required degree of velocity; whereas [43] the body in their center became piled up indiscriminately of all such materials of all possible kinds which did not acquire their regular motions, among which, since the lighter particles make up the largest part, it is easy to see that because, as the celestial bodies orbiting nearest to the center [are] also an outgrowth of denser kinds [of matter], the central body, however, contains in itself an indiscriminate mixture of all [sorts of materials], it has to be [of] a substance of denser kind than these [surrounding bodies].[12] In fact, even the moon is twice denser than the earth,[13] and this is 4 times denser than the sun,[14] which according to all supposition will be exceeded in still higher grades of density by the still deeper [closer] planets, Venus and Mercury.[15]

Our sight now turns to the relation which the masses of celestial bodies ought to have according to our theory in comparison with their distances in order to test the result of our system by the unerring calculations of Newton. It does not need many words to make it understandable that [because] the central body [is] the chief portion of its system, the sun must in a conspicuous way be greater in mass than the planets together, as this will also be valid about Jupiter with respect to its satellites and about Saturn in respect to its own. The central body forms [44] itself from the sediments of all particles [gathered] from the entire extent of its sphere of attraction, which could not acquire the most exact determination of the circular motion and the near relation to the common plane [of orbiting] and of which undoubtedly there must be an unusually larger amount than of the latter [others]. To apply this consideration especially to the sun: if one wants to estimate the width of space around [within] which the circularly orbiting particles, that have served for the planets as basic stuff, have farthest deviated from the common plane, then one assumes it to be somewhat larger than the width of the greatest deviation of the planetary orbits from one another. But now, inasmuch as they deviate on both sides from the common plane, their greatest inclination with respect to one another hardly makes $7\frac{1}{2}$ degrees. One can also represent all matter out of which the planets were formed as being spread out in that space which was enclosed between two surfaces from the center of the sun which enclose an angle of $7\frac{1}{2}$ degrees. But a zone going in the direction of a great circle with a width of $7\frac{1}{2}$ degrees is somewhat larger that 17th part of the surface of the globe,[16] the bodily space too between the two surfaces, which excise the spherical space to the width of the foregoing angle, is somewhat larger than the 17th part of the bodily content of the entire sphere. Also, according to that hypothesis, all matter [45] which has been applied to the formation of planets, make up about 17th part of that matter which the sun has gathered for its composition from that distance where the outermost planet stands from both sides [of the common plane of orbiting]. But this central body has an advantage of lump [mass] above the total content [of mass] of all planets which is to that not as 17:1 but as 650:1, as the calculation of Newton determines this;[17] but it can also be seen easily that in the higher [more distant] spaces beyond Saturn, where the planetary formations either cease or are rare anyhow, where only a few cometary bodies were formed[18] and where especially the motions of the basic stuff, inasmuch as they themselves did not succeed to acquire the regular equality of central forces [as well] as [is the case] in the region near the center, issue only in an almost universal sinking toward the center, and increase the sun with all matter from such far spread-out spaces that, I say, from these causes must arise for the sun-lump the [its] prominent greatness of mass.

But in order to compare the planets among one another with respect to mass, we first note that according to the manner of formation indicated above the quantity of matter, which comes to the putting together of a planet, arrives especially from the extent of its distance from the sun; 1. precisely, because the sun limits through its attraction [46] the sphere of attraction of a planet, but in similar circumstances [its attraction] does not set so strict [limits] to [the sphere of attraction] of the more distant [planets] than to the closer ones; 2. because the circle from which all particles come together [to] form a more distant planet, is drawn with a greater radius, also includes more basic stuff than the smaller circles; 3. because for the very last reason the width between the two planes of the greatest deviation [from the common plane of orbiting] is, in equal number of degrees, greater at great heights than at small ones. But this advantage of the more distant planets above the lower planets will be limited because the particles closer to the sun are of denser kind and in all likelihood also less dispersed than at greater distances; but one can easily estimate[19] that the former advantages for the formation of larger masses far exceed the latter limitations, and in general the planets which are formed at greater distance from the sun must obtain greater masses than the ones near. This happens also inasmuch as one represents the formation of a planet only as [one that goes on] in the presence of the sun; but when one lets several planets form themselves at various distances, then one will limit the extent of attraction of the other and this brings about an exception from the foregoing law. For that planet which is close to another with exceptional[ly large] mass, will lose very much from the sphere of its attraction and thereby [47] become much smaller than the relation of its distance from the sun alone would require. Although in general the planets are of larger mass inasmuch as they are more distant from the sun, just as in general Saturn and Jupiter, as the two chief pieces of our system, are the largest because they are most distant from the sun, yet there are deviations from this analogy in which, however, always transpires the hallmark of general formation which we assert about the celestial bodies: that, namely, a planet of exceptional size robs the nearest ones on both sides of the mass pertaining to them because of their distance from the sun; inasmuch as it appropriates a part of the material which should have gone to that [those] for its [their] formation. In fact, Mars, which because of its position should be larger than the earth through the force of attraction of so great a Jupiter which is near it, loses in its mass; and Saturn itself, although it has because of its height [distance] an advantage over Mars, is still not quite free from suffering a con-siderable loss[20] through Jupiter's attraction, and it seems to me that Mercury owes the exceptional smallness of its mass not only to the attraction of the so nearby mighty sun but also to the vicinity of Venus, which, if one compares its probable density with its size, must be a planet of considerable mass.[21]

[48] Now that all concurs as splendidly as one can wish to confirm the adequacy of a mechanical doctrine concerning the origin of the

world-edifice and of the celestial bodies,[22] we want, while we estimate the space in which the basic stuff of planets was spread out before their formation, to consider in what degree of thinness was that middle space filled and with what freedom or with how little obstacles could the particles floating around perform their regular motions. If the space which comprises in itself therein all the matter of the planets was contained in that part of the Saturnian sphere which from the sun out [os] between two planes about seven degrees far in all heights [distances] from one another, and therefore was the 17th part of the entire sphere, which one can describe with the radius of the height [distance] of Saturn, then we ought, in order to compute the change [thinning out] of the planetary basic stuff, which filled that space, only to set the height [distance] of Saturn [at] 100,000 earth-diameters;[23] then the whole sphere of the Saturnian orbit will exceed the space-content [volume] of the earth-globe by 1000 bimillions.[24] Thus, if we take instead of the 17th part only the 20th, the space in which the elementary basic stuff floated must exceed still by 50 bimillions the volume of the earth-globe.[25] [49] If one now sets, following Newton, the mass of planets with their companions at 1/650 of the Sun-lump, then the earth, which is only 1/169282th of it,[26] will be related to the total mass of all planetary matter as 1 to $276\frac{1}{2}$;[27] and if one therefore brought all this matter to the same specific density with the earth, there would arise out of it a body which would take up a space $277\frac{1}{2}$ times greater[28] than the earth. If we therefore take the density of the earth in its entire lump not much greater than the density of solid matter which one finds beneath its uppermost surface, just as this is not required otherwise by the properties of the figure of the earth,[29] and these upper materials [we take at] about 4 or 5 times thicker than the water,[30] but the water [we take at] 1000 times heavier than the air,[31] then the matter of all planets, if it were spread out to the thinness of the air, would take up an almost 14 times hundred-thousand times greater space than does the earth-globe.[32] This space compared with the space, in which according to our assumption all the matter of the planets was spread out, is thirty million times[33] smaller than that; also, the dispersion of planetary matter in that space entails an equally many times [greater] thinning out, than the thinness which the particles of our atmosphere have. In fact, this magnitude [degree] of dispersion, unbelievable as it may appear, was, however, neither unnecessary nor unnatural. It had to be as great as possible [50] to secure for the floating particles all freedom of motion, almost as much as in an empty space and to diminish infinitely the resistance which they could cause to one another; they could, however, even of themselves take on such a state of thinning out, which one

124

must not doubt, if one knows a little the expansion which matter suffers when transformed into vapor; or when one, to remain with the heavens, considers the thinning out of matter in the tails of comets which, even with an unheard width of their diameter, which exceeds the diameter of the earth well [over] hundred times,[34] are nevertheless so transparent that the small stars can be seen through them;[35] which our air, when illuminated by the sun, does not permit in a [with its] height which is many thousand times smaller.[36]

I conclude this section by adding an analogy which in and by itself alone can raise the present theory of the mechanical formation of celestial bodies above the probability of hypotheses into a formal certainty.[37] If the sun is composed of the particles of the same basic stuff of which the planets were formed and if the difference consists only in that in the former the materials of all kinds are piled up without difference, in these [latter], however, they were disturbed at various distances according to the condition of the density [51] of their kinds; then, if one considers the matter of all planets united together, a density must arise in their mixture which is almost equal to the density of the sun's body. This necessary consequence of our system finds a fortunate confirmation in the comparison which Mr de Buffon, this so worthily famous philosopher,[38] has presented between the densities of the total planetary matter and of the suns of theirs [of their sun]; he found a similarity between the two as that between 640 and 650.[39] If unartificial and necessary consequences from a theory find in the real relations of nature so fortunate confirmations, can one really believe that a mere chance produced this correspondence between theory and observation?[40]

THIRD SECTION

of the eccentricity of planetary orbits
and of the origin of comets.

One cannot make out of comets a special kind of celestial bodies which would completely differ from [52] the species of planets.[1] Nature works here as elsewhere through insensible deviations and, as she goes through all degrees of alterations, she ties together the distant properties with the close ones by means of a chain of intermediate members.[2] With the planets the eccentricity is a consequence of defects in those strivings through which nature endeavors to make the planetary motions exactly similar to a circle which she, however, can never fully attain owing to the intervening of various circumstances, but rather deviates from it more at greater distances [from the sun] than at near ones.

This determination [operation] leads through a steady ladder, across all possible degrees of eccentricity, from planets finally to comets; and although at Saturn it seems to be cut off by a great gap which wholly separates the cometary species from the planets, we have already remarked in the First Part[3] that presumably there may be still other planets beyond Saturn which through a greater deviation from the circular curving of orbits come closer to the course of comets and that only because of absence of observation or of its difficulty that this affinity has not since long become represented as visibly to the eye as to reason.[4] [53]

We have already adduced in the First Section of this Part a cause which makes eccentric the path of a celestial body which forms itself from the basic stuff floating around, if one also assumes that this stuff possesses in all its places forces exactly bent for circular motion. For because the planet gathers that stuff from heights [distances] widely separate from one another, where the velocities of circular courses are different, they come together on the planet with various [but] for them appropriate degrees of orbital motion which differs from the measure of velocity which is proper for the distance of the planet, and adduce to it thereby an eccentricity inasmuch as these various impacts of particles fail to offset completely one another's deviation [from the velocity appropriate to the planet].

If the eccentricity had no other cause, it would be moderate everywhere; it would be less even with those small and from the sun very distant planets than with the near and great ones;[5] if one in particular assumed that the particles of the basic stuff really had beforehand sufficient circular motions. But since these determinations do not agree with observations, because, as was already noted, the eccentricity increases with distance from the sun and the smallness of masses seems to make much rather an exception to the increase [54] of eccentricity as we see this in Mars,[6] [and] thus we are necessitated to limit the hypothesis about the exact circular motion of the particles of basic stuff in that as they in regions near the sun come very close to the exactness of that determination but they deviate from it the more the farther these elementary particles float from the sun. Such a modification of the basic proposition of the free circular motion of the basic stuff is more appropriate to nature. For regardless of the thinness of space which seems to leave them freedom to limit one another to the point of the completely bent equality of central forces,[7] yet no less considerable are the causes which prevent this goal of nature from its complete implementation. The more distant are the spread-out parts of basic stuff from the sun, the weaker is the force which brings them to sinking; the resistance of the lower parts [of this stuff], which should bend their fall sideways and force it to set its direction vertically away from the circle-ray [radius], diminishes in the measure in which these parts sink forth under it, either to incorporate themselves into the sun or to set up orbits in nearer regions.[8] The specifically prominent lightness of this higher [more distant] matter does not permit to those parts to achieve the [measure of] sinking motion, which is the basis of all, with that impact which is required to cause the bending of resisting [55] particles;[9] and perhaps that these distant particles still hinder one another to overcome finally after a long period to this uniformity, they already form among themselves small masses as the beginnings for so many celestial bodies, which gather themselves from weakly moved stuff, have a more eccentric motion whereby they sink to the sun, and on their way become deviated from vertical fall through the incorporation of speedily moving parts, finally, however, remain comets, if those spaces in which they were formed have become cleared and empty through sinking down to the sun or through the gathering in various lumps.[10] This is the cause of the eccentricity of planets increasing with distance from the sun and of those celestial bodies which are therefore called comets, because they markedly exceed the former in this property.[11] There are though still two exceptions which break the law of the eccentricity increasing with distance from the sun, which one notices in both the smallest planets of our system, [namely], in Mars and Mercury; but in the former the cause is presumably the vicinity of the so great Jupiter, which, while berobbing through its attraction on its side Mars of particles [destined] for its formation, leaves to Mars especially only place to stay away from the sun,[12] [and] thereby arises an overweight of central force and [with it] eccentricity.[13] What [56] concerns Mercury, the lowest but also the most eccentric among the planets, it is easy to perceive that because the sun in its axial rotation does not at all approach the [orbital] velocity of Mercury,[14] the resistance which the sun presents to the matter in the space surrounding it, not only berobs the nearest particles of their central motion, but also this contrary trend may easily extend as far as Mercury and its orbital velocity will thereby considerably be diminished.[15]

The eccentricity is the most prominent distinctive mark of comets. Their atmospheres and tails, which, because of the heat expand at their closer approach to the sun, are only the consequences of the former [i.e. eccentricities],[16] although in times of ignorance they served as unusual symbols of fright to announce destinies imagined by the vulgar.[17] The astronomers, who pay more attention to the laws of motion than to the strangeness of shape, note another property which distinguishes the species of comets from planets, namely, that unlike these, they do not tie themselves to the belt of zodiac but set up their orbits freely in all regions of the heavens. This peculiarity has a single cause [identical] with [that of] eccentricity. If therefore the planets have their orbits enclosed within the narrow district of the zodiac,[18] [this is only so] because the elementary matter [57] around the sun takes on circular movements, [and] in vain tries at each orbiting to cross the plane of reference and [thus] does not permit the bodies already formed to deviate from that plane toward which all matter tends from both sides; then the basic stuff of the space far removed from the center, which moves feebly through attraction, cannot acquire free circular impulses for the very same reason which produces eccentricities, is not capable [either] of accumulating itself at that height [elevation] with respect to the plane of reference of all planetary motions in order to retain mainly in that track all the bodies formed there; much rather the scattered basic stuff, as it is not confined to a special region, just as [is the case] with the lower planets, piles up with equal ease now on one now on the other side and far from the plane of reference just as often as near it in order to form celestial bodies. Therefore the comets descend to us with all unfetteredness from all regions; still those whose first place of formation is not too far elevated above the planetary orbits will display less deviation from the [ideal] confines [shape] of their orbits,[19] and just as well less eccentricity.[20] Concerning their deviations, this lawless freedom of comets increases with the distance from the center of the system and in the depths of the heavens transforms itself into a complete absence of revolutions, [an absence] which freely abandons [58] the most outwardly formed bodies to their fall into the sun and sets the last limits to the systematic constitution [of the planetary world-edifice].

I presuppose in this sketch of cometary motions that in respect of their direction they for the most part have it in common with the planets. This seems to me to be undoubtedly so with those near comets[21] and this uniformity cannot vanish in the depths of heavens until the point where the elementary basic stuff in the greatest feebleness of motion displays in all directions the rotation arising from the downward sinking because the time which is required to make them [cometary motions] uniform through the association of lower motions in respect to direction, is too long for it to be able to stretch to that point so that the [full] formation of nature may be attained in the lower regions. There will [therefore] be also comets which perform their orbiting in the opposite side [direction], namely, from East to West; although I would almost be persuaded by causes, which

I here abstain from adducing,[22] that out of the 19 comets with which this peculiarity has been observed,[23] optical appearance may have given the reason for this with perhaps a few of them.

I must still note something about the masses of comets and about the density of their stuff.[24] [59] As a rule, in the higher [more distant] regions of the formation of these celestial bodies, for reasons adduced in the previous sections, the masses to be formed ought to be always greater in the measure in which the distance increases. And it is believable that some comets are larger than Saturn and Jupiter; but it is not believable that this greatness of masses always so increases. The dispersion of the basic stuff, the specific lightness of its particles make slow the formation [of bodies] in the most removed regions of cosmic space; the unspecified spreading out of that stuff in the entire inexhaustible reach of that extent, without a determination [specification] to pile up in a certain plane, provides, instead of a single considerable formation, for many smaller ones and the absence of a central force draws the greatest part of particles down to the sun without their being collected into [large] masses.

The specific density of the stuff out of which the comets arise is of greater interest than the size of their masses. Presumably, since they form themselves in the highest [outermost] regions of the world-edifice, the particles of their composition are of the lightest kind[25] and it must not therefore be doubted that this is the most prominent cause of vaporous globes and tails whereby they make themselves known from other celestial bodies. This dispersion of the cometary material into vapour cannot be mainly ascribed to the working [60] of the solar heat; in their vicinity to the sun some comets hardly reach the depth of the earth-orbit; many remain [stop their descent toward the sun somewhere] between the orbit of the earth and of Venus and then return back.[26] If such a modest degree of heat dilutes and thins out the matter on the surface of those bodies to such an extent, then they must consist of the lightest kind which suffers through warmth more thinning out than any other kind of matter in the entire nature.[27]

One cannot relate these vapours so often rising from the comet to the heat which its body has retained from its former vicinity to the sun; for one may still surmise that a comet has, at the time of its formation, already passed through several revolutions with greater eccentricity and these have only become smaller gradually; but the other planets, of which one may surmise the same do not show this phenomenon. They would, however, show it on their body if the kinds of lightest matter, which are [also] included in the composition of planets, were as abundant [in them] as in the comets.

The earth has something on it that can be compared with the

expansion of cometary vapor and of their tails.* The finest particles which the sun's working draws from its surface [61] pile up around one of the poles when the sun performs the half circle of its course at [toward] the oppositely set hemisphere [of the earth].[29] The finest and most effective particles, which rise in the burning earth-belt,[30] become, after they have reached a certain height in the atmosphere, forced through the working of the sun's rays to recede and pile up in those regions which are turned away from the sun and are buried in a long night and compensate the inhabitants of the ice-zone [arctic] for the absence of the great light [of the sun] which [thus] sends to them all the effects of its warmth even in this great distance.[31] The very same force of the sun's rays which produces the northern light, would produce a vapory circle [shell] with a tail of the finest and volatile particles, were these to be found as abundant on the earth as on the comets.

FOURTH SECTION

of the origin of the moons and of the
motions of planets around their axes.

The tendency of a planet to form itself from the range of elementary material is also the cause of its axial revolution [62] and generates the moons which must orbit around it. What the sun with its planets is on a large scale, a planet, which has a far-reaching sphere of attraction, represents it on a small scale, namely, [as] the chief piece of a system whose parts are set in motion through the attraction of a central body. The self-forming planet, as it moves [draws] for its formation the particles of the basic stuff from the entire reach [of its sphere of attraction] will generate from all these sinking motions by means of their interactions circular motions and finally such that issue in a common direction and a part of which obtain the proper measure of the free circular course and find themselves in that restriction near a common plane. Just as [is the case with] the planets around the sun, in that space too moons will be formed around these planets if the extent of the attraction of such celestial bodies provides favorable circumstances for their formation. What in addition has been said about the origin of the solar system can be applied with sufficient similarity to the system of Saturn and Jupiter. The moons all will direct the orbits of their revolution in one side [direction] and in almost one plane, and this [happens] for the same causes which

---

* This [something] are [sic] the northern lights.[28]

130

determine this analogy on the large scale. But why move these companions in their common direction rather toward one side [direction], toward which the planets orbit, [63] rather than toward another? Their orbitings are not produced by the circular motions [of the planets], they merely recognize only the attraction of the planet as a cause, and in respect of this all directions are equal[ly possible]; a mere chance will chose among all these possible directions that in which the sinking motion of the stuff issues in orbits. In fact, the circular course of the planet does nothing to impress on the stuff, from which the moons must be formed around it, revolutions around itself; all particles around the planet move in the same motion with it around the sun and are also in respective rest toward one another. The attraction of the planet alone does all.[1] But the circular motion which must arise from the attraction, because this is in and by itself indifferent in respect to all directions, needed only a small external specification to issue much rather in one side [direction] than in another; it obtains this small degree of steering from the advancing of elementary particles which move simultaneously around the sun, though with greater velocity, and come into the planet's sphere of attraction.[2] For this forces the particles nearer[3] the sun, which orbit with faster velocity, to abandon already from afar the direction of their track and to rise in an elongated curving above [ahead of] the planet. These particles, because they have a greater degree of velocity than the planet itself, [64] as they are brought through this attraction into sinking towards the planet, give to their sinking a rectilinear fall and also to the fall [sinking] of the rest a bending from west to east[4] and only this slight steering is needed in order to bring about that the circular motion into which the fall, which the attraction produces, should take much rather this than the other direction. For this reason all moons will agree in their direction with the direction of the orbiting of the planet.[5] But also the plane of their path will not deviate far from the plane of the planetary orbits because the matter out of which they form [themselves] will, for the same reason which we have adduced in general about the direction [or orbits], also be directed to the most exact determination of them, namely, the coincidence [of them] with the plane of the chief orbit.

One sees clearly from all this what are the circumstances under which a planet may obtain trabants. The force of attraction of it must be great and consequently the extent of its sphere of action far extended so that thereby the particles moved through a high fall toward the planet, regardless of that [part of them] which is taken away by resistance, may nevertheless acquire velocities appropriate to free revolution, [just] as enough stuff is available in this district [of the earth] for the formation of the moon,[6] which cannot happen with a small attraction. Therefore only the planets with large mass and with [65] great distance [from the sun] are endowed with companions. Jupiter and Saturn, the 2 greatest and also most distant planets have most moons. To the earth, which is much smaller than those, only one was allotted; and Mars, to which because of its distance some share in this advantage pertained, goes away empty because its mass is so small.[7]

It is a satisfaction to recognize how this very attraction of the planet, which supplied this stuff for the formation of moons and simultaneously determined the motion of them, extends even to its own body and imparts to it through the same procedure through which it builds itself a rotation around its axis in the general direction from west to east. The particles of the downward-sinking basic stuff which, as was said, obtain a universal motion from west to east, fall mostly on the surface of the planet and mix themselves with its small lump,[8] because they do not have the proper degree [of velocity] to maintain themselves in freely floating circular motions.[9] As they now come into a combination with the planet, they must, as the parts of it, continue the same turning around in the same direction, which they had before they became united with it. And because in general it can be seen from the foregoing that the multitude of particles which the lack of required motion plunges down [66] to the central body must exceed very far the number of others which can acquire the appropriate degree of velocity, thus it can also easily be grasped why this [central body] will by far not have in its axial rotation the velocity to provide on its surface to gravity the counterweight with the fleeing force,[10] still, however, [that velocity] will become much speedier in the case of planets with greater mass and greater distance than with nearer and smaller planets. In fact, Jupiter has the speediest axial rotation which we know,[11] and I do not know in what [other] system could one harmonize this with a body whose lump exceeds all others, if one could not consider its motions as the effect of that very same attraction which this celestial body exerts according to the mass of this very lump. Were the axial rotation an effect of an external cause, then Mars should have a faster [rotation] than Jupiter; because this very same moving force moves more a smaller body than a larger and one ought to be puzzled for good reason how, since all [orbital] motions [velocities] decrease farther from the center, the velocities of rotations increase with those same distances,[12] and with Jupiter they could be three and a half times faster than [would be required by the velocity of] its yearly motion.[13]

Since one is forced to recognize in the daily rotation of planets the very same cause [67] which is nature's universal source of motion, namely, attraction, this kind of explanation will secure its correctness through the natural advantage of its basic notion and through the unartificial consequences [that follow] from it.

But if the very formation of a body produces the axial rotation, then all globes in cosmic space must easily have it; but why does the moon not have it?, [a body] which to some seems to produce (though falsely) that kind of revolution whereby it turns always the same side towards the earth, [a revolution which is] much rather of the kind of an overweight of one hemisphere[14] than of a real swing of revolution.[?] Did it not have to rotate formerly faster around its axis and, through I do not know what causes, which gradually decreased that motion, has been brought to this smaller and exact residue [of rotation]? One need to solve this question only in respect to one planet, [and then] the application arises from it by itself for all [other cases]. I keep this solution for another occasion, because it has a necessary connection with that task which the Royal Academy of Science in Berlin had set up for prize for the year 1754.[15]

The theory which must explain the origin of axial rotations must also be able to derive from the same causes the position of their axes with respect to the plane [68] of their orbits.[16] One has reason to wonder why the equator of the daily rotation is not in the same plane with the plane of moon-orbits which move around these same planets; for this motion, which directs the orbiting of a trabant, has through its stretching out to the body of the planet produced its rotation around the axis and has to impart to it the same specification in direction and plane. Celestial bodies, which have no satellites move around them, put themselves still through that same motion of particles, which served for their stuff, and through the same law, which confined those bodies to the plane of their periodic orbits into an axial rotation which [latter] for similar reason had to coincide with their orbital planes concerning direction. In consequence of these causes the axes of all celestial bodies clearly had to stand perpendicularly to the planetary system's general plane of reference which does not deviate much from the ecliptic.[17] But they are perpendicular only in the two most important pieces of this world-edifice, in Jupiter[18] and in the sun; [as to those of] the others, whose rotation is known, [they] lean their axes towards the plane of their orbits, Saturn more than the others, the earth however more than Mars, whose axis is directed also nearly perpendicular toward the ecliptic.[19] The equator of Saturn (insofar as this can be ascertained through the direction of its ring) leans through an angle of 31 degrees[20] to the plane [69] of its path; the [axis of the] earth [leans] however only with $23\frac{1}{2}$ [degrees toward the direction] of its path. One can perhaps ascribe the cause of these deviations to the inequality in the motions of the stuff which came together for the formation of the planets. The foremost motion of particles was in the direction of the plane of its [planet's] orbit around its center, and there was the plane of reference around [near] which the elementary particles piled up to make the motion around [near] it as circular as possible and to pile up material for the formation of satellites which therefore never deviate far from the orbital path [plane of the planet itself].[21] Had the planet built itself mostly only from these particles, then its axial rotation would have in its first formation deviated from it [that plane] as little as [do] the side-planets [satellites] which move around it; but it built itself, as the theory presented this, rather of particles which sank downward on both sides and whose quantity or velocity did not seem to deviate from it so completely that the one half-globe [hemisphere] could not have acquired a small overweight of motion over the other and thereby some deviation of the axis [from the direction perpendicular to the plane of orbiting].

Regardless of these reasons, I present this explanation only as a conjecture which I do not dare to settle. My real opinion tends to be that the [plane of] rotation of planets around the axis has fairly exactly coincided with the plane of their yearly path in the original state [70] of their formation and that the causes were on hand to shift this axis from its first position. A celestial body, which goes over from its first fluid condition into the state of solidity, suffers, even when it becomes fully formed in such a way, a great change in the regularity of its surface. This will become firm and hardened, inasmuch as the deeper materials have not yet sufficiently sunk according to the measure of their specific gravity; the lighter kinds, which were intermingled in its lump, got finally, after they had differentiated themselves from the others, below the uppermost firmed rind and produce the great caves, [of] which the greatest and largest are under or near the equator,[22] into which the said rind finally sinks [and] produces manifold inequalities, mountains, and caves. If now in such a way, as this obviously had to come about with the earth, the moon, and Venus, the surface has become uneven, then it could no longer provide the balance of revolution on its axial rotation on all sides. A few protruding parts of considerable mass, [which] could find no other [similar] parts that could provide for them the countereffect of swing [revolution] on the opposite side, had to shift immediately the axis of rotation and put it in such a position around which the materials maintained [71] themselves in equilibrium. The same cause, which in the full formation of a celestial body transformed its surface from the condition into abrupt inequalities, this universal cause, which is recognized in all celestial bodies which the telescope can discover clearly enough, has put them into the necessity of altering somewhat the original position of their axes. But this alteration has its limits not to be too much in excess. The inequalities generate themselves, as already mentioned, more beside the equator of a rotating celestial globe than far from it; toward the poles they rapidly vanish, concerning which [point] I reserve another occasion to adduce the causes.[23] Therefore masses which most protrude above the even plane [of the surface of the earth] will occur near the equinoctial [equatorial] circle, and since these strive owing to the advantage of the swing [momentum] to get closer to it, [they] can lift at most by a few degrees the axis of the celestial body from the perpendicular position from [with respect to] the plane of its path.[24] In consequence of this a celestial body, which has not yet fully formed itself, will still have this right-angled position of the axis toward its orbit, [a position] which it will perhaps change only in the course of long centuries. Jupiter still seems to be in this condition. The superiority of its mass and size, the lightness of its stuff have made it necessary for it to overcome the firm standstill of its materials a few centuries [72] later than other celestial bodies.[25] Perhaps the interior of its lump is still in the motion to sink the part of its composition toward the center according to the condition of their gravity and to overcome [to] the status of solidity through the sep-aration of the thinner kinds from the heavy ones. In such a situation the materials on its surface cannot yet appear quiet. Upheavals and ruins still dominate on it. The telescope itself has assured us about this. The shape [appearance] of this planet changes constantly,[26] while the moon, Venus, and the earth keep it unchanged.[27] One can for good reason imagine the completion of the period of the formation [to take place] several hundred years later in a celestial body which exceeds our earth in size more than twenty-thousand times[28] and falls behind it 4 times in density.[29] When its surface will have achieved a quiet constitution, then without doubt [the] far greater inequalities than those which cover the earth-surface will, together with the velocity of its swing, impart in not-too-long a course of time[30] to its rotation that steady status which the balance of forces will require on it.

Saturn, which is 3 times smaller than Jupiter,[31] can perhaps because of its greater distance have the advantage of a speedier formation; at least [73] its much faster axial rotation and the large ratio of its centrifugal force to gravity on its surface (which has to be presented in the following section), which presumably the inequalities produced thereby on it, soon gave through a shifting of the axis the protuberance on the side of the excess [mass].[32] I readily grant that this part of my system which concerns the position of the planetary axes is still imperfect and fairly far from being [ready to be] subjected to geometrical calculation.[33] I much rather disclose this frankly than to ruin the neatness of the remaining [part of the] doctrine through all sorts of covertly illusory reasons[34] and to give it a weak side. The following section may provide a confirmation of the credibility of the entire hypothesis whereby we wish to explain the motion [formation] of the world-edifice. [74]

FIFTH SECTION

of the origin of the ring of Saturn and the calculation of the daily rotation of this planet from its relations.

Owing to the systematic constitution of the world-edifice, its parts hang together through a gradual alteration of their properties and one can assume that a planet situated in the most distant region of the world will have characteristics almost such as the nearest comet would take on, if it were to be raised through the diminishing of [its] eccentricity into the planetary species.[1] We shall accordingly look at Saturn as if it had described in a manner similar to cometary motion several orbits with greater eccentricity and had been gradually brought to a track more similar to a circle.* The heat, which it had incorporated in itself in its vicinity to the sun, lifted from its surface the light stuff which, as [75] we know from the previous sections, is of extreme thinness in the highest [most distant] celestial bodies, [and] lets itself be expanded by small degrees [of] heat. Meanwhile, after the planet has been brought after some revolutions to the distance where it now floats, it gradually lost in such a moderate [even] climate the absorbed heat and the vapours, which from its surface kept expanding around it, receded more and more[3] in order to rise into tails.[4] New [vapours] did no longer arise so often to increase the old ones; in short, the surrounding vapours remained through causes, which we shall immediately adduce, floating around it and retained its former comet-like nature in a permanent ring while its body breathed away the heat and finally has become a quiet and purified planet. Now we want to point out the secret, which enabled the celestial body to retain its rising vapours [in a] freely floating [state]; nay, which has changed them from an atmosphere expanding around it into the form of an everywhere separate ring. I assume: Saturn had a rotation around its axis; and nothing more than this is needed to unveil the whole secret.[5]

---

* Or, what is more probable, that in its comet-like nature, which it still now has in itself owing to its eccentricity,[2] it has an expanded cometary atmosphere, before the lightest stuff of its surface becomes completely scattered.

No other driving mechanism, than this only one, has brought about through an immediate mechanical result the said phenomenon on the planet; and I dare to assert that in the entire [76] nature but a few things can be traced to such a comprehensible origin as this specialty of the heavens let itself be developed from the raw state of the first formation.

The vapours rising from Saturn had the motion in themselves and put them freely forth at the height [to] where they had risen, [from the point] which they had as parts of it [Saturn] in its revolution around the axis.[6] The particles which rose near the equator of the planet must have had the fastest [motions], and farther from there toward the poles all the much weaker [slower] motions, the greater was the latitude of the place from where they rose. The relation of specific weight assigned to the particles the various heights to which they rose; but only those particles could assert [maintain] the places of their distance in a steadily free circular swing, whose distances, in which they were set, required such a central force which these [particles] could make with the velocity which was their own through the exact rotation; the rest, inasmuch as they could not be brought through interaction with others to this exactitude, must either recede with the excess of motion from the sphere of the planet,[7] or through the lack of it became forced to sink back to it. The particles scattered through this entire extent of the vaporous globe strived, owing to the same central laws,[8] to cut across from both sides the extended [77] equatorial plane of the planet and, while they held one another in that plane from both hemispheres, they pile up there themselves; and because I postulate that the said vapours are those which the planet sends up last for its cooling, all the scattered vapour-material will gather beside that plane and leave empty the spaces on both sides. In this new and altered direction they will nevertheless set forth the very same motions which keeps them floating in free concentric circular orbits. In such a way the vapour circle now changes its shape, which was a filled sphere, into a form of a spread-out plane which exactly coincides with the equator of Saturn, but even this plane must for the very same mechanical reasons assume finally the form of a ring, whose outer rim will be determined by the solar rays' effect which through its force scatters and farther removes those particles which moved to a certain distance from the center of the planet,[9] just as it does this with the comets,[10] and thereby designates the outside border of its vapour circle. The inside rim of this developing ring will be determined through the relation of the velocity of the planet under its equator.[11] For in that distance from its center where this velocity produces a balance [78] with the attraction of the place, there is the greatest nearness in which the particles arising from its body can describe circular orbits through the proper motion [deriving] from the axial rotation. The nearer particles, because they need for such an orbiting a greater velocity, which they nevertheless cannot have because even at the equator of the planet the motion is not faster, will thereby obtain eccentric courses which cut across one another, weaken one another's motion, and finally crash together back into the planet from which they had lifted themselves.[12] Thus we now see the most wondrously peculiar phenomenon, whose sight has since its discovery[13] put astronomers at all times in [the state of] wonderment and [in connection with] whose cause no one has ever been able to muster even a probable hope to discover [it], [namely, to see it] to arise in an easy mechanical way freed of all hypotheses.[14] What happened to Saturn would, as can easily be perceived from this, just as regularly happen to that comet which had sufficient[ly large] axial rotation, if it were to be placed in a steady height [distance] in which its body could gradually cool. Nature is fruitful in splendid developments, [insofar as she is] in the state of her forces [being] left to themselves, even in [her state of] chaos, and the formation subsequent to it brings along such magnificent relations and harmonies for the common benefit of the creature that in the eternal and unchanging laws of their essential properties they offer for recognition with unisonal certainty [79] that great Being in which by means of their common dependence they unite to a total harmony. Saturn has great advantage from its ring; it increases its day and illuminates under so many moons its night in such a measure that one easily forgets there the absence of the sun.[15] But should one therefore deny that the universal development of matter through mechanical causes has, without being in need of specifications other than its universal ones, the ability to bring forth relations which produce benefits for the intelligent creature? All beings hang together from one cause, which is God's intelligence; they therefore can entail no other results than such which carry with them the presentation of perfection in the very same divine idea.[16]

We now want to calculate the time of the axial rotation of this celestial body from the relation of its ring according to the foregoing hypothesis of its generation. Because all motions[s] of the ring's particles is [are] a motion embodied by the axial rotation of Saturn, the fastest motion among those which these particles have will coincide with the fastest rotation which is found on the surface [80] of the planet, that is, the velocity with which the ring's particles orbit in its interior rim[17] is equal to that which the planet has on its equator. One can, however, find easily that velocity inasmuch as one seeks [to derive] it from the velocity of one of Saturn's trabants, through [the procedure] that one takes it in the relation of the square root of distances from the center of the planet.[18] From the velocity thus found, there immediately follows the time of Saturn's rotation around its axis; *it is six hours, twenty-three minutes and fifty-three seconds.*[19] This mathematical calculation of an unknown motion of a celestial body, which perhaps is the only prediction of its kind in natural science proper,[20] awaits confirmation from the observations of future times.[21] The still presently known telescopes do not enlarge Saturn so much that the spots, which one can surmise [to be present] on its surface, could be thereby discovered [in order] to see through their displacement its rotation around the axis.[22] But the telescopes have not perhaps yet reached all that perfection which one can hope from them and which the industry and skill of artisans seem to promise to us. If one once got to the point of settling our speculation through visual evidence, what a certainty would [not be achieved by] the theory of Saturn, and what a splendid credibility [81] would not thereby be achieved by the entire system [of our cosmogony] which is based on similar reasons![23] The time of the daily rotation of Saturn carries with it also the ratio of the centrifugal force to the gravity on its surface; it is to that as 20:32.[24] The gravity is [therefore] only about 3/5 times greater than the centrifugal force. This so large a ratio necessarily causes a very considerable difference of the [polar and equatorial] diameters of this planet and one could expect that this difference must become so great that the observation [of it] in the case of this planet, however little enlarged by the telescopes, must clearly come into sight, which however does not happen[25] and therefore the theory could thereby suffer a disadvantageous impact. A thorough scrutiny wholly removes this difficulty.[26] According to the Huygensian hypothesis,[27] which assumes that the gravity in the planet's interior is throughout the same, the difference of the [polar and equatorial] diameters has a twice smaller ratio to the diameter of the equator than the centrifugal force has to gravity below [at] the poles. For example, since in the earth's case the centrifugal force of [at] the equator is 1/289th of the gravity at the poles, the diameter of the equatorial surface must be 1/578 times greater than the [polar] axis of the earth. The cause is this: because, according to the presupposition, in the interior of the earth-lump in all close points to the center [82] gravity is as great as on the surface, the centrifugal force decreases, however, with the approaches to the center, the same [force] is not everywhere 1/289th of the gravity but much rather the entire decrease of weight of the fluid column[28] in the equatorial plane is for that reason not 1/289th but one half of it, i.e. 1/578th of it. On the contrary, in the hypothesis of Newton[29] the centrifugal force, which gives rise to the axial rotation[30] has the same ratio to the gravity of the place in the entire plane of the equator as far as its central point; because this force in the interior of the planet (when it is assumed to be of the same density throughout) decreases with distance from the center in the same proportion as the centrifugal force, so that it is always 1/289th of the former. This causes a lightening of the liquid column in the equatorial plane and even the rise of that column by 1/289th, which difference of the diameter will still be increased in this theory by the fact that the shortening of the axis brings about an approach of the parts to the center, together with an increase of gravity, but the elongation of the equatorial diameter brings about a recession of parts from that very same center and therefore a decrease of their gravity, and from this reason the flattening of the Newtonian spheroid so increases that the difference of the diameters will be raised from 1/289 to 1/230.[31]

[83] According to these reasons the diameters of Saturn are in still a larger ratio to one another than 20:32; they must come fairly close to 1:2. A difference, which is so great that the least attention would not miss it, small as Saturn may appear through the telescopes.[32] But from this one can only infer that the presupposition of equal density, which seems to be fairly correctly adduced in the case of the earth's body,[33] in Saturn's case would too far deviate from the truth; which [fact] is already in itself probable in the case of a planet whose lump consists of the lightest materials in the greatest part of its content and [which] much more freely allows the sinking down to the center to parts of heavier kind in its composition, according to the quality [measure] of their gravity, than [according] to [the gravity of] those celestial bodies whose much thicker stuff delays the settling down of materials and lets them become solid before this sinking down can happen.[34] Inasmuch as we also presuppose in the case of Saturn that the density of its materials increases in its interior with the approach to the center, this gravity no longer decreases in that ratio;[35] but the growing density offsets the lack of parts which are placed above the height of the point which is inside the planet and contribute nothing to its gravity [84] through their attraction.*[35] When this special density of the deepest material is very great, it transforms, in virtue of the laws of attraction, the gravity, which decreases in the interior toward the center, into an almost uniform [force], and sets the ratio of diameters close to the Huygensian ratio which is always the half of

* For according to the Newtonian laws of attraction, a body which is in the interior of a ball will be attracted only from that part of it which is described by the distance, which it has from the center, spherically around it. The concentric part outside this distance does, because of the balance of its attractions which offset one another, nothing to move the body either toward the center or away from it.

the ratio between the centrifugal force and gravity; consequently, as these are to one another as 2:3,[36] the difference of diameters of this planet [Saturn] becomes not 1/3 but 1/6 of the equatorial cross section [diameter];[37] which difference will finally be hidden by the fact that Saturn, whose axis makes with the plane of its path always an angle of 31 degrees,[38] never presents its position straight toward the equator, as is the case with Jupiter, which [circumstance] diminishes the foregoing difference almost by a third part,[39] according to appearance. Under such circumstances, and especially because of the so great a distance of this planet, it can easily be seen that the [85] flattened shape of its body will not strike the eyes so easily as one may think; nevertheless the astronomy, whose advance especially depends on the perfection of its tools, will perhaps through their aid be put in the position to achieve, if I do not flatter myself too much,[40] the discovery of so remarkable a property.

What I say of Saturn's figure can in a sense serve in the science of heavens for a general remark. Jupiter, which according to an exact calculation has on its equator a ratio of gravity to centrifugal force of at least as [great as] $9\frac{1}{4}:1$,[41] should, if its lump were of a uniform density throughout, according to the doctrines of Newton,[42] have a still greater difference than 1/9 between its axis and its equatorial diameter. But Cassini has found it only as 1/16,[43] Poned [Pound] 1/12, sometimes 1/14;[44] at least all these various observations, which prove by their difference the difficulty of this measurement, agree inasmuch as they set it much smaller than it should be according to Newton's system, or even more according to the hypothesis of uniform density.[45] And if one therefore changes the presupposition of uniform density, which would cause the so-great-a-deviation of theory from observation, into the more likely presupposition, where the density [86] of the planetary lump is set to increase toward its center, one not only will see the observation verified in Jupiter's case, but one may clearly understand in the case of Saturn, a planet much more difficult to measure [observe], the cause of a lesser flattening of its spheroidal body.

From the generation of the Saturnian ring we have been prompted to risk the daring step to determine through calculation the time of its axial rotation which the telescopes are not able to discover. Let us increase this test of physical prediction in the case of this planet still with another [test] which has to wait for the witness of its correctness from more perfect instruments of future times.

According to the presupposition that the ring of Saturn is a piling-up of particles which, after they had arisen as vapours from the surface of this celestial body in virtue of the swing which they have from its axial rotation and still carry it on, maintain themselves in the height of their distance moving freely in circles, these particles do not have the same periods of revolution in all their distances from the center; but [the periods of] these particles relate [to one another] as the square roots of the cubes of their distances, if they should maintain themselves floating through the laws of central forces.[46] Now, according to this hypothesis, the time in which the particles of the interior rim [of the ring] are [87] orbiting is about 10 hours,[47] and the time of the circular orbiting of particles in the exterior rim is, according to the appropriate calculation, 15 hours;[48] thus when the lowest [nearest] parts of the ring had performed their orbiting three times, the most distant parts did this only twice. It is, however, probable, that, should one estimate the impediment, which the particles at their great dispersion in the plane of the ring present to one another to be as low as one may wish, the remainder of more distant particles gradually delay and hold up in each of their orbitings the faster moving lower [closer] parts,[49] whereas these [latter] must impress a part of their motion upon those higher parts for a faster revolution, which [process], if this interaction would not finally be interrupted, would last as long until the parts of the ring would all be brought to the point [where] both the lower and the more distant ones would revolve in equal time, so that in which state they would be in respective repose to one another and would make upon one another no impact through [their] edging away. But such a state, should the motion of the ring issue in it, would completely destroy the ring, because, if one takes the middle of the plane of the ring and posits that the motion remains there in the state in which it previously was and must be in order that it may perform a circular course, the lower particles, because they do not maintain themselves floating in their heights [distances] but [88] cross each other in slanting and eccentric motions the more distant ones, become however, through the impression [on them by the nearer particles] of a greater motion than the[ir] motion ought to be before, [owing to] the central force of this distance, turned away from the sun [Saturn][50] more than the outer border of the ring is determined by the sun's effect, would through that effect become dispersed behind the planet and carried away.

But one need not fear [the coming about of] all this disorder. The mechanism of the motion generating the ring leads to a specification which puts the ring, through the very causes which should destroy it, into a safe condition by the fact that the ring becomes divided into several concentric circular stripes which, because of the intervening spaces that separate them, have no longer any association with one other. For, while the particles, which orbit in the interior rim of the ring, carry somewhat forward the higher [more distant] particles through their faster motion and speed up their orbiting, thus the increased degree[s] of velocity cause in these an excess of centrifugal force and a receding from the place where they floated. If one, however, presupposes that while these [higher particles] tend to separate from the lower ones, they have to overcome certain connectedness which, whether it consists [in the cohesive properties] of dispersed vapours, nevertheless ought to seem with these [particles] not entirely meaningless, [and] thus this increased degree of swing will tend [89] to overcome the said connectedness, but it will not overcome it as long as the excess of centrifugal force, which it applies in equal times with the lowest ones, does not go above the central force of its place [and does not] exceed this cohesion [interconnectedness]. And for this reason, the interconnectedness must remain in a certain breadth of a stripe of the ring, although, because its parts perform their orbiting in equal time, the higher [particles] exert a trend to tear themselves away from the lower ones, but not in a greater width because, inasmuch as the velocity of these particles moved [moving] around in equal times increases with the distances more than it should according to the central laws, when this velocity has exceeded the degree, which the interconnectedness of vapour particles can achieve, they [these higher particles] must tear themselves away and assume a distance which is proportionate to the excess of the force of revolution over the central force of the place. In this way the intervening space will be determined which separates the first stripe of the ring from the rest; and in a similar way, the accelerated motion of the higher parts produces, through the speedy orbiting of the lower particles and their connectedness which tries to prevent the separation, the second concentric ring from which the third stands apart by a certain intervening space. One could calculate the number of these circular stripes and the width of their intervening spaces, if one knew the degree of interconnectedness which hangs these particles to one another;[51] but we can [90] be satisfied to estimate in general with a good degree of probability the Saturnian ring's composition which prevents its destruction and maintains its floating through free motions.

This conjecture satisfies me in no small measure through the hope that it will eventually be seen confirmed through actual observations. A few years ago it was reported from London that while one observed Saturn with a new Newtonian telescope improved by Mr Bradley, it appeared that its ring was a composition of many concentric rings which were separated by intervening spaces.[52] This news was not set forth since.*[55] The [91] instruments of sight have opened for understanding informations about the outermost regions of the world-edifice. If now it is largely up to those instruments to make new steps in that respect, then one can very well hope from the attention of the [this] century all that which can enlarge man's insights, that it will especially turn toward a side [direction] which offers it the greatest hope for important discoveries.[56]

If, however, Saturn, was so fortunate to produce for itself a ring, why no other planet has shared in this advantage? The cause is obvious. Since a ring must develop from the evaporations of a planet, which it exhales in its raw [92] state and [since] its axial rotation must give [them] the swing which they have only to maintain when they have reached the height, where by means of that implanted motion of gravitation they can achieve with respect to the planet the exact balance, then one can easily determine by calculation to what height the vapours must rise from a planet if they, through the motions which they had under [at] its equator, ought to maintain themselves in free circular motion, if one knows the diameter of the planet, the time of its rotation, and the gravity on its surface. According to the law of central motion the distance of a body, which can orbit in free circle around a planet with a velocity equal to its axial rotation, will be in such a relation to the semidiameter of the planet as the centrifugal force at its equator is to the gravity [there].[57] For these reasons the distance of the inner rim of Saturn's ring was as 8, if its semidiameter is taken as 5, which two numbers are in the same ratio as 32:20, which [numbers], as we have previously remarked,[58] express the proportion between the gravity and the centrifugal force at the [its] equator. For the same reasons, if one posited that Jupiter must have had a ring generated in such a way, its smallest semidiameter would exceed ten times[59] the half thickness of [93] Jupiter, [a distance] which would extend to the point where its outermost trabant moves around

---

* After I have written this down, I find in the Memoirs of the Royal Academy of Sciences in Paris from 1705 an essay of Mr Cassini, about the trabants and ring of Saturn on the 571th page of the Second Part of the Steinwehrian translation,[53] a confirmation of this conjecture, which leaves almost no further doubt about its correctness. After Mr Cassini submitted an idea, which in a sense might have a small approximation to the truth which we have established, although it is improbable in itself, namely, that the ring of Saturn may perhaps be a swarm of small trabants which from Saturn [91] would appear just as the Milky Way does from the earth (which thought may be the case if one takes the vapour particles for these small trabants which swing around it [Saturn] with equal motion), he says further below: "This thought was confirmed by observations made in the [those] years when the ring of Saturn appeared wider and more open. For then one saw the width of the ring to be divided in two parts by dark elliptic line whose part after [nearest] the globe [of Saturn] was brighter than the most distant one. This line also marked a small intervening space between the two parts, just as the distance of the globe from the ring is shown by the greatest darkness between both."[54]

it and therefore for these reasons as well [the formation of a ring around Jupiter] is impossible, and also because the evaporation of a planet cannot extend so far from it. If one now wanted to know why the earth obtained no ring, one will find the answer in the magnitude of the [its] semidiameter which its inner rim alone should have had, [a magnitude] which must have become [as] great [as] 289 earth-semidiameters.[60] In the case of slower moving [rotating] planets the generation of a ring recedes even farther from [the realm of] possibility; nor remains there [another] case where a planet could have, in the manner in which we explained it, obtained a ring, than the case in which the planet is the one which really has it, [a circumstance] which is no small confirmation of the credibility of our way of explanation.

What makes me, however, almost assured [concerning the fact] that the ring, which surrounds Saturn, did not come into existence for it in the universal way and through the universal law of formation which dominates throughout the system of planets and created for Saturn also its trabants, that, I say, this external matter has not provided its [the ring's] stuff to that end, but that it [the ring] is a creature of the planet itself, which owing to the heat has lifted its most volatile parts and through its own axial rotation has imparted to them the swing for turning around, is this [circumstance] that the [94] ring is not, as are the other trabants of the planet and in general all orbiting bodies which are in the accompaniment of the[ir] planets, directed in the universal plane of reference of planetary motions but deviates very much from it,[61] which is a certain proof[62] that it has not been built from the universal basic stuff and obtained its motion from its downward sinking, but has ascended from the planet long after its completed formation, and through the planet's implanted revolving forces has obtained, as its separate part, a motion and direction relating to its axial rotation.

The satisfaction of having grasped one of the rarest peculiarities of the heavens in the entire extent of its being and generation has led us into such a detailed treatise. Let us, with the permission of our obliging readers, pursue where possible that treatise to the extreme [of its implications], so that, after we have in a pleasant manner abandoned ourselves to arbitrary notions with a kind of unrestraint, we may return again with all the more caution and care to the truth.[63]

Could one not imagine that the earth once had a ring just as Saturn [has now one]? It could have arisen from its surface, just as from that of Saturn and had maintained itself for a long time inasmuch as the earth had been slowed down from a much speedier rotation [95] than the present one through who knows what causes to the present degree [of rotation], or that one entrusts to the sideways-

145

sinking basic stuff [the role] of having formed it according to the rules we have clarified above; [all of] which must not be taken exactly so if one wants to satisfy one's penchant for the peculiar. But what an advantage for beautiful explanation and consequence does such an idea present to us[!]. A ring around the earth! What a beauty of a spectacle for those who were created for inhabiting the earth as a paradise; how much comfort for these [happy beings] on whom Nature wanted to smile on all sides![64] But this is still nothing [in comparison] with the confirmation which such a hypothesis can borrow from the record of the history of creation and which is of no small recommendation for approval for those who believe that they do not desecrate but confirm the honor of revelation when they avail themselves of that hypothesis in order to give prestige thereby to the extravagances of their wit.[65] The water of the firmament, which the Mosaic description [of the creation of the world] mentions, has already caused no small trouble to [its] interpreters.[66] Could not one avail himself of this ring to help oneself out of this difficulty? This ring without doubt consisted of watery vapours and, in addition to the advantages which it could provide for the first inhabitants of the earth, one could still let it break up on a [specially] needed occasion to punish with floods the earth which [96] made itself unworthy of such a beauty. Either a comet, whose attraction brought its regular movements into confusion,[67] or the cooling of the region of its locality united its scattered vapory parts and [made them] crash in one of the most gruesome cloudbursts down to the earth's surface. It is well known what the result was. The whole world [earth] went down in the water and in addition imbibed in those foreign and fleeting vapours of the unnatural rain that slow poison which brought all creatures closer to death and destruction. The form of a pale and light [faint] bow had now disappeared from the horizon, and the new world which could never remember that sight without a feeling of fright [of] that fearful instrument of divine wrath,[68] saw perhaps with no less bewilderment in the first rain that colourful arch which seemed according to its shape to imitate the former, but was to be, through the assurance of a reconciled heaven, a sign of grace and a monument of a lasting maintenance of the new transformed surface of the earth.[69] The similarity of shape of this memorial sign with the indicated event [occurrence of the ring] could recommend itself to those who are given to the prevailing inclination to bring into one system the miracle of revelation with the ordinary laws of nature.[70] I find it more advisable to sacrifice completely the [97] fleeting approval, which such agreements may awaken, to the true satisfaction which springs forth from the regular interconnections when physical analogies support one another for the designation of physical truths.

SIXTH SECTION

of the zodiacal light

The sun is surrounded with a subtle and vapory being [essence] which in the plane of its equator surround it with only a small extendedness on both sides to a great height [distance] about which one cannot be sure whether, as Mr von Mairan[1] portrays it in the form of a lens ground protrudingly (*figura lenticulari*) [in lentil-shape], it touches on the surface of the sun, or, as does the ring of Saturn, stands everywhere apart from it. Be it one or the other [case], enough similarity is left to put this phenomenon in comparison with the ring of Saturn and to derive it from a common origin. If this expanded matter is an outflow from the sun, as it is most probable [advisable] to consider that matter [98] to be such, then one cannot miss the cause which has brought it to the plane common with the sun's equator. The lightest and most volatile stuff, which the sun's fire raises from its surface and has for long raised it already, will through the same effect be driven far beyond it and remains, according to the measure of its lightness, floating at a distance where the repelling effect of [the sun's] rays[2] will provide equilibrium to the gravity of these vapory particles, or they will be supported by the flux of new particles which continually come towards them. Now, since the sun, inasmuch as it revolves around, similarly impresses its [rotational] motion on these vapours torn away from its surface, these maintain a certain swing for orbiting whereby they tend, according to the central laws,[3] to cut from both sides across the extended equatorial plane of the sun in the circle [orbit] of their motion, and therefore, because they press towards it in similar quantity from both hemispheres, they pile up there with equal forces and form an expanded plain in that plane relating to the sun's equator.

But regardless of this similarity with Saturn's ring, there remains an essential difference which makes the phenomenon of zodiacal light very deviating from it. The particles of the former maintain themselves through [99] the implanted rotational motion in freely floating circular orbits; but the particles of the latter become kept at their height [distance] through the force of the sun's rays, without which the motion indwelling in them from the sun's rotation[4] would fall far short of keeping them from falling [off] in [from their] free swinging around.

147

For as on the surface of the sun the axial rotation's force fleeing from the center is not even 1/40,000th of the attraction [there],[5] these rising vapours must recede [to a distance of] 40,000 [solar] semidiameters[6] from the sun to find for the first time in such a distance a gravity which can provide the balance to the motion imparted to them. It is thus certain that this phenomenon of the sun is not to be assigned to it in a manner similar to Saturn's ring.

Similarly, there remains a no small likelihood that this necklace of the sun recognizes perhaps the same cause which the entire nature recognizes, namely, the formation from a universal basic stuff whose parts, as they float around in the highest [most distant] regions of the sun's world, have, only after the complete formation of the entire system of the sun, sunk in a late [retarded] fall with weakened motion but still bent from west to east and through this kind of orbiting cut across the extended equatorial plane of it [sun], [and] as they stayed there through their piling-up from both sides, have occupied [100] in that position an expanded plain where in part owing to the repulsion of solar rays, in part owing to their actually acquired circular motion, they now maintain themselves in steadily similar height [distance]. The present explanation has no other merit than that which befits conjectures and [makes] no [other] claim than only to an arbitrary [benevolent] approval; the judgment of the reader may turn to that side which appears to him the most worthy of acceptance.

SEVENTH SECTION

from the creation in the entire extent of its infinity
according to space as well as to time

The world-edifice puts one into a quiet astonishment by its immeasurable greatness and by the infinite manifoldness and beauty which shine forth from it on all sides. If now [on the one side] the presentation of all this perfection excites the imagination, on the other side another kind of enthralment seizes the understanding when it considers how so much splendor, so much greatness flows from a single [101] universal rule with an eternal and right order. The planetary world-edifice, in which the sun, from the center of all orbits, makes with its mighty attraction the inhabited globes to orbit, was, as we have already seen, entirely formed from the originally spread-out basic stuff of all world-material. All the fixed stars, which the eye discovers in the hollow depth of the heavens and which seem to indicate a kind of waste, are suns and centers of similar systems.[1] The analogy allows not even here to doubt that these were formed and generated in the same way in which that [system] in which we find ourselves [was formed and generated] from the elementary matter which filled the empty space, this infinite range of divine presence.

If now all worlds and world-orders recognize this same kind of origin, if the attraction worked [in an] unrestricted and universal [manner and] the repulsion of elements [was] equally thoroughly effective, if in [respect of] the infinite the great and the small [are] both small, did not have all the world-edifices to assume among one another an interrelating constitution and a systematic connection, [just] as on the small scale the celestial bodies of our solar world, such as Saturn, Jupiter and the earth, which in themselves are systems individually and yet hang together in a still [102] larger system as [its] members? If in this immeasurable space, in which all suns of the Milky Way have formed themselves, one assumes a point around which through I do not know what cause the first formation of nature from chaos has begun, [then, as a result,] there will have arisen the greatest mass and a body of most unusual[ly] large attraction, which has thereby become capable of forcing all systems, [being] in [the process of] formation around it in an enormous sphere, to sink toward it as their center and to establish around it in the whole a similar system as the same elementary basic stuff, which formed the planets, made around the sun on the small scale. Observation renders this opinion almost indubitable.[2] Through its position related to a common plane, the host of stars forms just as much a system as do the planets of our solar edifice around the sun. The Milky Way is the zodiac of these higher world-orders which deviate from its plane as little as possible and whose streak is always illuminated by their light, just as the zodiac of planets [is illuminated] by the shine of these globes, although it glimmers only in few points here and there. Each of these suns forms in itself a special system with the planets orbiting around it; but this does not prevent [them] from becoming parts of a still greater system, just as Jupiter or Saturn, regardless of their own accompaniment, are confined within the systematic constitution [103] of a still greater world edifice. Cannot one recognize the same cause and manner of generation in such an exact agreement in [their] arrangement?

If now the fixed stars form a system whose range is determined by the sphere of attraction of that body which is found in the center, will not [also] arise more solar systems and, so to speak, more Milky Ways, which have been generated in the limitless field of cosmic space? We have spotted with astonishment figures in the sky which are[3] nothing else than such fixed star systems confined to a common plane, if I am allowed to express myself thus, which in [their] different positions present to the eye elliptical shapes according to [their] weakened glimmer: they are systems with, so to speak, infinite times infinitely greater[4] diameter than the diameter of our solar-edifice, but without doubt formed in the same way, ordered and arranged by the same causes, and maintain themselves, as does this [solar system of ours], in their constitution through a similar driving mechanism.

If one again looks upon these star systems as members in the great chain[5] of the entire nature, one has just as much cause as before to think of them as being in mutual attraction and in connections which form [104] in virtue of the law of first formation dominating throughout the entire nature, a new [and] still greater system which, through the attraction of a body of incomparably mightier attraction, will be ruled, as were all the former [systems], from the center of their regular positions. The attraction, which is the cause of the systematic constitution among the fixed stars of the Milky Way, works also even at the distances of those world-orders to remove them from their positions and to bury the [entire] world in an inevitably impending chaos, if the regularly distributed orbital forces did not present the counterweight to [the force of] attraction and both, [while] in connection, would not produce that correlation which is the basis of the systematic constitution. The attraction without doubt is just as an extensive a quality of matter as the coexistence which forms space, inasmuch as it connects the substances through mutual dependences, or to speak more properly, the attraction is precisely that universal relation which unites the parts of nature in one space; it also stretches out over the entire extension of that space into all reaches of its infinity. If light reaches us from these distant systems, the [that very] light which is only an impressed motion, must not much rather the [force of] attraction, this original source of motion which is earlier than all [other] motions that [and] needs no foreign cause [and which] cannot be stopped by any impediment [105] because it works in the very interior of matter, nay even in the universal standstill of nature without any [external] push, must not, I say, the attraction had to put in motion these fixed star systems, regardless of their immeasurable distances, in the unformed dispersion of their stuff in the beginning of nature's stirring, [into a motion] which, as we have seen on a small scale, is equally the source of the systematic connection and of the lasting stability of their members which secures them from collapse?

But what will finally be the end of the systematic arrangements? where will the creation [the created realm] itself cease? It is well said[6] that in order to think of creation in relation to the power of the Infinite Being, it must have no limits. One does not come closer to the infinity of God's creative force if one encloses the space of its manifestation within a sphere described by the radius of the Milky Way than if one wants to confine that power within a globe which is one inch in diameter. All that is finite, [also] has its limits and a definite ratio to unity, [and] is equally far removed from the infinite. Now, it would be senseless to set Godhead in motion[7] with an infinitely small part of his creative ability and to imagine his infinite force, the wealth of a true inexhaustibility of nature and worlds to be inactive and locked up in [106] an eternal absence of exercise.[8] Is it not much more proper, or to say better, is it not necessary[9] to represent the very essence of creation [created realm] as it ought to be, [namely], to be a witness of that power which can be measured by no yardstick? For this reason the field of the manifestation of divine attributes is just as infinite as these themselves are.* Eternity is not far reaching enough [107] to contain the witnesses of the Highest Being, [in the case] where they are not connected with the infinity of space. It is true, the development, the form, the beauty, and perfection are relations of basic pieces [elements] and substances which make up the stuff of the world-edifice, and one notices this in the establishments which the wisdom of God still achieves all the time; it is also most appropriate to that wisdom that they should evolve from these universal laws implanted in them through an unforced sequence. And therefore one can posit with good basis that the ordering and arrangement of the world-edifice should gradually happen [take place] from the supply of the created nature-stuff; the the basic matter of it, whose qualities and forces lie at the basis of all changes, is an immediate consequence[15] of the divine being; that being must at once be so rich [and] so complete that the development of their compositions in the flow of eternity may spread out over a plan which includes in itself all that can exist, which admits no measure [limit], in short, is infinite.[16]

If now the creation [created realm] is infinite also with respect

---

* The notion of an infinite extension of the world finds opponents among metaphysicians[10] and has only recently found one in Mr M. Weitenkampf.[11] If, because of the supposed impossibility of a quantity without [definite] number and limits,[12] these gentlemen cannot accommodate themselves to this idea, then I wanted only to ask in passing: whether the future course of eternity will not comprise in itself a true [definite] infinity of varieties and changes and whether this infinite series is not already at once entirely present to the divine mind? If it was now possible that God can make real in a series of [events] following upon one another the notion of infinity which is represented at once to his mind, why that divine mind should not be able to represent the notion of another infinity in a *conjoined connection* relating to space[13] and thereby make the extent of the world to be without limits? While one seeks to answer this question, I will avail myself of the opportunity which presents itself to remove the difficulty in question through an explanation drawn from the nature of numbers whereby one, through proper appraisal, can see it as a question in need of clarification: whether that, which has been *brought forth* through a power directed by the Highest Wisdom to reveal herself, may not relate as a differential magnitude[14] to that what she *could have brought forth*.

to space or was at least really [infinite] with respect to matter already from the beginning,[17] but [and] is ready, with respect to form or development, to become infinite, then the cosmic space will be enlivened with worlds without number and without end. Will now then that systematic connection, which we have weighed before in all parts specially, extend also to the whole and hold together the entire universe, the all of nature, in one such system through the connection of attraction with centrifugal force? I say, yes; if only single separate world-edifices, which had no unified relation among one another to the whole, were on hand, one could, if one assumed this chain of members as truly infinite, very well think that an exact equality of attraction of their parts on all sides, could safely keep these systems from the collapse with which their mutual attraction threatens them.[18] But for this [to happen] such an exactly measured determination is required in those distances [continually] bent [altered] by attraction that even the smallest displacement in the universe would entail the downfall [of it] and would hand it over in long periods, which however must finally reach their end, to collapse. A world-constitution, which without a miracle does not maintain itself, does not have the character of steadiness which is the hallmark of God's choice;[19] one also hits the mark far more appropriately concerning that choice if one makes from the entire creation [created realm] a singl system [109] which makes related to a single center all worlds and world-orders that fill the entire infinite space. A scattered swarming of world-edifices, separated as they may be from one another by no matter what great distances, would rush with unhindered propensity toward doom and destruction if there were not set up a certain relational arrangement through systematic motions against a universal center, the center of attraction of the universe and the pivotal point of the entire nature.

One can assume with probability that it was around this universal center of the sinking of the entire nature, of the developed as well as of the raw [state of it], where without doubt is found the lump of the most exceptional[ly large] attraction,[20] which holds in its sphere of attraction all worlds and [world]-orders which time has brought forth and eternity will bring forth, that nature made the start of her formation and that the systems are piled up there most densely; father from that point the systems peter out with ever greater degree of dispersion. One could take this rule from the analogy of our solar-edifice and this constitution can further serve [the purpose] that in great distances not only the universal central body but also all systems [110] orbiting nearest around it unite their attraction and they, as if from one lump, exert [it] on systems of still greater distance. This will then become helpful in that entire nature will be grasped in the entire infinity of its stretching out in one single system.[21]

In order to trace out the erection of the universal system from the mechanical laws of a matter striving to [its own] development, there must have been, in the infinite space of the spread-out elementary basic stuff, at some point of that basic stuff the thickest piling-up,[22] so that through the special formation occurring there a mass may be produced for the entire universe, [a mass] which served for it as a point of support. It is true that in an infinite space no point can have the privilege to be called the center; but through a certain relation, which is based on the essential degree [gradation] of the density of the primeval stuff, according to which gradation that stuff piled up considerably thicker right at its creation at a certain point and increases in its scattering with distances from that point, such a point can have the privilege to be called the center;[23] and it will become really such through the formation of the central mass by the strongest attraction in it, [and] toward which all the remaining elementary matter, caught in particular formations, [111] sinks, and thereby, however far the evolution of nature may stretch, it will make only one single system in the infinite sphere of creation.

What is, however, the most important, and insofar as it requires approval, is most worthy of attention, is that in consequence of the ordering of nature in this system of ours, the creation or rather the formation of nature first begins at this center and will gradually spread out with steady progress in all farther reaches in order to fill the infinite space with worlds and [world]-orders in the progress of eternity. Let us dwell on this presentation [idea] for a moment with silent satisfaction. I find nothing which can raise the spirit of man to a nobler astonishment insofar as it opens for him a view into the infinite field of omnipotence than this part of the theory which concerns the successive completion of creation.[24] If one grants to me that the matter, which is the stuff for the formation of all worlds, was spread out in the entire infinite space of divine presence not uniformly but according to a certain law which perhaps related to the density of particles and according to which form a certain point, as the place of the thickest piling-up, the dispersion [thinning out] of the primordial stuff increased with distances from this center [112], then the formation will have started next to that center at the original stirring of nature and then in progressive succession of time the [increasingly] farther space has gradually formed worlds and world-orders with a systematic constitution relating to that center. Each such finite period, whose length has a proportion to the magnitude of the work to be completed, will always bring into formation only a finite sphere [as measured]

153

from that center; the remaining infinite part will meanwhile struggle with aberration and chaos, and the farther away it is from the state of completed formation, the farther is its distance from the sphere of the already fully formed nature. Consequently, although from the place of our abode in the universe we have a look into, as it appears, a fully completed world and into, so to speak, an infinite host of world-orders which are systematically connected, still we find ourselves actually only in a vicinity to the center of the entire nature where she has already evolved from the chaos and acquired her appropriate perfection.[25] It we could overstep [the boundary of] a certain sphere, we would spot there the chaos and the dispersion of elements which have according to the measure as they find themselves closer to that center, in part abandoned the raw state and are closer to the perfection of formation, whereas with [increasing] degrees of distance they are [113] gradually lost in a complete dispersion. Who [we] would see how the infinite space of divine presence, in which the supply for all possible formations of nature is available, [lies] buried in a silent night, full of matter, to serve for stuff for the world to be generated in the future, and [full] of mainsprings to put that matter in motion which starts with a weak stirring those motions whereby the immeasurability of that desolate space still ought to be enlivened. Perhaps a series of millions of years and centuries[26] will have flown past before the sphere of developed nature in which we find ourselves, arrived at the [stage of] perfection which now attends it; and perhaps there will pass an even larger period, until nature makes an equally great step [back] in[to] the chaos; but the sphere of developed nature is incessantly busy in expanding itself. Creation is not the work of a moment.[27] After it has made the start in the bringing forth of an infinity substances and matter, it is efficient throughout an entire sequence of eternity with an ever growing degree of fruitfulness. Millions and entire mountains [bundles] of millions of centuries will flow by, within which always new worlds and world-orders form themselves one after another in those reaches [so] distant from the center of nature and reach perfection; they achieve [114] regardless of the systematic constitution which is among its parts, a universal relation to the center which has become the first point of formation and the center of creation through the attraction-capability of its outstanding mass.[28] The infinity of future time-sequence, in which eternity is inexhaustible, will throughly enliven all spaces of the presence of God and will gradually place them into the regularity which is appropriate to the magnificence of His plan; and if one could, so to speak, condense the entire eternity with a bold presentation into one concept, one could also see the entire infinite space filled with world-orders and the creation as completed. But because in fact the remaining part of the time-sequence of eternity is always infinite and the [part] already flown by is finite,[23] the sphere of developed nature is always only an infinitely small part of its being which has in itself the seed of future worlds and tends to develop from the raw condition of chaos in longer or shorter periods. Creation is never completed. Though it has once started, but will never cease. It is always busy in bringing forth more scenes of nature, new things and new worlds.[30] The work which it accomplishes has a proportion to the time which it applies to that work. It needs nothing less than eternity in order to enliven [115] the entire limitless reaches of infinite spaces with worlds without number and without end. One can say of creation what the most sublime among German poets writes of eternity:

> Infinity! Who measures thee?
> Before thee worlds are as days and men as moments.
> Perhaps the thousandth sun is rounding now,
> And thousands still remain behind.

> As a clock animated by a weight
> Speeds by a sun moved by God's power:
> Its drive runs down, and another strikes,
> You, however, remain and count them not.
> von Haller.[31]

It is of no small satisfaction [for man] to launch with his imagination across the frontier of completed creation into the space and see the half raw nature in the vicinity of the sphere of developed world, lose itself gradually through all grades and shades of imperfection in the entirely unformed space. Is it not, however, a blameworthy boldness, one would say, to throw out a hypothesis and appraise it as a plan [worthy] of the delight of the intellect, [a plan] which is perhaps quite arbitrary, if one asserts that nature is developed only in an infinitely small part of it and infinite spaces still struggle with the chaos [116] in order to display in the course of future times entire hosts of worlds and world-orders, in all appropriate order and beauty? I am not so devoted to the consequences which my theory presents that I should not recognize how the conjecture about the successive expansion of creation through infinite spaces, which contain the stuff for that, cannot completely dispose of the objection of undemonstrability.[32] I still expect from those who are able to appraise the degree of probability that such a chart of infinity, though it comprises a plan which seems to be destined to remain forever hidden to human understanding, will not therefore be immediately looked upon as a phantasm, especially if one takes for help the analogy[33] which must lead us always in such cases where the understanding lacks the thread of unquestionable demonstrations.

One can, however, also support the analogy with plausible reasons and the insight of the reader, inasmuch as I can compliment myself with such [his] approval, will perhaps increase them with still more important ones. For if one assumes that creation does not carry with it the character of stability, insofar as it does not oppose to the universal tendency of attraction, which works through all its parts, an equally thoroughgoing specification which [117] can sufficiently resist the inclination of the former toward destruction and disorder if it has no distributed forces of orbiting which, in connection with the tendency toward the center, establish a universal systematic constitution [embodying stability], then one will be forced to assume a universal center of the entire universe, which holds all its parts together in a connected relation and makes only one system out of the entire being of nature. If one attaches to this the notion about the formation of celestial bodies from the scattered elementary matter, as we have outlined it in the foregoing [sections], though here not [as] confined to a separate system but extended over the entire universe, then one will be forced to conceive such a distribution of the basic stuff in the space of the original chaos which naturally brings with it a center of [for] the entire creation, so that the active mass which comprises in its sphere the entire nature can be brought together [related] to this [center], and the thoroughgoing relation can become operative whereby all worlds make up only one single edifice. But in the infinite space hardly a kind of distribution of the primordial basic stuff can be conceived which should set a real center- and sinking-point of the entire nature, unless it is arranged according to a law of increasing dissipation [starting] from that point to all far [farthermost] reaches.[34] This law, however, sets simultaneously a difference [differentiation] in time which needs a system [118] in the various regions of infinite space to come to the ripening of its development, so that this period is the shorter, the closer is the building-place of a world-edifice to the center of creation, because there the elements of the stuff are piled up more densely and, on the contrary, the longer time [is] required, the more extended is the distance, because there the particles are more scattered and come together later for [the] formation [of a world-edifice].

If one weighs the entire hypothesis, which I lay out, in the entire extent of what I have said as well as of what I still will specially present, then one will not at least take the boldness of its demands as being incapable of deserving an excuse. One can reckon the inevitable tendency, which each world-edifice [which has already been] brought to perfection has [in a] gradually [increasing degree] toward its destruction, among the reasons which can assure that the universe in other regions becomes conversely fruitful in [producing new] worlds to offset the lack which it has suffered at one [specific] place. The entire piece of nature which we know, whether it is only an atom with respect of that which remains hidden above or below our horizon, still confirms this fruitfulness of a nature which is without limits, because it is nothing else but the exercise of divine omnipotence itself.[35] Uncounted animals and plants become [119] destroyed daily and are a sacrifice to transitoriness; but nature, through an inexhaustible capability of generating, brings forth no fewer [animals and plants] in other places and fills out the emptiness. Considerable pieces of the earth's surface, which we inhabit, become again buried in the sea, from which a favorable period had brought them forth;[36] but in other places nature completes the defect and brings forth other regions, which were hidden in the depths of water, in order to expand over these [regions] new riches of her fruitfulness. In such a way worlds and world-orders fade away and are devoured by the abyss of eternity; however, creation is always busy in setting up new formations in other celestial regions and in repairing the loss with gain.

One need not be astonished over finding transitoriness even in the great[est] of God's works. All that is finite, [all] that has a beginning and cause, has on itself the hallmark of its limited nature; it must pass away and have an end. The duration of a world-edifice has through the excellence of its arrangement a steadiness which, according to our notions, comes close to an infinite duration.[37] Perhaps thousands, perhaps millions of centuries will not annihilate it; but because the futility, which is grafted on their finite natures, steadily works on their destruction, eternity will contain [120] in itself all possible periods to usher in finally the moment of their doom through a universal decay.[38] Newton, this great admirer of God's attributes [as ascertained] from the perfection of His works, who with the deepest insight into the excellence of nature united the greatest reverence toward the revelation of divine omnipotence,[39] saw himself forced to announce to nature its doom through the natural inclination which the mechanics of motion has for it [in store].[40] If, through the essential course of frailty in great spans of time even in [its] very smallest part which one may conceive, a systematic constitution approaches the condition of its confusion, then there must occur a moment in the infinite course of eternity where this gradual diminution exhausts all motion.

We must not, however, bemoan the decay of a world-edifice as a true loss of nature. She demonstrates her richness in a kind of waste [exchange] which, while some parts pay tribute to transitoriness, maintains itself undamaged through innumerable new products in the entire extent of her perfection. What an uncountable amount of flowers and insects perishes every cold day; but how little does one miss them, regardless [of the fact that] they are the splendid artefacts of nature and pieces of evidence of divine omnipotence;[41] in another place this loss will be offset by overflow. Man, [121] who seems to be the masterpiece of creation, is himself not exempted from this law. Nature demonstrates that she is just as rich, just as inexhaustible in bringing forth the most excellent among creatures as [she is with respect] to the least appreciated creatures and that their decay is a necessary nuance in the manifoldness of her suns because their production costs her nothing. The harmful effects of polluted air, the earthquakes, the floods wipe out entire nations from the surface of the earth,[42] but it does not appear that nature thereby suffers some loss. In a similar way entire worlds and systems leave the stage after they have played their role. The infinity of creation is great enough to view in relation to it[self] a world or a Milky Way of worlds [in the same way] in which man looks upon a flower or an insect in comparison with the earth. Thus, while nature decks out eternity with changing shows, God remains busy in an unceasing creation to shape the means for the formation of still greater worlds.

Who, because he is the Creator of all, sees
   with the same eye
A hero go under and a small sparrow fall,
Sees a bubble burst and an entire world perish.
                                        Pope
                        after Brockes' translation[43]

   Let us accustom our eye to these terrible convulsions, as well as to the customary ways of providence, and consider them with a kind of approval. And in fact, nothing is more befitting the richness of nature than this [approval]. For if a world-system exhausts in the long course of its duration all variety which its arrangement can hold, if it now has become a superfluous member in the chain of being, then nothing is more befitting than that in the theater of the ongoing changes of the universe that [factor should] play the last role which taxes each finite being, namely, that each should bring its levy to transitoriness. Nature shows, as has been thought [mentioned], this rule of her procedure already in the small part of her being which the eternal fate has prescribed to her in [her] entire [being], and I say it again, that the greatness [size] of what must go under is not here in the least objectionable; for everything which is great will be small, nay becomes a mere point, of one compares it with the infinite,[44] which the creation will represent in the unrestricted space throughout the sequence of eternity.

It seems that this end, imposed on those worlds as well as on all things of nature,[45] is subject to a certain law whose consideration gives to the theory a new feature of respectability. According to that law that end occurs in those cosmic bodies which are closest to the center [123] of the universe, just as the generation and formation first started near that center; from there decay and collapse spread out into the farther distances to bury finally through a gradual collapse of motions in a single chaos all world[s] which has [have] completed its [their] period[s]. On the other hand, nature is unremittingly busy on the opposite border of the developed world in building worlds from the raw means of scattered elements and while she ages on one side beside the center, she is young on the other side and fruitful in new begettings. Accordingly, the developed world finds itself confined in between the ruins of a collapsed and the chaos of an undeveloped nature: and if one imagines, what is likely, that a world which has already reached perfection may last a longer time than what it needs to be formed, then regardless of all devastations which the transitoriness incessantly serves up, the extent of the universe will nevertheless increase.

If, however, finally one still leaves room for an idea which is just as probable as it is befitting the constitution of divine works, then the satisfaction, which such a portrayal of the alterations of nature pro-vokes, will rise to the highest degree of [124] of approval.[46] Can one not believe that nature, which was capable of placing herself from chaos into a regular order and a skilful system, will not be in the position to restore herself from the new chaos, into which the dimi-nution of her motions had lowered her, just as easily and to renew the first combination? After the standstill of the [world] machine has brought them to rest, cannot the springs, which brought the stuff of scattered matter into motion and order, be put again in effectiveness through expanded forces and confine themselves to harmony according to the same universal rules whereby the original formation got under way? One will not hesitate too long to admit this, if one considers that after the final dullness of orbital motions in the world-edifice crashed the planets and comets together into the sun, the glow of this body must obtain an immeasurable increase through the mixture of so many and great lumps, especially since the [more] distant globes of the solar system, in consequence of our previously demonstrated theory, contain in [the entire] nature the lightest and in fire the most effective stuff.[47] This fire, set by new nourishment and most volatile matter into the greatest vehemence, will without doubt not only dissolve again everything into the smallest elements, but these too will again expand and scatter with an expansive force proportional to the heat [125] and with a velocity, which will not be weakened by any resistance of [in] the intervening space, into these same distant spaces which they have occupied before the first formation of nature in such a way so as, after the vehemence of the central fire has been dampened through an almost complete dispersion of their mass[es], to repeat the old begettings and systematically related motions and to present a new world-edifice through the combination of the forces of attraction and repulsion. If in such a way a particular planetary system has fallen into decay and through the essential forces has restored itself from it, if this play has more than once repeated itself, then perhaps there will finally approach the period which will gather in the same way into one chaos the great system, in which the fixed stars are members, through the decay of their motions.[48] One can here doubt even less that the unification of so infinite an amount of fire-storehouses as these burning suns are, together with the retinue of their planets, will scatter the stuff of their masses, dissolved by the unspeakable glow, into the old space of their sphere of formation and there the materials become available through these mechanical laws for new formations from [by] which the desolate space can become enlivened with worlds and systems. If we then follow this phoenix of nature,[49] which burns itself out only to revive from its [126] ashes rejuvenated, across all infinity of times and spaces; if one sees how nature even in the region where she decays and ages is inexhaustible in new acts, and [how] on the other frontiers of creation in the space of unformed raw matter she progresses with steady steps on behalf of the expansion of the plan of divine revelation, in order to fill eternity as well as all spaces with her wonders, then one's spirit, which reflects on all this, plunges into a deep astonishment; but still unsatisfied with this so great a subject, whose transitoriness cannot sufficiently satisfy the soul, he wishes to know at close range that Being, the greatness of whose intellect is the source of that light which spreads out over the entire nature also as if from a center. With what kind of awe must not the soul look at her own being when she considers that she still has to live through all these changes;[50] she can say to herself what the philosophical poet says of eternity:

When therefore a second nothing[ness] will bury this world,
When from the entire all nothing remains but its place,
When other heavens, by other stars brightened,
Will have their courses completed, [127]

160

You will be as young as now, equally far from your death,
You will be still in for eternity just as you are today.

von Haller.[51]

Oh, happy is that soul when under the tumult of elements and the dreams [rubbles] of nature he is always set at a height from where he can see the ravages, which the frailty of the things of the world causes, roar by under his feet. [Such] a happiness, which reason not once dares to wish for, revelation teaches us to hope for with assurance.[52] When therefore the chains, which keep us tied to the futility of creatures, will fall away in the moment which is appointed for the transformation of our being, then the immortal soul, freed from the dependence of finite things, will find the enjoyment of true happiness in communion with the Infinite Being. The entire nature, which has a universal harmonious relation to the approval of Godhead, can do no otherwise than to fill with everlasting satisfaction that rational creature which finds himself united with that primordial source of all perfection. Nature, seen from this center, will show on all sides complete certainty and complete fitness. The changing scenes of nature are not able to displace the restfulness of the happiness of a spirit which has once been raised to such [128] a height. While he already tastes in advance this condition with a sweet hope, he can exercise his mouth in those songs of praise with which some day all eternity shall resound:

When Nature fails, and day and night
    Divide Thy works no more,
My ever grateful heart, O Lord,
    Thy mercy shall adore.

Through all Eternity to Thee
    A joyful song I'll raise;
For, Oh! Eternity's too short
    To utter all Thy praise.

Addison after Gottsched's translation.[53] [129]

ADDITION TO THE SEVENTH SECTION

Universal theory and history of the sun in general

There is still a major question whose solution is indispensable in the natural science of the heavens and in a complete cosmogony.[1] Why will, namely, the center of each system be taken by a flaming body? Our planetary world-edifice has the sun for a central body, and the fixed stars, which we see, are in all appearance centers of similar systems.

In order to understand why in the formation of a world-edifice the body which serves as the center of attraction must become a fiery body, while the remaining globes of its sphere of attraction remained dark and cold globes, one only need to recall the manner of the begetting of a world-edifice which we have sketched in detail in the foregoing [sections].[2] In the far extended space, in which the diffused elementary basic stuff lends itself to formations and systematic motions, the planets and comets form themselves only from that part of the elementary basic stuff sinking toward the center of attraction which through the fall and reciprocal action of the [130] collected particles will be specified for the exact confinement of direction and velocity which will be required for [their] revolution. This part, as was presented above, is the least of the entire amount of the downward-sinking matter and is only the waste of denser kinds [of matter], which through the resistance of other [parts] could attain to this degree of [required] exactness. There are found in this mixture floating kinds of outstanding lightness, which, impeded by the resistance of [across] space, do not through this fall press through to the appropriate velocity of periodic revolutions and which consequently become driven down together on the sun in [owing to] the dullness of their impulse.[3] Since now even these lighter and volatile parts are also the most efficient to maintain fire,[4] we see that through their increase the [chief] body and center of the system obtains the advantage of becoming a flaming body, in a word, a sun. On the contrary, the heavier and forceless stuff and the lack of these fire-nourishing particles make of the planets only cold and dead lumps which are robbed of such quality.

This increase of so light materials is also [the reason] why the sun has received the specific lesser density, by which it falls even behind our earth, the third planet in distance from it, four times in density; [131] although it is natural to believe that in this center of the [planetary] world-edifice, as in its lowest place [point], the heaviest and densest begettings of matter ought to be found, whereby the sun, without the addition of so great an amount of lightest stuff, should exceed the density of all planets.

The mingling of denser and heavier kinds of elements to these lightest and most volatile [kinds] serves likewise to outfit the central body for the most vehement glow which ought to burn and keep [burning] on its surface. For we know[5] that the fire, in whose nourishing stuff thick materials are found mingled with the volatile [kinds], has a great advantage of vehemence for those flames which will be maintained only by the light begettings. But this mixing of some heavy kinds among the lighter ones is a necessary consequence of our doctrine about the formation of celestial bodies, and has still that [additional] profit that the might of glow does not suddenly dissipate the flammable matter of the [sun's] surface and that the same [mighty glow] will be gradually and steadily nourished by the afflux of nourishment from the interior.

After the question has now been resolved,[6] [namely], why the central body of a great star-system is a flaming globe, that is, a sun, it does not seem to be superfluous to deal for a while yet with this subject [132] and to explore with a careful scrutiny the condition of such a celestial body; especially, since the conjectures can here be derived from stronger reasons than they commonly use to be in the investigations of the constitution of distant celestial bodies.[7]

At the very first I firmly state that one cannot doubt that the sun is truly a flaming body and not a mass of molten and glowing matter heated to the highest degree [of temperature] as some, because of certain difficulties which they think to be present in the former opinion, wanted to conclude.[8] For if one considers that a flaming fire has that essential advantage above any other kind of heat that it, so to speak, is efficient even in itself, instead of diminishing or exhausting itself through [the process of] sharing, but rather it obtains thereby more strength and vehemence and requires only stuff and nourishment for maintenance to last forever; the glow, on the contrary, of a mass heated to the highest degree [of temperature] is a mere passive status[9] which through the association of contacting matter unceasingly diminishes and has no forces of its own to spread itself out from a small beginning, or come again alive in the case of diminishing; if one, I say, considers this, one can sufficiently perceive already from this—I leave aside other reasons[10]—that this quality [of being aflame] must be ascribed with probability [133] to the sun,[11] the source of light and warmth in each world-edifice.

If now the sun or the suns in general are flaming bodies, then the first property of its surface, which will be derived from this, is that air must be found on it, because no fire burns without air. This circumstance gives occasion to remarkable consequences. For, first, if one puts the atmosphere of the sun and its weight in relation to the solar lump, in what state of compression will that air not be[12] and how capable will it not be thereby of maintaining the most vehement degree of fire through its spring-force [elasticity]? In this atmosphere there arise in all probability also the smoke-clouds from those materials dissolved by fire which, as cannot be doubted, have in themselves a mixture of gross and light particles which, after they had risen to a height that provides for them cooler air, storm down in heavy tar-

and brimstone-rains and bring new nourishment to the fire. Even this atmosphere, for similar reasons as on our earth, is not free of the movements of winds which, however, must far exceed in vehemence in respect to all that imagination can picture for itself. If some region on the surface of the sun, either through the choking power of out-breaking vapours or through the scarce afflux [134] of flammable materials, falls behind in the outbreak of flame, then the air above it cools somewhat and, while it contracts, gives to the place next to it [the opportunity] to push into its space with a force proportional to the excess of its expansion, in order to rekindle the extinguished flame.[13]

For all that, all flame always devours much air and there is no doubt that the spring-force [elasticity] of the volatile air-element, which surrounds the sun, must in some time suffer thereby no small disadvantage. If one applies here on a large scale that [conclusions] which Mr Hales has verified through careful experiments in connection with the working of flame in our atmosphere,[14] then one can consider the ever-present striving of smoke particles coming from the flame to annihilate the elasticity of the solar atmosphere as a chief knot whose resolution is connected with difficulties. For if the fire, which burns over the entire surface of the sun, takes into itself the air which is indispensable for its burning, [then] the sun is in danger of becoming extinguished if the greatest part of its atmosphere becomes devoured. True, the fire through the dissolution of certain materials [in it] also generate air, but the experiments show that always more [air] will be devoured than generated.[15] If a part of the solar fire is robbed under [the impact of] choking vapours of the air which serves [135] for its maintenance, violent storms, as we have already remarked, will try to disperse and lead away those vapours. But on the whole one will be able to make comprehensible the replacement of this necessary element [of air] in the following way, [namely], if one takes into consideration that since in a flaming fire the heat works only above it and only very little below it,[16] if it becomes choked through the adduced cause, its vehemence turns against the interior of the solar body and necessitates its deep gorges to let the air enclosed in their caves break forth and rekindle anew the fire;[17] [and] if one places, through a freedom which is not forbidden in a subject so unknown,[18] in the bowels of this [body] especially materials which, as salpeter,[19] are inexhaustibly productive in elastic air, then the solar fire cannot easily suffer defect over long periods in the afflux of always renewed air.

Nonetheless, one sees the clear hallmarks of transitoriness[20] even in this priceless fire which nature has set up for a torch of the world.

There comes a time when all will be extinguished. The withdrawal of the most volatile and finest materials which, scattered [as they are] by the vehemence of heat, never again return and [but] increase the stuff of the zodiacal light, [so that] the piling-up of unburnable and burnt-out materials, that is, ashes, on the surface [of the sun], [and] finally also [136] the lack of air will set for the sun a target [end], because its flame will essentially be extinguished and eternal darkness will occupy its place where now is the center of light and life for the entire world-edifice.[21] The recurring effort of its fire to rekindle again through the openings of new chasms, whereby it perhaps presents [restores] itself before its [final] decay, could give an explanation of the disappearance of some fixed stars.[22] There may be suns which are near their extinction and which still a few times tended to revive from their debris. Whether this explanation deserves approval or not, one can still avail himself of this consideration in order to perceive that since an inevitable collapse threatens the perfection of all world-orders, be it in one way or another, one would find no difficulty in the law, presented above, of their decay through the trend of the mechanical arrangement which, however, will be especially worthy of acceptance because it entails the seeds of renewal[23] in the [their] very mixing together with the chaos.

Finally, let us present closely to the power of imagination[24] such a specially wondrous object as a burning sun is. One sees at a glance wide seas of fire which raise their flames against the sky; raging storms whose fury doubles the vehemence of the former [137] which, while they swell over their shores, now cover the elevated regions of this celestial body, now sink back into their confines; burnt out rocks which stick out their fearful peaks from the flaming gorges and whose inundation or unveiling by the waving fire-elements causes the alternating appearance and disappearance of sunspots;[25] thick vapours which put out the fire and which through the power of winds rise, [and] form dark clouds which in fiery downpourings storm down again and as burning streams gush from the heights of the firm solar land* into the flaming valleys; [138] the crash of elements; the debris

---

* I ascribe not without reason[26] to the suns all the unevenness of firm land, mountains, and valleys, which we find on our earth and other celestial bodies. The formation of a celestial globe, which changes from a fluid state to a firm [dry] state, brings along necessarily such inequalities. When the surface hardens, inasmuch as in the fluid interior part of such a mass the materials sink according to the measure of their gravity toward the central point, the particles of the elastic air- or fire-element, which finds itself intermingled in these materials, become ejected and pile up under the meanwhile solidified crust, under which they produce great and, in proportion to the solar lump, enormous cavities into which the uppermost crust finally sinks in with manifold inbendings and thus prepares thereby elevated regions as well as valleys and floodbeds of further seas of fire.

of burnt out materials; and the [entire] nature resounding with destruction which, together with the abominable status of her derangements, works for the beauty of the world and for the benefit of creatures.

When therefore the centers of all great world systems become flaming bodies, this must above all be conjectured about the central body of that inexhaustible system which the fixed stars make up. Will now, however, this body, whose mass must have a proportion to the greatness of its system, if it were a self-illuminating body or a sun, not strike the eye with special brilliance and magnitude? However, we see no fixed star so exceptionally distinguishing itself glimmer forth among the celestial host. In fact, one need not be concerned if this does not happen. If it were to exceed 10,000 times our sun in greatness [size], it would, if one assumes its distance to be 100 greater than that of Sirius, appear no larger and brighter than this [star].[27]

Perhaps, however, it is reserved for future times to discover at least [139] the region where the center*[28] of the fixed-star system to which our sun belongs is to be found, [140] or perhaps to determine where one should set the central body of the universe at which all parts of it aim with uniform sinking. Concerning [the whole topic of] what ought to be the constitution of this fundamental piece of the entire creation and what can be found on it, we want to leave [all this] for Mr Wright of Durham to determine, who with a fanatical inspiration elevated on this happy place, as if on the throne of the entire nature, a mighty being of divine kind [endowed] with spiritual

---

* I have a conjecture according to which it appears to me very probable that in the system of stars, which form the Milky Way, the Sirius or Dog-star is the central body and occupies the center toward which all are related. If one looks upon this system according to the sketch of the First Part of this treatise, as a swarm of suns which are piled up toward a common plane, which is stretched out on all sides from the center and through [still] forms a certain, so to speak, circle-shaped space which through minor deviations of it from the reference plane extends itself in width somewhat on both sides [of that plane]; then the sun, which similarly finds itself near that plane, will see the appearance of this circle-shaped whitish glimmering zone as broadest on that side, according [with respect] to which it finds itself closest to the outermost limit of the system, because it is easy to guess that it will not maintain itself exactly in the center. Now the streak of the Milky Way is widest in the part between the sign[s] of the Swan and of the Archer. Consequently this will be the side where our sun is closest to the outermost periphery of the circle-shaped system;[29] and in this part will we hold the place, where the star-images of the Eagle and the Fox stand with the Goose, to be especially nearest to them all, because it is there, from that in-between space, where the Milky Way divides itself, that the greatest visible dispersion of stars shines forth. [140] If one therefore draws a line roughly from the place near the tail of the Eagle through the middle of the plane of the Milky Way to the opposite point, this line must pass through the center of the system and in fact it exactly comes to Sirius,[30] the brightest star in the entire sky, which because of this fortunate [and] with its prominent figure so harmonious an agreement seems to deserve that one should hold it for the central body. It would, according to this concept, be also seen exactly in the streak of the Milky Way, if the position of our sun, which at the tail of the Eagle deviates somewhat from the plane of the Milky Way, had not caused the optical distance [shift] of the center toward the other side of such zone.[31]

attraction- and repulsion-forces which, being operative in an infinite sphere around itself, draws all virtues to itself but drives back the vice.[32] We do not want to give free rein [141] to the boldness of conjectures, to which we have perhaps allowed too much, to the point of [indulging in] arbitrary fictions.[33] Divinity is everywhere equally present in the infinity of the entire cosmic space; everywhere, where there are natures capable of launching themselves forward beyond the dependency of [on] creatures to the communion of the Highest Being, [this latter] is equally near. The entire creation is permeated by its [His] forces, but only the one who knows how to free himself from the [grasp of a] creature, [only the one] who is so noble to perceive that in the enjoyment of this primeval source of perfection is the highest degree of beatitude alone and solely to be sought, he alone is capable of finding himself nearer to this true point of reference of all excellence than to something else in the entire nature. However, when I, without sharing in the enthusiastic presentation of the [that] Englishman,[34] must conjecture[35] about the different degrees of the world of intellects from the physical relation of their dwelling places to the center of creation, then I should want to seek with greater probability the most perfect classes of rational beings farther from that center than near it. The perfection of creatures endowed with reason, insofar as it depends on the condition of matter in whose bonds they are enclosed, comes very much to the fineness of stuff whose influence determines them for the presentation of the world and for [their] reaction to it.[36] The inertness and resistance of matter limits very much [both] the freedom of the [142] spiritual [rational] beings for action and the clarity of their sensations of external things, it makes dull their faculties inasmuch as matter does not respond with appropriate lightness [agility] to the motions of those faculties. Therefore if one, as this is [should seem] likely, posits the densest and heaviest kinds of matter near the center of nature and, conversely, the increasing degree[s] of fineness and lightness of it in the greater distances, according to the analogy which prevails in our world-edifice, then the result is comprehensible. The intelligent beings, whose birthplace and sojourn are closer to the center of creation, are sunk into a stiff and immovable matter, which keeps their forces captive in an insuperable inertness and is just as capable of transmitting and imparting the impressions of the universe with the necessary clarity and lightness [agility]. One will have to count these thinking beings into the low class; on the contrary, this perfection of the world of spirits [intellects], which rests on its mutual dependence on matter, will grow as a steady ladder[37] with distances from the universal center. Accordingly, one has to place the worst and most imperfect begettings of thinking nature in the deepest abasement toward this point of [universal] sinking and it is there where this excellence of beings finally loses itself with all nuances of diminution in the complete lack of consideration [143] and thought. In fact, if one considers that the center of nature constitutes at the same time also the beginning of her formation from the raw means and [that] her [outer] border [is contiguous] with the chaos; if one adds to this that the perfection of [an] intelligent being has an outermost border of its beginning where their [its] faculties collide with unreason, but [that there are] no fences for progress above which those faculties could not be raised, but that from that [other] side onward a complete infinity lies before it, then if there ought to be a law according to which dwelling places are distributed to rational creatures according to the order of their relation to the common center, one will have to put the lowest and most imperfect begetting, which is also the beginning of the species of the world of spirits [intellects], to that place which is to be called the beginning of the entire universe, so that together with that universe they may fill in similar progress all infinity of time and space with degrees, growing into infinity, of perfection of the ability of thinking and bring themselves gradually closer to the goal of highest excellence, namely, to divinity, but without every being able to reach it. [144]

EIGHTH SECTION

General proof of the correctness of a mechanical doctrine of the arrangement of the world-edifice in general, and of the certainty of this present doctrine in particular.[1]

One cannot view the world-edifice without recognizing the most excellent disposition in its arrangement and the certain signatures of God's hand in the perfection of its correlations. After having pondered and admired so much beauty, so much splendour, reason rightly becomes indignant over the bold madness which takes it upon itself to ascribe all this to chance and to lucky approximation. The highest wisdom and infinite power must have carried it out, or else it would be impossible that so many objectives converging into one end should be found in the constitution of the world-edifice. It still remains to be decided whether the plan of the constitution of the universe has been deposited by the highest intellect into the essential dispositions of eternal natures and planted in the general laws of motion so that it may evolve from them unhindered in a manner fitting a most perfect order; or whether the general properties of the constituent parts of the world have the complete inability [145] to harmonize and not [even] the slightest trend for union, and need therefore a foreign hand [so as] to move into that compactness and co-ordination which permits perfection and beauty to be seen [everywhere in nature]. An almost universal prejudice has overtaken most philosophers against the ability of nature to produce through its general laws anything orderly,[2] as if it were a challenge to God's ruling the world if one looked in the forces of nature for the original formations and as if these forces were a principle independent of God and [equivalent to] an eternal blind fate.

If, however, one considers that nature and the eternal laws, which are prescribed to substances for their interaction, are not a principle autonomous and necessary regardless of God, that precisely because nature displays in them so much correspondence and order which she produces through general laws, it is to be recognized that the beings of all things must have their common origin in a certain basic being and that they show but mutual relations and harmony only because their properties have their source in a single highest intellect whose wise idea has placed them into close relations and implanted into them that capacity by which they bring forth only beauty, only order [146] according to the conditions of their efficiency, if one, I say, ponders this, then nature will appear for us more worthy than she is commonly regarded and one will expect from her unfolding nothing but harmony, nothing but order. When, however, one gives room to an unfounded prejudice that the general laws of nature in and by themselves bring along nothing but disorder[3] and [that] all co-ordination to usefulness, which shines forth in the constitution of nature, shows God's immediate hand, then one is obliged to turn the entire nature into a miracle. One then must not deduce from the forces implanted in matter the beautiful coloured bow, which appears in raindrops when these absorb the colors of sunshine, on account of its beauty, the rain on account of its usefulness, the winds on account of their indispensable advantages that serve human needs in infinite ways, in brief, [one must not do this in connection with] all changes of the world which bring along appropriateness and order. The initiative of the investigators of nature, who have given themselves to such philosophy, will have to make a solemn apology before the judgment seat of religion. There will in fact be no longer any nature; there will only be a God in [behind the appearance of] the machine to bring about the changes in the world. But then what will do that very specific means, the certainty of demonstrating the [147] Most High Being from the essential impotency of nature, for an effective convincing of the Epicureans? When the natures of things produce through the eternal laws of their beings nothing but disorder and absurdity, they will precisely because of this demonstrate the character of their independence of God; and what kind of notion can one make for himself of a God who is merely listened to, as if by constraint, by the general laws of nature and whose wisest plans they resist in and by themselves? Will not the enemy of Providence derive so many triumphs over these false axioms as he is able to note coincidences, which the general working laws of nature produce without any special restriction, and will for him such examples be in short supply? On the contrary, let us also conclude with all the more fairness and correctness: nature, left to her general properties, is fertile in truly beautiful and perfect fruits which in themselves show not only concordance and perfection, but also well harmonize with the entire realm of their being, with the needs of man, and with the glory of divine attributes. From this it follows that their essential properties can have no independent necessity; but that they must have their origin in a single Intellect as in the ground and fountain of all beings, in which they are planned according to common correlations. [148] All that mutually relates to a reciprocal harmony must be mutually interconnected in a single being from which they altogether depend. Thus there is clearly a Being of all beings, an infinite Intellect and self-sufficient Wisdom, from which nature, even according to her mere possibility, draws her origin in the entire meaning of specifications. Hence one should not contest the capability of nature as sharing in the being of a Most High Being;[4] the more perfect is she in her development, the better her general laws lead to order and harmony, [and] all the more certainly is she a proof of the Godhead from whom she borrows these relations. Her productions are no longer the effect of imprecision and the consequences of haphazard; all flows forth from her according to unchanging laws, which must display her skill because they are but aspects of the all-wise plan from which disorder is banished. It is not the haphazard concurrence of Lucretius' atoms that built the world; implanted forces and laws, which have the wisest Intellect for source, are an unchanging origin of that order which emanates from them not accidentally but necessarily.

If one is able to shake off an old unfounded prejudice and a foul philosophy which try to hide under a pious complexion [149] a slothful ignorance, then I hope to found on incontrovertible grounds a firm conviction, [*first*] *that the world recognizes for the origin of its constitution a mechanical development unfolding from the general laws of nature; and second, that the kind of mechanical genesis which we have presented is the true one.*[5] If one is to judge whether nature has sufficient ability to bring about the order of the world-edifice through a mechanical series of her laws of motion, then one has first to ponder how simple are the motions which celestial bodies observe and that in view of what is demanded by a greater exactness these motions imply nothing else than what is involved in the general laws of the forces of nature. The orbital motions consist in the combination of the sinking force which is a certain consequence of the properties of matter, and of the thrustlike motion which can be regarded as the effect of the former as a velocity resulting from the downward sinking in which only a certain cause[6] was necessary to deviate sideways the vertical fall. After the required determination of these motions [is done], nothing further is necessary to maintain them forever.[7] They exist in the empty space through the connection of the once-imposed thrustlike force with the attraction deriving from essential natural forces and suffer no further changes. The analogies themselves [150] demonstrate in the harmony of these motion so clearly the reality of a mechanical origin that one can entertain no doubt on that score. Therefore,

1. These motions have a universally conform direction, so that among the six main planets [and] the ten trabants[8] there is not one that would move in a direction other than from west to east in their advancing [orbital] motion as well as in their rotation around their axes. These directions are, in addition, so precisely co-ordinated that they deviate but little from a common plane, and this plane, to which all is related, is the equatorial plane of the body which in the center of the entire system rotates in the same direction around its axis and which through its overwhelming attraction has become the point of attraction of all motions, and consequently has to participate in them as completely as possible. A proof, that all motions together arose and became determined in a mechanical way corresponding to the general laws of nature and that the cause, which either imposed or directed the sidewise motions, dominates the entire realm of the planetary edifice and obeys therein the laws which is observed by any matter which finds itself in a space commonly moved together, is that all the different motions ultimately assume one single direction and make themselves together [151] related as exactly as possible to one single plane.

2. The velocities are so determined as they ought to be in a space in which the moving force is in the center, namely, they decrease in steady degrees with the distances from it, and vanish in the farthest reaches into a total dullness of motion which bends sideways the vertical fall but very little. From Mercury on, which has the greatest orbital force,[9] one sees these forces gradually diminish, and to be so minute in the outermost comets as this is possible in order that they may not fall straight into the sun. One cannot object that the laws

of central motion in circles demand that the orbital velocity has to be all the greater the closer is [a body] to the center of the universal sinking; for why should even these celestial bodies near that center have circularly shaped orbits; why are not the nearest ones very eccentric and the most remote ones going around in circles, or rather, since they all deviate from that measure geometrical exactness, why does that deviation increase with distance? Do not indicate these relations the point to which all motion originally tends and has, according to the measure of [its] nearness [to that center], reached even greater degrees [of exactness] before other factors had its directions changed into the present ones?

[152] Should one, however, now except the constitution of the world-edifice from the universal laws of nature in order to ascribe them to the immediate hand of God, then it becomes immediately evident that the adduced analogies openly contradict such a notion. For, to begin with, concerning the general agreement in direction it is clear that there is no ground here why the celestial bodies should have orbits directed in exactly one single direction if the mechanism of their origin has not determined it. For the space in which they move is resisting [them to an] infinitely little [extent] and limits their motion very little either towards one or the other side; also, God's choice would not, without some smallest motivation, be bound to a single determination, but would evidence itself with greater freedom in all sorts of deviations and differences.[10] Moreover, why do the orbits of planets relate so closely to a common plane, namely, to the equatorial plane of that great body which in the center of all motion rules their orbitings? This analogy, instead of showing in itself an impelling basis for fitness, is rather the cause of a certain disturbance which would be eliminated through a free deviation of the planetary orbits [from the common plane]; because the [mutual] attractions of planets disturb to some extent even now the uniformity of their motions[11] and would not be obstructing one another [153] if they were not so closely drawn to a common plane.

Even more than all these analogies does the most evident mark of the hand of nature point to the absence of most precise determination in those relations which she tried to achieve. For if it were the best that the planetary orbits should be placed almost in a common plane, why are not they exactly so and why has a part remained of that deviation which should be diminished? If therefore the planets, [which are] close to the orbit of the sun, had thus received the magnitude of centrifugal force holding the attraction in balance, why is there still something lacking to complete equality and why are their orbits not completely circularly round if only the wisest intention, supported by the greatest capability, had considered the production of this arrangement?[12] Is it not to be perceived clearly that the cause, which had set the orbits of celestial bodies, insofar as it strived to bring those orbits to a common plane, could not carry it out completely, and similarly, that the force, which dominated the celestial space when all matter, now formed into globes, obtained its orbital velocities, aimed at bringing them near the center into a balance with the sinking force, but could not achieve complete exactness?

Is not to be recognized here the customary procedure of nature which through the interaction of different influences is always made to deviate from the quite exact determination and will one find the causes of this arrangement solely in the ultimate objectives of an immediately present highest Will? One cannot, without displaying hard-headedness, deny that the much vaunted way of explanation of the properties of nature [which is wont] to justify itself by the presentation of its utility, here did not measure up to the hoped-for test. With respect to the benefit of the world, it was certainly indifferent whether the planetary orbits were completely circular or whether they were slightly eccentric; whether they should wholly coincide with the plane of their general attraction, or whether they should somewhat deviate from it; rather, if it was [not] necessary [for them] to be limited by this kind of correspondence, it was best to have them [left] entirely to themselves [in no orderly relation to one another]. If it is true what the philosopher said that God always does geometry,[13] [and] if this shines forth even in the ways of the general laws of nature, then certainly this rule ought to be perfectly traceable in the immediate works of the omnipotent Word and these should show on themselves the perfection of geometrical exactness. The comets belong to these shortcomings of nature. One cannot deny that in view of their orbits and the changes they thereby suffer, they ought to be regarded [155] as imperfect members of creation which neither can serve to provide comfortable habitats for rational beings, nor can they be useful for the best of the entire system by serving, as was once thought, as nourishment for the sun; for it is certain that most of them can reach that goal no sooner than at the collapse of the entire planetary system. Within the doctrine about the immediate highest arrangement of the world, [but] without a natural development from universal natural laws, such a remark would be repulsive, [regardless of] whether it is quite certain [sound]. Only in a mechanical art of explanation are the beauty of the world and the manifestation of omnipotence glorified thereby in no small measure. Nature, insofar as she comprises all possible grades of variety, stretches her realm over all begettings from perfection to nothing, and her shortcomings themselves are a sign of the overflow in which her essence is inexhausted.

One may very well believe that the afforded analogies would much prevail over prejudice to [and] make worthy of acceptance the [doctrine of the] mechanical origin of the world-edifice, were it not for certain reasons which, being taken from the nature of things themselves, appear to contradict entirely that doctrine. The celestial space, as already thought [noted] several times, is empty or at least [most] filled with infinitely thin matter, [156] which consequently can provide no means to impress common movements on the celestial bodies. This difficulty is so significant and valid that Newton, who had reason to trust the insights of his philosophy as much as any [no] other mortal, saw himself necessitated to give up all hope here to explain through the laws of nature and the forces of matter the imparting or orbital forces present in the planets, regardless of all correspondence which pointed to a mechanical origin.[14] Although it is a distressing decision for a philosopher to give up, in case of a complicated condition which is still very distant from simple basic laws, the effort of investigation and to be satisfied with a reference to the immediate will of God, still Newton recognized here the borderline which separates nature and the finger of God,[15] the course of the established laws of the former and the hint of the latter. After the perplexity of so great a philosopher it seems to be a presumption to hope for a lucky advance in a matter of such difficulty.

But that very difficulty, which deprived Newton of the hope to understand from the forces of nature the centrifugal force distributed to the celestial bodies [planets] whose direction and determinations constitute the systematic aspect of the world-edifice, [157] has become the very source of the notion which we have presented in the previous sections. It supports a mechanical doctrine, but such a one which is far removed from that which Newton found unsatisfactory and on account of which he had rejected all underlying [mechanical] causes, because (if I am allowed to say this) he erred in that he held that doctrine for the only one [acceptable] among all possible of its kind.[16] It is quite easy and natural, by means of the very difficulty of Newton, to arrive through a brief and basic inference at the certainty[17] of that mechanical way of explanation, which we have submitted in this essay. If one assumes (as one cannot help admitting it) that the foregoing analogies establish it with the greatest certainty that the harmonious and with respect to one another orderly interrelated motions and orbits of celestial bodies indicate a natural cause as their origin, then this [cause] nevertheless cannot be the material which now fills the celestial space. It therefore must be that [material] which had previously filled those spaces and whose motion was the basis for the present orbits of celestial bodies after it had coalesced into globes and cleaned thereby the spaces which one now sees to be empty or [it must be] the material which immediately emanated from it, whose materials [particles], which the planets, the comets, nay the sun consist of, had to be [158] spread out in the space of the planetary system and in this condition had set themselves in motions, which they maintained as they united into distinct lumps and formed the celestial bodies which comprise all the world-material that had previously been scattered. One is here not too long at a loss to discover the driving mechanism which can set in motion this material of a self-building nature. The source of it was the drive of that matter which brought under way the unification of masses, the force of attraction which is essentially inherent in matter and is so well fit, at the first stirring of nature, for [the role of] the first cause of motion. The direction, which in the case of that force always aims at the center, poses no problem here; for it is certain that the fine stuff of dispersed elements, which is in a perpendicular motion, had, both because of the multiplicity of points of attraction and because of the impediments which is posed by the mutual crossing of the lines of directions, to deviate into various sideways motions where the certain law of nature, which makes that all matter contracting through mutual interaction reaches such a final status in which one [particle] causes to the other as little change any more as possible, has produced the uniformity of direction as well as the corresponding degrees of velocities, which at every distance are weighed according to the central force and through which connection the elements cannot strive to stray [159] from one another upward or downward; thus all elements are made to orbit not only in one direction but also in nearly parallel and free circles around the common point of attraction in the thin celestial space. These motions of the part had to endure henceforth as planetary globes were being formed out of them and now exist, through the connection of the once implanted impulse with the central force, for unlimited future times.[18] On this so comprehensible ground rest the uniformity of directions in planetary orbits, the precise relation to a common plane, the measure of centrifugal force according to the attraction of the point, the decrease with distance of the exactness of these analogies, and the free deviation of the outermost celestial bodies in both sides as well as in opposite direction [of motion]. Thus these signs of mutual dependence in those determinations of formation point, with obvious evidence, at a material originally set in motion and spread across the entire space, so also proves the entire absence of all matter in this henceforth empty celestial space, apart from that matter out of which the bodies of planets, of the sun, and of the comets are put together, that in the beginning this matter had to be in that state of expansion. The ease and correctness [19] with which from these assumed principles all phenomena of the world-edifice had been derived in the [160] previous sections is a fulfillment of such a conjecture and gives it a value which is no longer arbitrary.

The certainty of a mechanistic doctrine, especially of ours, about the origin of the world-edifice will be raised to the highest peak of conviction [20] if one considers the formation of celestial bodies, the importance [density] and size of their mass according to the relations which they have with respect to the distance from the center of gravitation. For firstly, the density of their material, if one weighs them in the totality of their lump, is decreasing with the distance from the sun; a property which points so clearly at the mechanical properties of the first formation that one cannot deny it any more. They are put together of such materials in which those of the heavier kind obtain a deeper [closer] place with respect to the common center of sinking, [whereas] those of the lighter kind a more distant position, which condition is necessary in all kinds of natural formation. But in the case of a construction flowing directly from the divine Will there is not the slightest ground to chance upon the relations in consideration. For even if it could equally appear that the more distant globes should consist of a lighter material so that they could still experience the necessary effect from the smaller force of the sun's rays, [161] yet this is merely a goal which bears on the constitution of the material to be found on its surface and not on the deeper kinds of its interior lumps, for upon these the sun's heat never makes any effect, which [lumps] also serve to produce the planet's attraction which must make the bodies surrounding it sink toward it and therefore should not have the least relation to the strength or weakness of the sun's rays. If, however, one asks why are the densities, as derived from the calculations of Newton, of the earth, Jupiter, and Saturn with respect to one another as 400, $94\frac{1}{2}$ and 64, [21] then it would be senseless to ascribe the cause to God's intention which apportioned them according to the degrees of the sun's heat; for then our earth can serve as a counterexample in which the sun makes its effect through its rays only into so small a depth below the surface that the part of its lump, which must have some relation to it, amounts at most not even to a millionth part of the whole of which the rest in respect of that intention is quite indifferent. [22] If also the stuff, which the celestial bodies consist of, has an orderly relation mutually harmonizing with the distances, and the planets can no longer confine one another, as they now stand apart in empty space, their material must have previously been in a condition where they could make a common effect on one another so that they should confine themselves to places proportionate to their [162] specific gravity, which could not have happened otherwise than that their parts had, before their formation, been spread out in the whole space of the system and had, according to the general laws of motion, obtained places which belong to their densities.

The relation among the magnitude[s] of planetary masses which increases with distance is the second ground which clearly proves the mechanical formation of celestial bodies and especially our theory of it. Why do the masses of celestial bodies increase approximately with the distances?[23] If one follows a doctrine which ascribes all to the choice of God, then one can think of no other purpose why the more distant planets must have greater masses so [than] that they could, through the greater strength of their attraction, catch thereby into their spheres one or several moons which should [then] serve to make pleasant the sojourn of inhabitants who are appointed to them. But this purpose could just as well be achieved through a considerable density in the interior of their lump and why should then the lightness of material flowing from special grounds, [a lightness] which is contrary to that relation, remain, and be so overthrown through the preponderance of volume that the mass of the superior planets be more important than of those below? When one does not keep in mind the art of the natural formation of these [163] bodies, one will be hard put to give account of these relations; but by keeping it in view nothing is easier than to understand this disposition. As the material of all celestial bodies was still spread out in the space of the planetary system, the attraction formed from these particles globes which undoubtedly had to become the greater, the farther the place of their sphere of formation was from that universal central body, which from the center of the entire space limited and prevented, as far as it could, that unification through a specially powerful attraction.

One will notice with satisfaction the marks of such a formation of the celestial bodies from the initially spread-out basic material at the sides of the intervening spaces, which separate their orbits from one another and which according to this notion ought to be regarded as empty compartments from which the planets have taken the material for their formation. One can see how these intervening spaces between the orbits have a relation to the magnitude of masses which were built from them. The width between the orbit of Jupiter and Mars is so great that the space enclosed there exceeds the regions of all lower planetary orbits taken together; but that space is worthy of the greatest among all planets, namely, of that which has more mass than all the others together.[24] One cannot ascribe this separation of

Jupiter from Mars to the purpose that their attractions had to impede one another [164] as little as possible. For on such a basis the planet between two orbits would always find itself closest [closer] to that of the two whose attraction united with its own can in the least disturb the[ir] respective orbitings around the sun; consequently, closest [closer] to that which has the smallest [smaller] mass. Since now according to the correct calculations of Newton the force by which Jupiter can influence the course of Mars is like $1/12912$ to $1/200$ to the force which it exerts on Saturn through mutual attraction,[25] one can thus easily make the calculation as to how much closer Jupiter ought to find itself to the orbit of Mars than to that of Saturn, if its distance would have been determined through the purpose of their external relation and not through the mechanism of their formation. But the situation is quite different; since a planetary orbit with respect to the orbits that are above and below it is often[26] farther from the one in which a smaller planet moves than from the track of that with a larger mass, but the width of space around each planet always has a proper relation to its mass, it is thus clear that the [mechanical] kind of formation had to determine these relations and that, because these properties as well as their causes and their consequences seem to be tied together, one will do best if one considers the spaces enclosed between the orbits as the function of that very same material out of which the planets [165] were formed; whence it immediately follows that the sizes of those spaces ought to be proportioned to the masses of planets,[27] which relationship is, however, in the case of more distant planets, increased through the greater scattering of elementary material in those regions. Therefore of two planets, which are fairly similar to each other with respect to mass, the more distant one must have a greater space of formation, that is, a greater distance from both nearest orbits, both because its material is in itself of specifically lighter kind, and also because it was more scattered than in the case of the one which was formed closer to the sun. Therefore, although the earth together with the moon does not yet seem to be similar [equal] to Venus in bodily content,[28] it nevertheless requires around itself a larger space of formation, because it had to build itself from a more scattered material than that lower planet. About Saturn it is to be assumed on this ground that its sphere of formation is far more extended on the farther side than on the side closer to the center (as this also holds of almost all planets; and therefore the space intervening between Saturn's orbit and the track of the celestial body immediately above, which one can assume to exist above it,[29] will be much wider than the space between that same planet and Jupiter.

In the planetary world-edifice everything proceeds by gradations,

178

in proper relations to the first generating force which next to the center was more effective than in distant regions, into [166] all unlimited reaches. The decrease of the impressed thrustlike force, the deviation from the most exact harmony in the direction and position of orbits, the densities of celestial bodies, the frugality of nature with respect to the space of their formation; all [this] decreases with gradations from the center into the farthest distances; all [this] shows that the first cause was tied to the mechanical rules of motion and did not act through a free choice.[30]

But, what shows so clearly, as anything else, the natural formation of celestial globes from a basic matter originally spread out in the space of heavens, which is now empty, is that correspondence which I borrow from Mr Buffon, which, however, in his theory has not at all the profit it has in ours.[31] For, according to his remark, if one takes together the planets whose masses one can determine by calculation, namely, Saturn, Jupiter, the earth, and the moon,[32] they constitute a mass whose density is to the density of the sun as 640 to 650, against which, since they are the chief pieces in the planetary system, the remaining planets, Mars, Venus, and Mercury, can hardly deserve to be counted;[33] then one will readily wonder at the remarkable similarity which dominates between the material of the total planetary edifice, if one considers it as taken as one lump, and [167] the mass of the sun. It would be an irresponsible levity to ascribe this analogy to an incident, [namely,] that materials, so infinitely different in their multiplicity that even on our earth some of them 15 thousand times exceed one another in density,[34] should nevertheless come in the whole so close to the relation of 1 to 1; and one must admit that when one considers the sun as a medley of all sorts of matter, which are separate from one another in the planetary edifice, then all together seem to have been formed in a space which originally was filled with a uniformly spread-out matter, and gathered on the central body without any distinction, but were assorted by the direction of the High[est Being] for the formation of planets. I leave it to those who cannot admit the mechanical formation of celestial bodies to explain, if they can, this so special correspondence from the motives of the choice of God. I will finally stop basing on more proofs a matter of so convincing an evidence as is the development of the world-edifice from the forces of nature. When one is able to remain unmoved in the presence of so many demonstrations, one must either be deeply in the fetters of prejudice or be quite capable of launching oneself above the jumble of sundry opinions to the consideration of the purest truth.[35] It is to be believed that nobody, except the demented, [168] on whose consent one must not count, can disregard the truth of this theory,[36] if the correspondences, which the world-edifice provides in all its connections for the benefit of intelligent creatures, did [does] not seem to have for its basis something more than the mere universal natural laws. One also rightly believes that the skilful dispositions, which aim at a worthy goal, must have a wise intellect for [their] origin and one will be wholly satisfied, when one considers that the natures of things recognize no other source than this primordial source, [and that] their essential and general conditions must have a natural inclination for steady and mutually harmonious consequences. One should not be reluctant, if one considers the dispositions of the world-constitution aiming at the mutual benefit of creatures, to assign them to a natural consequence from the universal laws of nature; for what proceeds from these is not the effect of a blind chance or of a mindless necessity; it is based ultimately on the highest Wisdom from which the universal dispositions borrow their harmony. Only one conclusion is entirely correct: if order and beauty transpire in the constitution of the world, then there is a God. But the other is no less established: if this order could derive from the universal laws of nature, then the entire nature is an effect of the highest Wisdom.[37]

[169] If, however, one is resolved to see the immediate application of divine wisdom in all dispositions which bespeak of mutual harmony and useful ends, insofar as one assigns no harmonious results to the development from the general laws of motion, then I would counsel that in the contemplation of the world-edifice one should not direct one's eye at a single one among the celestial bodies, but rather on the entirety [of them]; so that one could once and for all extricate oneself from that illusion. If the steep inclination of the earth's axis against the plane of its yearly course should be, through the pleasant change of seasons, a proof of the immediate hand of God, then one is allowed to postulate only that arrangement in other celestial bodies; but one realizes that it varies in each of them and that in that variety there are some celestial bodies which do not have it all; thus, for instance, Jupiter whose axis is perpendicular to the plane of its orbit, and Mars whose axis is almost perpendicular,[38] which two enjoy no differences of seasons and are still just as well the works of the supreme Wisdom as are the others. The accompaniment of moons in the case of Saturn, Jupiter, and the earth may seem to be special dispositions of the highest Being, if the free deviation from this goal through the entire system of the world-edifice had not shown that nature, without suffering an extraordinary constraint in her free behavior, had produced these specifications. Jupiter has four moons, Saturn five, [170] the earth one, the remaining planets none; as if it seemed irrelevant whether these, because of their longest nights, were not more in need

[of moons] than the others. If one admires the proportional equality of the centrifugal forces impressed into the planets with the central trends of their distance as the cause by which they orbit around the sun almost in circles and become fitted, through the constancy of the thereby distributed heat, as habitats of intelligent creatures, and [if one nevertheless] sees [in] these [effects] the immediate finger of the Almighty, then one will immediately be led back to the universal laws of nature, if one considers that this planetary disposition gradually dissolves with all degrees of diminution in the depth of heavens, and that even the highest Wisdom, which has its pleasure in the orderly motion of planets, has not excluded the defect by which the system ends, inasmuch as it ends in complete irregularity and disorder.[39] Nature, regardless [of the fact that] she has an essential inclination for perfection and order, includes in the extent of her manifoldness all possible varieties, including even defects and deviations.[40] This very same unlimited fruitfulness of hers has brought forth the inhabited celestial globes as well as the comets, the useful mountains and the harmful crags, the habitable lands and empty deserts, the virtue and the vice.[41]

UNIVERSAL

NATURAL HISTORY

AND

THEORY OF THE HEAVENS.

THIRD PART,[1]

which
contains an essay on a comparison, based on the
analogies of nature, between the inhabitants of the various
planets.

He who knows the relation of all worlds from one part to the other,
He who knows the quantity of all suns and each planetary orb,
He who recognizes the various inhabitants from each and every star,
To him alone is possible to grasp and to explain to us,
Why things are as they are.

Pope[2]

Universal

Natural History

and

Theory of the Heavens.

THIRD PART.

APPENDIX,
of the inhabitants of the stars [planets].

Since I hold that the character of philosophy is dishonored when one uses it to assert with levity [and] with some appearance [of plausibility] free flights of fancy, if [unless] one also declares that all this is merely to [174] entertain; therefore, I will in the present essay adduce no other proposition than such which can truly contribute to the enlargement of our knowledge and the probability of which is so well grounded that one can hardly refuse to let them be valid.[3]

It may seem though that in this kind of project, the freedom has no proper limits to poetize and that one, in judging the characteristics of the inhabitants of distant worlds, can with greater abandon give free rein to phantasy than would a painter in depicting the plants or animals of undiscovered lands, and that such thoughts can neither be well proven or refuted: still one must admit that the distances of celestial bodies [planets] from the sun embody certain relationships, which in turn entail a decisive influence on the various characteristics of thinking natures [beings] that are found there; whose manner of operating and feeling is bound to the condition of the material with which they are connected and [also] depends on the measure [intensity] of impressions which the [external] world evokes in them according to the properties of the relation of their habitat to [the sun,] the center of attraction and heat.

I am of the opinion that it is not even necessary to assert that all planets must be inhabited, although it would be sheer madness [175] to deny this in respect to all, or even to most of them.[4] In the richness of nature, where worlds and [world-]systems are but specks of sun-dust in respect to the whole of creation, there may very well exist barren and uninhabited regions that are not useful in the slightest for the purpose of nature, namely, for [making possible her] contemplation by intelligent beings. It would have to be admitted, even if one wanted to consider things on the basis of God's wisdom, that sandy and uninhabited deserts cover large tracts of the earth's surface and that there are in the ocean abandoned islands on which no man can be found. At any rate, a planet is much smaller in respect to the whole of creation than a desert or island in respect to the earth's surface.

It may well be that not all celestial bodies are yet fully developed; hundreds or perhaps thousands of years are needed before a great celestial body obtains a firm state of its material.[5] Jupiter seems still to be in that phase. The notable changes in its form at different times have long ago made astronomers suspect that it must undergo great convulsions and that it is not at all so quiet on its surface, as [this] should be [with] a habitable planet. If it has no inhabitant, or if it never should have one, would this not be still an infinitely smaller waste [176] of nature in respect to the immensity of the whole creation? And would it not be a sign of nature's poverty much rather than an evidence of her abundance, if she had to display with diligence all her richness at every point of space?

But it is more satisfactory to imagine that although Jupiter is not inhabited, it will be at a time when the period of its development is completed. Perhaps our earth had been around a thousand or even more years[6] before it found itself in the condition to support men, animals, and plants. It does not disrupt the purposefulness of a planet's existence that it should reach such [stage of] perfection only a few thousand years later. Precisely, because of this a planet will in the future stay longer in its state of perfection once it has reached it; for there is a certain law in nature: everything that has a beginning steadily approaches its decline and is all the closer to it, the farther it gets from its starting point.[7]

One cannot indeed help agreeing with the satirical portrayal by that witty author from The Hague[8] who, after listing the general news from the r.[egister][9] of sciences, knew how to present the humorous side of the idea about all celestial bodies being [177] necessarily inhabited: "Those creatures," says he, "which live in the forests on the head of a beggar, had long since considered their location as an immense ball, and themselves as the masterpiece of creation, when one of them, endowed by Heaven with a more refined spirit, a small Fontenelle[10] of his species, unexpectedly became familiar with the head of a nobleman. Immediately he called together all the witty heads of his quarters and told them with excitement: 'We are not the only living beings in nature; see, there, that new land, more lice live there'." When the unfolding of this conclusion provokes a laughter, it does not happen because it departs, to wit, very far from man's ways, but because the same error, which with man has a similar cause for its basis, seems to deserve more excuse with these [ways of his].

Let us judge without prejudice. This insect, which both in respect to its way of life and insignificance well expresses the condition of most men, can with good reason be used for such a comparison. Because, according to its belief, nature is infinitely well adapted to its existence, the insect holds as irrelevant the entire remainder of nature which does not imply a direct reference to its species as the center of her aims. Man, standing [178] immensely removed from the uppermost rank of beings, is indeed bold to flatter himself in a similar delusion about the necessity of his own existence. [But] the infinity of nature includes within herself with the same necessity all beings which display her overwhelming richness. From the highest class of thinking beings to the most abject insect, no member [of that chain] is indifferent to nature; and nothing can be missing [from it] without breaking up the beauty of the whole, which consists in interconnectedness. There everything is determined by universal laws which nature makes operative through the connection of their originally implanted forces. Because in her procedure nature displays only aptitude and order, no particular purpose should disturb and interrupt her course. In its first stage the formation of a planet was but an infinitely small effect of nature's fruitfulness; and it would now be senseless that her well-established laws should be subservient to the particular aims of that atom [which man is]. If the condition of a celestial body sets obstacles to its being inhabited, then it will be uninhabited, although in and for itself it would be more beautiful that it should have inhabitants of its own. The splendor of creation loses nothing thereby: for the infinite is among all magnitudes the one which by the subtraction of a finite part is not diminished. One would [however] imply this by complaining that the space between [179] Jupiter and Mars in unnecessarily empty,[11] and that there are comets which are not populated.[12] In fact, that insect may appear to us as insignificant as possible, still nature is more interested in maintaining its whole species than in supporting a small number of prominent creatures of which an infinite number would remain, even though an entire region or locality would be berobbed of them. Because nature is inexhaustible in producing both [the highest and the lowest], one sees both left mercilessly, in their preservation and decay, to [the course of] universal laws. Did the owner of those populated forests on the beggar's head ever make greater devastations among the species of that colony [of lice], than did the son of Philip[13] in the species of his fellow citizens when his evil genius put it in his head that the world has been produced only for his sake?

At any rate, most planets are certainly inhabited, and those that are not, will be one day.[14] What relationship will then be produced among the different kinds of those inhabitants through the relation of their place[s] in the world-edifice to the center, out of which diffuses the heat which keeps all alive? For it is certain that this heat produces specific relationships in the materials of those celestial bodies in proportion to their distances [from the sun]. Man, who [180] among all rational beings is the best known to us, although at the same time his inner nature remains for us an unexplored problem,[15] should in this respect serve as the foundation and general reference point. Here we do not wish to consider him in his moral traits, and not even in the physical construction of his built: we merely wish to investigate as to what limitations his ability to think and the mobility of his body, which obeys that [the former], would suffer through [the changes of] the properties of matter with which he is linked and which are proportioned to the distance from the sun. Whatever the infinite distance between the ability to think and the motion of matter, between the rational mind and the body, it is still certain that man—who obtains all his notions and representations through the impressions which the universe through the mediation of bodies evokes in his soul, both in respect of their meaning and of the readiness to connect and compare them, which man calls the ability to think—is wholly dependent on the properties of that matter to which the Creator joined him.[16]

Man is so created as to receive the impression and stirrings which the [external] world must evoke in him through that body which is the visible part of his being, and the material of which serves not only to impress on the invisible soul that dwells [181] in it the first notions of external objects, but also to recall and connect them interiorly, in short, [that body] is indispensable for thinking.* In the measure in

---

* It is clear from the principles of psychology[17] that in virtue of the actual arrangement along which the creation made soul and body dependent on one another, the former not only must obtain all concepts about the universe through union with the latter and under its influence, but that also the exercise of the faculty of thinking depends on the latter's disposition and borrows from its support the needed ability.

which his body develops, the faculties of his thinking nature also obtain the corresponding degree of perfection, and they reach a definite and mature status only when the fibres of his [body-]instrument achieve the strength and endurance which is the completion of their development. Those faculties develop in him early enough through which he can satisfy the needs to which he is subject through his dependence on external things. In some men the development stops at that level. The ability to combine abstract notions and to master the bent of passions through a free application of considerations takes place later; in some never in their whole lives; in all, however, it is rather weak: it serves the lower forces [instincts] which it rather should dominate and in whose mastering consists [182] the excellence of his nature. When we consider the lives of most men, this creature seems to have been created to absorb fluids, as does a plant, and to grow, to propagate his species, and finally to age and die. He of all creatures least achieves the goal of his existence, because he uses his outstanding faculties [mostly] for such purposes which other creatures accomplish more securely and conveniently with far inferior [faculties]. He would even become the most despicable at least in the eyes of true wisdom, if the hope of a future life did not elevate him and if a period of complete development were not in store for the faculties enclosed in him.

If one looks for the cause of impediments, which keep human nature in such a deep abasement, it will be found in the crudeness of matter into which his spiritual part is sunk, in the unbending of the fibers, and in the sluggishness and immobility of fluids which should obey its stirrings.[18] The nerves and fluids of his brain deliver to him only gross and unclear concepts, and because he cannot counterbalance in the interior of his thinking ability the impact of sensory impressions with sufficiently powerful ideas, he will be carried away by his passions, confused and overwhelmed by the turmoil of the elements that maintain his [bodily] machine. The efforts of reason to rise in opposition [183] and to dissipate this confusion with the light of the ability to judge will be like the flashes of sunlight when thick clouds continually obstruct and darken its cheerful brightness.

The grossness of the stuff and of the texture in the build of human nature is the cause of that sluggishness which keeps the faculties of the soul in perennial dullness and feebleness. The handling of reflections and of representations enlightened by reason is a tiresome condition into which the soul cannot place itself without opposition, and out of which the soul would, through the natural inclination of the bodily machine, soon fall back into the passive condition, where the sensory impressions determine and rule all its activities.

The sluggishness of his ability to think, which is a consequence of its dependence on gross and rigid matter, is the source not only of depravity but also of error. Through the difficulty which is connected with the effort to dissipate the cloud of confused notions and to distinguish and separate the universal knowledge obtained through the comparison of ideas from the sensory impressions, one's thinking readily yields to overhasty approval and acquiescence in the possession of a view which, because of the sluggishness of its nature and because of the resistance of matter can hardly permit to be looked upon from another side.[19]

Because of this dependence, the spiritual faculties disappear together with the vigor of the body: when owing to the slackened flow of fluids advanced age [184] cooks only thick fluid in the body, when the suppleness of the fibers and the nimbleness in all motions decrease, then the forces of the spirit too stiffen into a similar dullness. The agility of thought, the clarity of representation, the vivacity of wit, and the ability to remember lose their strength and grow frigid. Concepts ingrained through long experience offset somewhat the departure of these forces, and reason would even more evidently betray its incapacity, should not the strength of passions that need its rein also diminish simultaneously and even sooner.

It becomes evidently clear from all this that the forces of the human soul become hemmed in and impeded by the obstacles of a crude matter to which they are most intimately bound; but is even more noteworthy that this specific condition of the stuff has a fundamental relation to the degree of influence by which the sun in the measure of its distance enlivens them and renders them adapted to the maintenance of animal economy [regimen]. This necessary relation to the fire, which spreads out from the center of the world-system to keep matter in the necessary [degree of] excitation, is the basis of an analogy which will be firmly stated[20] in respect to the different inhabitants of planets; and in virtue of that relationship each and any class of theirs is tied through the necessity [necessary structure] of their nature [185] to the place which has been assigned to it [that nature] in the universe.

The inhabitants of the earth and Venus cannot exchange their habitats without mutual destruction. The former, whose [bodily] building stuff is proportioned to the measure of heat of his distance [from the sun] and is therefore too light and volatile for a greater heat, would in a hotter sphere suffer enormous upheavals and a collapse of his nature, which would arise from the dissipation and evaporation of his fluids and from the violent tension of his elastic fibers; the latter, whose grosser build and the sluggishness of the elements of his structure needed a greater influence of the sun, would in a cooler celestial region grow numb and perish in lifelessness. By the same token, much lighter and more volatile ought to be the matter of which the body of Jupiter's inhabitant is composed, so that the weak excitation which the sun can produce at that distance may move those [bodily] machines as powerfully as it performs this [function] in the lower regions [closer to the sun], and thus all would be summed up in a general notion: *The stuff, out of which the inhabitants of different planets as well as the animals and plants on them, are built, should in general be all the lighter and of finer kind, and the elasticity of the fibers together with the principal disposition of their build should be all the more perfect, the farther they stand from the sun.*

[186] This relationship is so natural and well grounded that not only the motivations of final purpose, which in natural science are generally looked upon as only weak reasons, lead to it, but also the proportion of the specific conditions of materials composing the planets (which are established from Newton's calculations[21] as well as from the foundations of cosmogony) confirm the same [relationship] according to which the stuff of which the celestial bodies are built is always of a lighter kind in those that are more distant than in those which are closer [to the sun], which [circumstance] should entail a similar relationship in the creatures that produce and sustain themselves on them.

We have established a comparison between the condition[s] of the material with which rational creatures on the planets are essentially united: and it may also easily be seen after the introduction of this consideration that these relations would entail a consequence also in respect of their spiritual faculties. If, accordingly, these spiritual faculties have a necessary dependence on the stuff of the [bodily] machines which they inhabit, then we can conclude with more than probable confidence:[22] *That the excellence of thinking natures, the promptness in their reflections, the clarity and vivacity of the notions that come to them through external impression, together with the[ir] ability to put them together, finally also* [187] *the skill in their actual use, in short, the whole range of their perfection, stand[s] under a certain rule, according to which these [natures] become more excellent and perfect in proportion to the distance of their habitats from the sun.*

Since this relationship has a measure of credibility, which is not far from demonstrated certainty, we find an open field for pleasant speculations that stem from the comparison of the characteristics of these various [planetary] inhabitants. Human nature, which on the ladder of beings occupies exactly the middle rung,[23] sees itself in the middle between the two extreme limits of perfection, from which both ends it is equally distant. When the consideration of the most elevated classes of rational creatures, which inhabit Jupiter or Saturn, hurts its pride and humiliates it through the knowledge of its lowliness, then a look at the lower rungs would bring it satisfaction and peace, [because] those on the planets Venus and Mercury are lowered far beneath the perfection of human nature. What an outlook worthy of wonderment! From one side we saw thinking creatures among whom a man from Greenland or a Hottentot would be a Newton, and on the other side some others who would admire him as [if he were] an ape: [188]

When recently the superior sages saw
What not long ago truly wonderfully
A mortal among us has done,
And how he unfolds nature's law, they wondered
That it was possible for such a thing
To happen through an earthly creature,
And looked upon our Newton as we look upon an ape.

Pope[24]

What advances of knowledge should not be achieved by the insight of those happy beings of the uppermost spheres of the heavens! What beautiful consequences would not this brightness of insights have on their ethical disposition! The insights of intellect, when they possess the proper degree of perfection and clarity, have much more vivid stirrings than do sensory allurements, and are able to overcome these and rule them victoriously. With what majesty would not God, who depicts himself in all creatures, depict himself in these thinking natures, which as an ocean undisturbed by the storms of passions would quietly receive and reflect his image! We do not wish to stretch such speculations beyond the limits prescribed to a physical treatise;[25] we merely wish to recall once more the analogy set forth above: *That the perfection of the spiritual world, just as well as the material [world] in [the realm of] the planets from Mercury to Saturn, or perhaps even beyond [189] (insofar as there are still other planets), increases and progresses in a straight-forward gradation according to the measure of their distance from the sun.*

Since this rule follows to an extent naturally[26] from the consequences of the physical relation of their habitats to the center of the world, to that extent it will conveniently be admitted; on the other hand, a real look at those magnificent establishments [habitats] which are skilfully adapted to the perfection of these [intelligent] natures in the higher [celestial] regions, confirms this rule so clearly that it can almost make a claim to being fully convincing. The agility of activities that are connected with the characteristics of an exalted nature matches much better the rapidly changing time periods of those spheres than does the slowness of slothful and less perfect creatures.

The telescopes teach us that the alternation of day and night on Jupiter takes place in 10 hours. What would the inhabitant of the earth do with that partition if placed on that planet? The 10 hours would hardly suffice for that [amount of] rest which that crude machine [of man's body] needs for recuperation through sleep. What a part of the following [remaining] time [of daylight] would not be demanded by the preparation for the business of awakening, dressing, and by the time given to eating, and how would a creature, whose activities take place with such slowness, not be confused and incapacitated [190] for anything productive, [and] whose 5 hours of work would be interrupted by the intervening of an equally long darkness? However, if Jupiter is inhabited by more perfect creatures, which combine more elastic forces and a greater agility in execution with a more refined build, then one may believe that those 5 hours are as much or even more for them than what the 12 hours of day provide for the lower class of humans. We know that the need for time is something relative, [a circumstance] which can be recognized and understood in no other way than from the magnitude of that which is to be done, compared with the speed of execution. Therefore the same time, which for one kind of creatures is but a moment, may very well be for another a long period in which a long sequence of changes unfolds through a fast chain of efficiency. Saturn has, according to the probable calculation of its rotation which we have presented above,[27] an even far shorter division of day and night, and [this] permits to assume even more excellent abilities in the nature of its inhabitants.

Finally, all ties together for a confirmation of the foregoing law. Obviously, nature has prodigiously spread out her provisions to the farthest regions of the world. The moons, which compensate for the industrious beings of those happy regions the absence of daylight through an adequate substitute, are in the greatest quantity [191] allocated there, and nature seems to have been careful to give all the aid to their effectiveness, so that at no time would they be deprived of [the opportunity of] applying it. In respect to moons Jupiter possesses an obvious advantage over all other lower planets, and Saturn over Jupiter, whose outfitting with a beautiful and useful ring that surrounds it makes [provides] even more probably still greater advantages for its condition;[28] on the contrary, the lower planets, in whose case such a provision would be uselessly wasted and whose class rather closely borders on [the realm of] unreason, do not share in such advantages or only to a very small extent.

But one cannot [should not] view (here I anticipate an objection that could foil all the foregoing harmony) the greater distance from the sun, this source of light and life, as a drawback against which the special features of abodes in the case of the more distant planets would merely serve in return to help them out to some extent, and [then conclude] that in fact the superior planets had in the world-edifice a less distinguished location and a position which was disadvantageous to the perfection of those abodes because they received a weaker influence from the sun. For we know that the working of light and heat is determined not through their absolute intensity but through the ability of matter which absorbs them and more or less resists their impact, [192] and that therefore the very same distance, which for a cruder matter can be called a proper climate, would destroy the more subtle fluids and would be for them of disastrous intensity; consequently, it takes a more refined stuff composed of more mobile elements to turn the distance of Jupiter or of Saturn from the sun into a felicitous location.

Finally, the excellence of natures in these higher celestial regions seems to be tied through a physical connection to a durability which is most proper to it. Decay and death cannot affect those excellent creatures to the extent to which they affect us lower beings. For the very sluggishness of matter and crudeness of the stuff, which in the lower stages [regions] are the specific principle of their debasement, are also the cause of that propensity which they have for [their] perishing. When the fluids, which nourish and make grow the animal, or man, incorporate themselves amidst its small fibers and add to its mass, can no longer enlarge those vessels and canals in spatial extension once the growth has been completed, these additional fluids of nourishment must therefore, owing to the mechanical drive which is expended for the nourishment of the animal, constrict and block the cavities of its vessels, and destroy the build of the whole machine through a gradually increasing numbness. It is believable that although decay affects even the most perfect natures, [193] nevertheless the advantage in the refinement of the stuff, in the elasticity of vessels, and in the lightness and efficiency of fluids of which those perfect beings that inhabit the more distant planets are composed, held up far longer this frailty, which is a consequence of the sluggishness of the cruder matter and secure for those creatures an endurance the length of which is proportional to their perfection, just as the frailty of the lives of men has a direct relation to their unworthiness.

I cannot leave these considerations without facing up to a doubt which may naturally arise from the comparison of these ideas with our previous statements. In respect to the abodes in the world-edifice, we have recognized in the greater number of satellites, which illuminate the planets of the most distant orbits, in the speed of their axial rotations, and in the composition of their stuff proportioned against the working of the sun, the wisdom of God that disposed so fittingly everything for the benefit of intelligent beings who inhabit them. But how would now one reconcile with the doctrine of purposiveness a mechanistic doctrine, so that what the highest Wisdom itself planned is entrusted to raw matter, and the rule of providence to a nature left to herself for its execution? Is the former [or the doctrine of purposiveness] not rather an understanding that the orderly disposition of the world-edifice could not have developed through the latter [or the mechanistic doctrine]?

[194] One will quickly quickly dissipate this doubt if one only recalls what was previously set forth in a similar connection. Should not the mechanism of all natural motions have a fundamental propensity for only such consequences that fittingly correspond to the project of the Highest Reason in the whole realm of interconnections? How could they [those motions] have erroneous trends and an uncontrolled dissipation in their origin when all their properties, from which these consequences follow, have been determined by the eternal idea of the Divine Intellect in which all [things] must necessarily be related to one another and fit together? If one reasons properly, how can one justify the kind of judging that one considers nature as a rebellious subject who only through some harness, which sets limits to her free behavior, can be kept in the tracks of order and common harmony, so long as one does not [also] think that nature is her own sufficient principle whose properties know no cause, and whom God strives, as well as this can be done, to force into the plans of his intentions? The better one learns to know nature, the better will one realize that the general properties of things are not alien to and separate from one another. One will be sufficiently convinced that they have essential affinities through which they are by themselves in harmony and support one another in achieving more perfect [195] dispositions, [namely,] the mutual influence of elements for the beauty of the material and even for the advantage of the spiritual world, and that in general the single natures of things already in the realm of eternal truths form, so to speak, within themselves a system in which one is related to the other; one will also forthwith recognize that the affinity

is proper to them through the community of origin out of which they have together their essential properties created.

And now to apply this repeated consideration to the present purpose. These general laws of motion, which in the world-system have assigned to the superior planets a distant place from the center of attraction and inertia, have placed them thereby also in the advantageous condition to display their formations at the farthest from the center of raw matter and therefore with greater freedom. They [those laws] have put them also in a regular relation to the influence of heat which, according to a similar law, also spreads out from that center. And it is precisely these regularities that make the development of celestial bodies in these faraway regions more unimpeded and the generation of motions depending on them much faster, and, to say it briefly, the system better established, so that finally the spiritual entities will have a necessary dependence on matter to which they are personally tied; therefore it is no wonder that [196] the perfection of nature is effected from both sides in a single connection of causes and from the same foundations. This harmony, on closer reflection, is not something sudden and unexpected, and because the latter [spiritual] entities are, through a similar principle, embedded in the general disposition of material nature, the spiritual realm will be more perfect in the faraway spheres for the same reason by which the bodily [world] is [more perfect there].

Thus in the entire span of nature all is tied together into an uninterrupted gradation through the eternal harmony which makes all members related to one another. The perfections of God have clearly revealed themselves on our levels and are not less majestic in the lower classes than in the higher:

> What a chain, which from God its beginning
> takes, which from [among] natures
> [Stretches] from heavenly and earthly, from
> angels, men, to beasts,
> From seraphim to worm. Oh distances
> which the eye never
> Can reach and view!
> From the infinite to you, from you to nothing!
>   Pope.[29]

We have set forth the foregoing considerations faithfully to the directive of physical relationships, which has kept them on the path of rational credibility. Should we permit ourselves one more escapade from these [197] tracks into the field of phantasy? Who shows us the limits where the well-founded probability ends and arbitrary fictions begin? Who is so bold as to dare an answer to the question whether sin would exercise its dominion also on the other globes of the world-edifice, or virtue alone has her regime set up there?

The stars are perhaps abodes of glorious souls,
As vice rules here, there virtue is the lord.

von Haller.[30]

Does not a certain middle position[31] between wisdom and unreason belong to the unfortunate faculty of being able to sin? Who knows, are not also the inhabitants of those distant celestial bodies too noble and wise to degrade themselves to [the level of] that stupidity which is inherent in sin, those, however, who inhabit the lower planets are grafted too fast to matter and endowed with all too weak faculties to be obligated to carry the responsibility of their actions before the judgment seat of justice? In such a way, only the earth and perhaps Mars (so that we would not be deprived of the miserable comfort of having companions in misery) would alone be in the dangerous middle road, where temptations of sensible stirrings against the domination of the spirit would possess a strong potential for seduction, [and] yet, this [spirit] cannot deny that it has the ability by which it [198] is in a position to put up resistance to them, provided its sluggishness would not rather take pleasure in being carried away by them; [in that position] where the dangerous middle point is between weakness and ability, there precisely those advantages, which put him above the lower classes, place him at a height from which he may sink again infinitely deeper below them. In fact, both planets, the earth and Mars, are the middle members of the planetary system, and perhaps not without probability an intermediate physical as well as moral constitution between the two extremes may be assumed about their inhabitants; however, I will readily leave these considerations to those who feel they can muster more repose in the face of undemonstrable considerations and more readiness in providing answer.[32]

CONCLUSION

It is not really known to us what really man is today, however self-awareness and reason should instruct us on this point; how much more may we err as to what he is to become eventually![33] Still the human soul's thirst for knowledge reaches out eagerly after these topics so distant from here and strives to find some light in such a dark [field of] knowledge.

Shall the immortal soul during the whole infinity of her future duration, which the [199] grave itself does not interrupt but merely transforms, remain tied forever to this point of space, to our earth? Shall she never share in a closer contemplation of the other wonders of creation? Who knows, is it not her destiny that she should once know at a closer range those faraway globes of the world-edifice and also the excellence of their establishments which excite so much her curiosity from a distance? Perhaps there are further globes of the planetary system in the process of evolving, so that after the completed course of time, which is prescribed to our sojourn here, there may be new habitats ready for us in other heavens. Who knows, whether the moons do not orbit around Jupiter to shine finally on us?[34]

It is permitted, it is pleasing to entertain oneself with such speculations; but nobody shall base the hope of future life on such uncertain pictures of the force of imagination. After frailty had exacted its due from human nature, the immortal soul will with a rapid swing raise herself above all that is finite and place her existence with respect to the entire nature in a new relationship which derives from a closer connection with the Highest Being. From there on, this more elevated human nature, which has the source of happiness in itself, will not let herself dissipate amidst external objects and search for repose in them. The whole aggregate of creatures, which has a necessary harmony for the pleasure of the Highest Primordial [200] Being, needs it also for its own [pleasure] which it will not reach except in the everlasting contentment.

In fact, when man has filled his soul with such considerations and with the foregoing ones, then the spectacle of a starry heaven in a clear night gives a kind of pleasure which only noble souls can absorb. In the universal quiet of nature and in the tranquillity of mind there speaks the hidden capacity for knowledge of the immortal soul in unspecifiable language and offers undeveloped concepts that can be grasped but not described. If there are among the thinking creatures of this planet lowly beings who, unmindful of the stirrings through which such a great vision can captivate them, are in the position of fastening themselves to the servitude of vanity, then how unfortunate is this globe to have been able to generate such miserable creatures! On the other hand, how fortunate is that same globe, since a road is open for them under most desirable conditions to reach a happiness and nobility which are infinitely far above those advantages which nature's most exceptional dispositions can achieve on all celestial bodies.

END

APPENDIX

The Only Possible Argument
for a Demonstration of the Existence of God

Seventh Consideration
Cosmogony
[149]

A hypothesis of the mechanical kind of explanation of the origin of celestial bodies and of the causes of their motions according to rules previously demonstrated.[1]

The shape of celestial bodies, the mechanism according to which they move and form a world system, similarly the various changes to which the position of their orbits is subject in the course of time, all this has become a part of the natural sciences which is formulated with so great a clarity and certainty that it is impossible to indicate a single other insight which would explain a topic of nature (which would come fairly close to this in its [150] complexity) in such an unquestionably correct manner and with such an obviousness. When one considers this, should not one also take the view that the condition of nature in which this [world-]edifice took its origin and in which the motions that now endure with so uniform and comprehensible laws were originally impressed into it, would also be easier to comprehend and become more tractable than perhaps most of the things for the cause of which we look in nature. [?] The reasons which favor this opinion are clear. All these celestial bodies are round masses and, as far as one knows, without [a complicated] organization and secret artificiality. The force, by which they are attracted is, according to all considerations, a basic force proper to matter, need not and cannot be explained. The thrustlike motions with which they perform their flight, and the direction along which that thrust was imparted to them, is together with the formation of their masses the chief point, nay the only one, about which one has to seek the first natural causes.

Uniform and by far not so complicated processes as are most others in nature, in which in general [151] the laws are not known with that mathematical exactitude according to which they take place, here on the contrary lie before one's eye in a most understandable plan. Nothing is so much in the way of the appearance [prospect] of [such] a fortunate outcome as the impression of the startling magnitude of such a piece of nature as the solar system, where the natural causes are all suspect because their adequacy appears well-nigh nothing and contrary to the creative rights of the Highest Cause. But cannot this be said also of the mechanism through which a great world-edifice, once it is already there, obtains its movements? Its entire maintenance is based on the same law by which a stone, thrown in the air, described its path; a uniform law, rich in regular consequences and worthy of being entrusted with the maintenance of an entire world-edifice.

From the other side one will say that one is not able to make clear the natural causes by which the most abject herb is produced according to fully comprehensible mechanical laws [152] and [yet] one presumes to explain the origin of a world-system in its main features. But was ever a philosopher in the position to make the laws, according to which the growth or the inner motion of an already existing plant takes place, as clear and mathematically certain as are those to which all motions of the celestial bodies do conform? The nature of objects is here quite different. The large, the astonishing is here infinitely more comprehensible than the small and admirable, and the formation of a planet together with the cause of the thrustlike motion by which it is launched to move in a circle, will in all likelihood be understood easier and clearer than the production of a single snowflake in which the precise correctness of a six-cornered star is in [all] appearance more exact than is the bending of the circle in which the planets move and in which the rays are more correctly related to a plane than are the orbits of these celestial bodies to the common plane of their orbital motions.

I will present the essay of an explanation of the origin of the world-edifice according to universal [153] mechanical laws, not of the entire nature's ordering, but only of the great masses and of their orbits, which form the rawest foundation of nature. I hope to say a few things which may give occasion to others for important speculations, although my essay is rough and unelaborated. Some [parts] of it has in my opinion a degree of probability which in a smaller object [topic] would leave little doubt and to which only the prejudice [on behalf] of a skill with greater requirements than the one accorded to the universal laws of nature can stand opposed. It often happens that one does not find at all those laws which one really looks for, but one rather stumbles along that road on other advantages which one does not suspect [beforehand]. Even such a profit would be a sufficient benefit, if it were to be gained upon reflecting on others, even though the main objectives of the hypothesis should thereby disappear. I will here presuppose the universal gravitation of matter according to Newton and his followers. Those who believe that they can annihilate through a definition of the metaphysics of their taste the conclusion of insightful men [154] from observations and from mathematical reasoning, may pass over the following theses as something which has only a remote parentage with the chief objective of this writing.

1. A broader view into the essence of the universe

The six planets with their attendants move in orbits which do not deviate from a common plane, namely, from the extended equatorial plane of the sun. The comets move, however, in orbits which differ very much from it and roam on all sides far out from this plane of reference. If now instead of so few planets or comets a few thousands of them would belong to the solar world, the zodiac would appear as a band illuminated by uncounted stars, or as a streak which dissolves into a sheer glimmer in which a few nearby planets [would be seen] in distinct light, the distant ones would, however, present a nebulous appearance [155] through the amount and dullness of light. For, because of the orbital motion by which they all together [seem to] stand around the sun, there would be always some in each part of the zodiac, even though as many others had changed their place. On the contrary, the comets would cover the regions on both sides of that zone in all possible dispersions. If we, prepared by this imagery (in which we have but multiplied in thought the amount of the bodies of our planetary world), direct our eyes at the farther reaches of the universe, we really see such a bright zone in which stars, although they are in all likelihood at very unequal distances from us, are nevertheless piled more thickly towards one and precisely that plane, whereas the celestial regions are on both sides [of that plane] covered with stars in all kinds of dispersion. The Milky Way, which I have in mind, has almost exactly the direction of a great circle, a feature worthy of all attention, and it can be seen from this that our sun and we with it find ourselves in that [156] host of stars which mostly crowd together towards a certain common plane of reference and the analogy here provides such ground to assume that these suns, to whose number also ours belongs, form a world systems which on a general [large] scale is arranged according to similar laws as our planetary world is on a small scale; that all these suns together with their attendants may have some kind of a center of their common orbits and that they do not appear to change their places only because of their immeasurable distance and the long time of their orbitings, if indeed some shift, however slight, of their positions has been observed; that the orbits of these great celestial bodies also relate to a common plane from which they do not deviate too much and that those, which occupy in smaller groupings the remaining areas of the sky, are similar to the comets of our planetary world.

From this conception which, I think, has the greatest probability, one may assume that if there are several such higher world orders [157] as the one to which our sun belongs, and which to anyone who is positioned in it produces the appearance of the Milky Way, a few of these in the depths of cosmic spaces will be seen as faint, glimmering places and, if the reference plane of another such ordering of fixed stars is directed steeply with respect to us, will appear as elliptical figures which in a small place represent from a great distance a solar system like the one from our Milky Way. And astronomy had long time discovered such places, although the opinion, which has been made of them, is very diverse as can be seen in Mr. Maupertuis' book on the figure of stars.[2]

I wish that this consideration would be greeted with some attention; not only because the notion which arises thereby about the [realm of] creation is astonishingly more impressive than it would be [otherwise] (inasmuch as an innumerable host of suns, like ours, form a system whose members are connected through orbital motions, these systems, however, which presumably are again innumerable [158] [and] of which we can spot a few, may themselves be members of a still higher ordering), but also because the very observation, guided by such a notion, of the fixed stars or much rather slowly wandering suns, can perhaps discover close to us something which escapes attention insofar as not a specific plan is to be investigated.

2. Reasons for a mechanical origin of our planetary world in general.

The planets move around our sun together in one direction and only with a small deviation from a common plane of reference which is the ecliptic, just as [do] bodies that are carried by some material which, insofar as it fills the whole space, directs their motion rotating around an axis. The planets gravitate together toward the sun and the magnitude of the sideways thrust must have an exact correctness [magnitude], if they are to be brought thereby into moving in circular orbits; and because in such a mechanical effect a [159] geometrical exactness is not to be expected, all these orbits deviate, although not too much, from circular rounding. They consist of materials which, according to Newton's calculations, have the smaller densities, the farther they are from the sun, just as anyone would find this natural, if they had been formed in the space, in which they float, from a world-stuff which is scattered there. For in the tendency with which everything sinks toward the sun, matter of denser kind must tend more toward the sun and pile itself up more in its vicinity than matter of lighter kind whose fall is more retarded because of its lesser density. The material of the sun is, however, according to de Buffon's remark, fairly equal to the density of that matter which the combined mass of all planets would have, [a point] which agrees well with [the doctrine of] a mechanical formation, according to which the planets could have formed at various heights [distances] from various kinds of elements, while all the remaining [parts of matter] that filled that space might have precipitated down to their common center, the sun.

[160] Anyone who regardless of this want to see such an edifice to be given over immediately into the hand of God without entrusting anything to mechanical laws, is forced to adduce something why he finds here necessary what he would not lightly admit [elsewhere] in natural science. For he can name no purpose why would it be better that the planets should orbit in one rather than in different direction, close to a plane of reference, rather than in all sorts of areas [planes]. The heavenly space is now empty and they [the planets] would present to each other no obstacles in all this [celestial] motion. I would readily grant that there may be hidden purposes which cannot be achieved according to universal mechanics and which no one knows, but [by the same token] no one is allowed to presuppose them if one wants to base an opinion on them, without being able to demonstrate them. For if finally God directly imparted the projectile force to the planets and had set their orbits, then it is to be assumed that they should not show the signs of imperfection and deviation which arise in each product of nature. If it was good that they should [161] relate to a plane, then it is to be assumed that He put their orbits exactly in it; if it was good that they should approach a circular motion, then one should believe that their orbits should be exactly a circle, and it cannot

be foreseen why there should remain exemptions from a most exact correctness in that which ought to be an immediate divine masterwork.

The members of the solar systems from its more distant regions, the comets, move in a very eccentric manner. They could, if an immediate divine action were the case, just as well move in circles even if their orbits deviated greatly from the ecliptic.[3] The advantages of so great eccentricity could in this case be devined [only] with [much] greater boldness, for it is sooner conceivable that a celestial body always moves in a celestial region, whatever it may be, at the same distance which has a certain co-ordination to that [same] distance [region], rather than that it is co-ordinated in an advantageous way to the great difference of distances; and what concerns the advantages which Newton [162] adduces,[4] it is clear that they do not have the slightest probability apart from the fact that they can serve as an objection to a purpose in the case of a presupposed immediate divine arrangement.

This fault of directly subordinating the edifice of the planetary world to divine purposes comes most evidently into sight when one wants to invent motivations for the density of planets decreasing inversely with the increase of distances. The effect of the sun, to wit, decreases in that measure[5] and it was proper that the density of bodies, which are to be warmed by it, would also be arranged in such a proportion. It is, however, known that the sun has an effect only into a small depth below the surface of a celestial body and from its influence to warm them one cannot also infer the density of the whole lump. Here the inference from the purpose is too great [far-fetched]. The means, namely, the diminished density of the entire lump, implies a far-reaching disposition which for the magnitude of the purpose [in question] is superfluous and unnecessary.

[163] In all products of nature, inasmuch as they bear appropriateness, order and advantage, there are in evidence agreements with divine purposes but also signs of an origin from general laws, whose consequences spread much further than to such single cases, and therefore in each special effect they show traces of a mixture of such laws which were not aimed merely at this single product. Therefore, deviations occur from the greatest possible precision with respect to a special purpose. However, an immediate supernatural arrangement, because its implementation does not presuppose the consequence from general laws of matter, will not be vitiated through intervening side-effects of these, but will produce the plan in the utmost possible exactness. In the parts of the planetary world closer to the common center there is a greater approach to complete order and true exactness which toward the boundaries of the system or far

[164] from the plane of reference to the sides turn into irregularity and deviations, just as one can expect from a structure which is of mechanical origin. In an immediately divine arrangement there can never occur imperfectly achieved purposes, but the greatest correctness and exactness are invariably in evidence just as this is true among other things in the build of animals.

3. Short summary of the probable manner of how a planetary system may be formed mechanically.

The proofs just presented on behalf of a mechanical origin are so important that even a few of them had previously prompted all investigators of nature to look for the cause of planetary orbits in natural forces of motion, especially because the planets orbit around the sun in the same direction in which it turns around its axis, and their orbits coincide so closely with its equatorial [165] plane. Newton was the great destroyer of all these vortices to which one remained strongly attached long after his demonstration [of their intenability], as can be seen in the case of the famous Mr. de Mairan.[6] The more certain and convincing proofs of the Newtonian philosophy showed obviously that such a thing as a vortex, which carried the planets around, had to be, cannot be found in the heavens and that in no way could a stream of such fluidity be in these spaces, so that even the tails of comets could continue their undisturbed motion straight through all these circles [vortices]. One could therefore safely conclude that insofar as the celestial space is now empty or infinitely thinned out, there could be no mechanical cause which impressed on the planets their circular motion. But to let suddenly all mechanical laws go by and to let through a daring hypothesis God directly launch the planets so that thereby they may move in circles in connection with their gravity, was too big a step to [let one] still stay within the confines of natural science. It becomes immediately obvious that there still remains a case where mechanical [166] causes of this arrangement [of planets] are possible, namely, if the space of the edifice of planets, which is now empty, was previously filled to accommodate a community of forces of motion through all the regions of that area within which the sun's attraction rules.

And here I can point out that condition which is alone is possible, which occurs in the one mechanical cause of celestial motions, [and] which for the proof of a hypothesis is of so considerable circumstance [weight] that one can boast of it but rarely. Since the [celestial] spaces are now empty, these must have been full beforehand, or else there could never be present a widespread influence of forces of motions driving around in circles. And, accordingly, this spread-out material had to coalesce afterwards upon the celestial bodies, that is, if I consider this more closely, these celestial bodies themselves were formed from the basic stuff spread out in the spaces of the sun-edifice and the motion which the particles of its composition had in the state of dispersion, [167] was left with them after their coming together in separate masses. Since then these spaces are empty. They contain no matter which could serve among these bodies for the imparting of a circular thrust. But they were not always so [empty] and we shall notice motions of which now there can be found no natural causes which are, however, the remnant of the absolutely oldest rough state of nature.

From this remark I will make only one step still to provide myself with a probable notion about the manner of evolution of these great masses and with a cause of their motions, while I leave to the inquiring reader the more thorough execution of a smallish sketch. When, therefore, the stuff for the formation of the sun and of all celestial bodies, which are the subject to the command of its mighty attraction, was spread out through the whole realm of the planetary world and there was somewhere in the place, which is now taken up by the lump of the sun, a material with stronger forces of attraction, there arose a general sinking hereto and the attraction of the sun's body has grown with its mass. It is easy to [168] see that in the general fall of particles from even the most remote regions of the world-edifice, matter of denser kind piled up in the deeper regions, where everything pushed toward the common center, in the measure in which they were closer to that center, although materials of all kinds of density were present in all regions. For only the particles of the heaviest kind could have the ability to press in this chaos through the mass of lighter particles so as to get closer to the [central] point of gravitation. In the motions, which originated from differently high fall[s] in the sphere around [that point], the resistance of the mutually impeding particles could never be so completely similar that the resulting velocities should not have issued in one side into a bending. And in this circumstance there is displayed a very general rule of the interaction of materials, [namely,] that they drive, or direct, and confine one another so long until they give one another the least resistance; accordingly, the sideways motion had finally to unite into a common rotation along one and the same direction. Thus the particles, of which the sun was formed, came upon it already [169] with that sideways motion, and the sun, formed of that stuff, had to have a rotation in that very same direction.

It is, however, clear from the laws of gravitation that in this rotating world-material all parts must tend to cut across the plane, insofar as they are not already found in it, which in the direction of their common rotation goes through the center of the sun and which, according to our conclusions, coincides with the equatorial plane of that celestial body. Accordingly, all these parts will have their greatest accumulation near the sun in the space which is near its prolongated equatorial plane. Finally, it is also very natural that the particles will have to hinder or speed up one another, or in one word, toss or drive one another so long until one cannot disturb the motion of the other; ultimately all will come into the state that [where] only those particles remain floating which have exactly the measure of sideways thrust which is required in the distance at which they are from [170] the sun to provide [such] counterweight to gravitation whereby each would swing around in concentric circles. This velocity is an effect of the fall [toward the center] and the motion sideways is a consequence of the counter thrust which endures as long as all has stayed by itself in the status of least impediment. The remaining parts, which could not achieve such an appropriate exactness, must, because of the always decreasing motion, sink to the center of universal gravitation, in order to increase the mass of the sun which, accordingly, will have a density which, taken on the average, is rather similar to the rest of matter in the space found around it, yet in such a way that according to the foregoing circumstances its mass will necessarily far surpass the amount of matter which in the district around it remains floating.

In this situation, which appears to me natural since a stuff spread-out for the formation of various celestial bodies in a narrow space [171] close to the elongated plane of the sun's equator will have the greater density, the closer it is to the center and will have swung around on all sides far out, according to central laws, with a thrust which was appropriate at this distance for a free circular motion, if one now posits that planets formed from these particles, then [in such a situation] it cannot fail [to obtain] that they should not have circular thrust whereby they should move in orbits which come close to circles, though they would somewhat deviate from it because they coalesced from parts of various elevations. It is also very natural that these planets which formed in very great heights (where the space around them is much greater, which permits that the difference of velocities of particles surpass the force through which they are attracted to the center of planets) should obtain greater lumps than those near the sun. I pass over the agreement with many other remarkable features of the planetary world, because it presents itself naturally.* In the farthest parts [172] of the system and especially in great distances from the plane of reference, bodies, the comets, forming there cannot have this regularity. And thus the space of the planetary world becomes empty after all [matter] has united into separate masses. Yet in later epochs particles sink down from the outermost borders of this sphere of attraction which may forever move freely in the celestial space and [such is] perhaps the stuff which the zodiacal light consists of.

4. Remark

The purpose of this consideration is especially to give an example of the procedure to which our previous proofs entitled us, that one indeed disposes the unfounded concern as if such an explanation from universal natural laws of a large [-scale] structure of the world would open a hole for the sinister enemy of religion to penetrate into its bastions [173]. According to my opinion the hypothesis as outlined above is at least enough to invite men of broader insight for a closer inspection of the plan embodied in it which is only a rough outline. My goal, inasmuch as it concerns this writing, is achieved if one, prepared through trust in regularity and order which can be forthcoming from universal natural laws, opens a freer field for natural science and can be moved to see a kind of explanation, either this or another, as possible and quite agreeable with the knowledge of a wise God.

Furthermore, it would be very worthy of the philosophical endeavor, after the vortex, the favorite tool of so many systems, had been banished outside the sphere of nature into Milton's limbo of futility,[7] that one investigated as something similarly appropriate whether, without the imagining of special forces, nature herself offered something that would explain the circular motion [174] of planets directed invariably in one direction, since the other [motion] of the central forces is given in gravitation as a permanent disposition of nature. Not in the least does the plan submitted by us departs from the rule of unity, because this thrustlike force itself will be derived as a consequence from gravitation, as being appropriate for particular

---

* The formation of a smaller system which belongs as a part to the planetary world, such as that of Jupiter and Saturn, together with the axial rotations of these celestial bodies will be grasped through analogy from this explanation.

motions, because these must be deduced as a consequence from forces present in matter even when it is at rest.

In addition I note that in spite of the first appearance of similarity [with this system], the atomistic system of Democritus and Epicurus has on the inference to an author of the world a bearing quite different from our plan. There the motion was eternal and without an author, and the collision, the rich source of so much order, [was] an approximation and chance for which there was never a basis. Here a familiar and true law of nature leads, after a very comprehensible presupposition, with necessity to order and because here a definite ground for issuing in order [175] is given and something which keeps nature in the track of well-adjustment and beauty, one will be led to assuming a cause from which the necessity of relatedness to perfection can be understood.

And meanwhile, to make clear through another example how the working of gravitation in connection with scattered elements is set for bringing forth regularity and beauty in a necessary way, I will add an explanation about the mechanical generation of the ring of Saturn which, so it seems to me, has as much probability as one can expect from a hypothesis. Let one only admit to me that Saturn was in the first world-epoch surrounded by an atmosphere the like of which one has seen in various comets, which do not come close to the sun and appear without tail, that the particles of the vaporous ring of that planet (to which we want to assign an axial rotation) have risen, and that, in consequence, these vapours, be it because the planet [176] cooled or for other reasons, began to sink again toward it downward, then the rest follows with mechanical correctness. Since all particles from the point of surface where they rose from must have had a velocity proper to that place in order to move around the axis of the planet, they all must by means of that side-thrust be driven to describe, according to the rules of central forces, free orbits around Saturn.*
But all those particles, whose velocity does not have the right amount which provides exactly the counterweight through centrifugal force to the [gravitational] attraction of the height at which they float, must necessarily push and retard one another until only those which can orbit in free circular motion according to central forces, [and are] driven around Saturn in circles, are left, whereas the remaining gradually fall back unto its surface. Now all these [177] circular motions must cut across the elongated plane of the equator of Saturn, [a consequence] which must be familiar to anyone who knows about

* Saturn moves around its axis according to the presupposition. Each particle which rises from it must therefore have this sideways motion and go on with that same motion at whatever height it reaches.

central forces; also finally the other particles of its erstwhile atmosphere will tend around Saturn toward a circularly round plane which includes the elongated equator of this planet and whose outermost edge will be cut off here through that very cause which in comets determines the limit of their atmospheres. This limbo of freely moving world stuff must necessarily become a ring or, rather, [any] conceivable motion can issue in no other figure than that of a ring. Since all of these particles can have their velocities for circular motion only from points on the surface of Saturn where they rose from, those must possess the greatest velocity which rose from its equator. Since among all distances from its center there is only one where this velocity is fit for circular motion and in all smaller distances [that velocity] is too weak, a circle in that limbo can be drawn from the center of [178] Saturn within which all particles must fall back to the surface of that planet, [whereas] all the remaining particles between that imaginary circle and of its outermost edge (consequently the ones contained within a ring-shaped space) will henceforth remain in motion around it freely floating in circular orbits.

After such a solution one reaches conclusions through which the time of the axial rotation of Saturn is given and, to wit, with so much probability, once one grants these reasons whereby it also becomes determined. For because the particles of the inner edge [of the ring] have precisely that velocity which is had by a point of the Saturn-equator, and since in addition this velocity has, according to the laws of gravitation, the measure proper to circular motion, one can find from the ratio of the distance of one of the trabants of Saturn to the distance of the inner edge of the ring from the center of the planet, together from the given time of the orbiting of the trabant, the time of the revolution of particles in the interior edge, [179] from this, however, and from the ratio of the smallest diameter of the ring to that of the planet [one can find] the time of its axial rotation. And thus one has from the calculation that Saturn must turn around its axis in 5 hours and about 40 minutes,[8] which [result], when one consults the analogy with the remaining planets, seems to harmonize well with the time of rotation of these.

And whether the assumption about a cometary atmosphere, which Saturn may have had in the beginning, is admitted or not, the conclusion which I draw from it for the clarification of my principal thesis remains, so it seems to me, fairly certain, [namely,] that if there was around it such a vaporous circle [disk], the mechanical origination of a floating ring must be a necessary consequence from it and that therefore the issuing, even from a chaos, of a nature left to universal laws aims at regularity.

NOTES

List of works frequently quoted

ADICKES, E.   *Kant als Naturforscher* (Berlin: W. de Gruyter, 1924–25)

BOROWSKI, L. E. *et al.*   *Immanuel Kant. Sein Leben in Darstellungen von Zeitgenossen/Die Biographien von L. E. Borowski, R. B. Jachmann und A. Ch. Wasianski* (Berlin: Felix Gross, 1912)

BUFFON   *Histoire naturelle, générale et particulière, avec la description du Cabinet du Roy. Tome Premier* (Paris: de l'Imprimerie Royale, 1749)

German translation: *Allgemeine Historie der Natur nach allen ihren besondern Theilen* . . . Erster Theil (Hamburg und Leipzig: bey Georg Christian Grund und Adam Heinrich Holle, 1750)

CHÉSEAUX, J. P. L. DE   *Traité de la comète qui a paru en décembre 1743 et en janvier, février et mars 1744* (Lausanne: M. M. Bousquet, 1744)

DERHAM, W.   *Astrotheology: Or a Demonstration of the Being and Attributes of God, from a Survey of the Heavens* (London: printed for W. Innys, 1715). For further editions, see note 30 to First Part.

German translation: *Astrotheologie, oder Himmlisches Vergnügen in Gott* (Hamburg: bey Theodor Christoph Felginers Wittwe, 1728). For further editions, see note 30 to First Part.

HASTIE, W.   *Kant's Cosmogony.* For full description, see note 3 to Section I of Introduction.

HERSCHEL, W.   *The Scientific Papers of Sir William Herschel*, edited with a biographical introduction by J. L. E. Dreyer (London: The Royal Society and the Royal Astronomical Society, 1912)

HUYGENS, CHR.   *Oeuvres complètes de Christian Huygens* (The Hague: Martinus Nijhoff, 1880–1950)

JACHMANN   see Borowski

JAKI, S. L.   *The Milky Way: An Elusive Road for Science* (New York: Science History Publications, 1972)

Planets and Planetarians: A History of Theories of the Origin of Planetary Systems (Edinburgh: Scottish Academic Press; New York: John Wiley and Sons, 1978)

KANT, I.

Kant's Gesammelte Schriften (Berlin: G. Reimer, 1902–), usually referred to as the Akademie Ausgabe, quoted here as AA

LALANDE, J. J. L. DE

Astronomie (Paris: chez Desaint & Saillant, 1764)

LAMBERT, J. H.

Cosmologische Briefe über die Einrichtung des Weltbaues (Augspurg: bey Eberhard Kletts Wittib., 1761)

English translation: Cosmological Letters on the Construction of the World-Edifice, with introduction and notes by Stanley L. Jaki (New York: Science History Publications; Edinburgh: Scottish Academic Press, 1976)

LOVEJOY, A. O.

The Great Chain of Being: A Study of the History of an Idea (1936; New York: Harper & Row, 1960)

MAUPERTUIS, P. L. M. DE

Ouvrages divers de Mr. de Maupertuis (Amsterdam: aux dépens de la Compagnie, 1744). For further description, see note 37 to Section II of Introduction.

NEWTON, I.

Isaac Newton's Philosophiae naturalis principia mathematica. The Third Edition (1726) with Variant Readings, assembled and edited by Alexandre Koyré and I. Bernard Cohen with the assistance of Anne Whitman (Cambridge, Mass.: Harvard University Press, 1972). Quoted here as Principia (Var. Ed.)

Sir Isaac Newton's Mathematical Principles of Natural Philosophy and his System of the World. Andrew Motte's translation (1729) revised and supplied with an appendix by Florian Cajori (Berkeley: University of California Press, 1962). Quoted here as Principia (Cajori).

STUCKENBERG, J. H. W.

The Life of Immanuel Kant (London: Macmillan, 1882)

VOLTAIRE

Oeuvres complètes de Voltaire (Paris: Garnier Frères, 1877–82)

WASIANSKI

see Borowski

WOLF, C.

Les hypothèses cosmogoniques. Examen des théories scientifiques modernes sur l'origine des mondes. Suivi de la traduction de la Théorie du Ciel de Kant (Paris: Gauthier-Villars, 1886)

WRIGHT, T.

An Original Theory or New Hypothesis of the Universe, Founded upon the Laws of Nature, and Solving by Mathematical Principles the General Phaenomena of the Visible Creation, and Particularly the Via Lactea. Compris'd in Nine Familiar Letters from the Author to his Friend (London: printed for the Author, and sold by H. Chapelle, 1750). Reproduced in facsimile edition with an introduction by M. A. Hoskin (London: Macdonald, 1971)

INTRODUCTION

I. *A New Translation*

1. Paisley: Alexander Gardner, 1926. Macmillan, who was also the first Hastie lecturer (1906–09) at the University of Glasgow, had at his disposal Hastie's correspondence and manuscripts, which I was unable to locate in spite of extensive inquiry.
2. Ibid., p. 226.
3. *Kant's Cosmogony as in His Essay on the Retardation of the Rotation of the Earth and His Natural History and Theory of the Heavens, with Introduction, Appendices, and a Portrait of Thomas Wright of Durham*, edited and translated by W. Hastie, D. D., Professor of Divinity, University of Glasgow (Glasgow: James Maclehose and Sons, 1900), cix + 205 pp.
4. *The Life of Professor Hastie*, see pp. 253–54.
5. The title given in the translation section (p. [1]) is only a shortened version of the full form which Hastie, curiously enough, chose to give in the Introduction of his *Kant's Cosmogony* (p. xxxix).
6. Here a passage from a letter which The Rev. Prof. Gavin White (Department of Ecclesiastical History, University of Glasgow) wrote to me on March 6, 1978, may seem relevant: "Hastie claimed to speak all kinds of languages which he scarcely knew, but it seems clear that he had good knowledge of German." The same letter also contains the information that when Cornelius P. Tiele, Professor of the History and Philosophy of Religion, at the University of Leyden, gave the Gifford Lectures at the University of Edinburgh in 1897, Hastie volunteered his services to translate Tiele's Dutch manuscript into English. When the translation was found gravely defective, Hastie "sued in Court of Session for libel, arguing that a cabal of Edinburgh academics had poisoned Tiele's mind against him in order to get the fees for translation." The incident is not reported in the biography by Macmillan, who mentions (p. 223) only that Tiele was among those scholars from the Continent who strongly supported Hastie's election to the chair of divinity in 1895.
7. The review appeared in the February 28, 1901, issue, pp. 413–15.
8. In the eyes of Hastie, Kant was a "thorough scientist" and a "faithful disciple of Newton" (*ibid.* p. xvii), claims which he had already found important to make in his study of Kant's political theories, which included his translation, with an introduction, of Kant's essay on perpetual peace, under the title, *Kant's Principles of Politics* (Edinburgh: T. & T. Clark, 1891; see especially,

pp. x–xii). It shows something of Hastie's miscomprehension of Kant's discourses on science that he extolled "the purely scientific spirit of Kant's own thought" over Hegel's and Schelling's writings on nature, and deplored those students of the latter two who had "little or nothing to say of Kant's incomparably greater merit as a scientific discoverer and a true scientist" (*Kant's Cosmogony*, p. xiv).

9. "From his Class Certificates it is clear that he was an excellent student both in Mathematics and Natural Philosophy" is all that is stated by the invariably admiring Macmillan. See *The Life of Professor Hastie*, p. 20.

10. *Kant's Cosmogony*, pp. xviii–xxvii.

11. As will be discussed in detail in Section V of this Introduction.

12. The letter is quoted in full in *The Life of Professor Hastie*, p. 254, together with a congratulatory letter by Sir William Huggins, of solar spectroscopy fame, which is even less specific than Kelvin's letter concerning Kant's cosmogony.

13. *Kant's Cosmogony*, p. xxvii. Hastie, as will be seen (see note 35 to Section V of this Introduction), intimated more than the record warranted, and in several respects he was misleading. Thus he mentioned R. A. Proctor's *The Universe and the Coming Transit* (London: Longmans, Green & Co., 1874), although Proctor discussed only Kant's explanation of the Milky Way (pp. 178–79). By referring to the account in S. Newcomb's *Popular Astronomy*, which between 1877 and 1900 went through well over a dozen editions and printings, Hastie could justly say that it made Kant's theory well known. He did not relate that Newcomb's account came to a close with a pointed reference to the failure of Kant's theory to satisfy the conservation of angular momentum. As to G. F. Becker's praise of Kant's theory, eagerly seized upon by Hastie, it contradicted Becker's admission that "the attempt which Kant made to create moment of momentum from the impact of nebulous matter is curiously out of accord with the rest of his investigations." See "Kant as a Natural Philosopher," *American Journal of Science* 5 (1898):107.

14 *Lettres philosophiques* (1734), in *Oeuvres complètes de Voltaire*, 22:130.

15. The topic is discussed in detail with extensive documentation in ch. 4, "The Fashion of Strange Moulds," of my Fremantle Lectures, *The Origin of Science and the Science of Its Origin* (Edinburgh: Scottish Academic Press, 1978).

16. *Kant's Cosmogony*, pp. ix and xxviii.

17. *Kant's Cosmogony* [etc.], translated by W. Hastie, revised and edited with an Introduction and Appendix by Willy Ley (New York: Greenwood Publishing Company, 1968). It will be quoted as *Reprint 1968*. The quality of Ley's Introduction may be gathered from his statement (pp. xiii–xiv) that Johann Heinrich Lambert was "professionally an architect with mathematical training but he had always been fascinated by astronomical matters," a statement which shows how the compounding of clichés can generate sheer fantasies. Ley also repeatedly refers (p. x) to Martin Kuntzen [sic] as Kant's teacher in mathematics and physics, a fallacy which will be aired later. Ley exculpates Kant's false quantitative result concerning the retardation of the earth's rotation on the ground that "the figures then current for the size and especially for the mass of the earth . . . were wrong" (p. xii), which, if true, would had already invalidated much of Book III of Newton's *Principia* and made impossible d'Alembert's, Clairaut's, Euler's, and many others' work in celestial dynamics.

18. *Reprint 1968*, p. vii.

19. Ley is best known for his *Rockets, Missiles and Space Travel* (originally published

in 1951), which together with its revised edition (New York: Viking Press, 1957) went through a dozen reprints by 1959. He also co-published with Wernher von Braun popular works on the exploration of the moon and Mars.

20. Among them, *Space, Time and Creation: Philosophical Aspects of Scientific Cosmology* (Glencoe, Ill.: The Free Press, 1957), reissued as Collier paperback (1961), and an anthology of cosmological texts, *Theories of the Universe: From Babylonian Myth to Modern Science* (Glencoe, Ill.: The Free Press, 1957), reissued as paperback in 1965.

21. This reprint of Hastie's translation was published under the title, *Universal Natural History and Theory of the Heavens* (Ann Arbor: University of Michigan Press, 1969), although, unlike *Reprint 1968*, it also contained Hastie's translation of Kant's essay on the earth's rotation. It will be quoted as *Reprint 1969*.

22. New York: Johnson Reprint Corporation, 1970. The title was *Kant's Cosmogony*. It will be quoted as *Reprint 1970*.

23. *Reprint 1969*, p. 22.

24. Ibid. The quotation was from Weizsäcker's Gifford Lectures, *The Relevance of Science* (London: Collins, 1964), p. 143.

25. Ibid. For a summary and discussion of Weizsäcker's and Kuiper's theories, see my *Planets and Planetarians*, pp. 227–30 and 234–35.

26. It seems that Jeffreys and Jeans, whose collisional theories dominated the scene during that period, were not particularly influenced by Chamberlin and Moulton, who made around 1900 a sharp break with what at that time was generally referred to as the Kant-Laplace hypothesis. See *Planets and Planetarians*, ch. 7, "Collisions Revisited."

27. As will be discussed below.

28. Charlier's lectures saw print in *Publications of the Astronomical Society of the Pacific*, vol. XXXVII (1925); for quotation, see p. 63.

29. *Philosophy* (New York; W. W. Norton, 1927), p. 80.

30. *Reprint 1970*, p. xl.

31. *Kant's Cosmogony*, pp. cviii–cix.

32. *Immanuel Kant's Critique of Pure Reason*, translated by N. K. Smith (London: Macmillan, 1929), p. 560.

33. Hastie seemed to be unaware of the fact that the effect had already been given in the 1880s its full and definitive scientific elaboration by Sir George Darwin who did not refer to Kant and who, needless to say, followed a very different approach. Nor did such forerunners of Darwin as C. E. Delauney and G. B. Airy refer to Kant. That Kant did not have confidence in his method and results may be surmised from two facts. First, he did not include them in the *Allgemeine Naturgeschichte* and in his lecture notes on physical geography. In the latter (see note 42 below) he took up the topic again and did so in such a way as to reveal his amateurism in dynamics. Second, he hesitated to ascribe an acceleration to the rotation of the earth owing to its shrinking in its molten stage. Instead, he went back to the idea of light particles ascending from the surface of a celestial body and heavy particles descending on it—which embroiled him time and again in verbose circumlocutions in the *Allgemeine Naturgeschichte*. A tentative reconstruction of Kant's calculation of the amount of the retardation of the earth's axial rotation as given by J. Rahts (AA 1:539–41) shows that on the basis of his assumptions Kant should have set as 200 million and not 2 million years the complete cessation of the earth's rotation with respect to the moon. Thus the increase of the earth's rotational period should have been 5 minutes in every 2000 years and not $8\frac{1}{2}$ hours.

While the latter result was patently impossible, Kant was not only in its favor, but he also failed to realize that even the former result would have been incompatible with the precision demanded by the celestial dynamics of his time. Kant apparently based his calculation on Prop. xxvi of Book II of the *Principia*, a proposition, which like many other propositions of that Book, is faulty.

34. The remark is in Lambert's letter of Nov. 13, 1765, to Kant, a reply to Kant's inquiry concerning priority with respect to the explanation of the visual appearance of the Milky Way. Translation is from *The Milky Way*, pp. 199–200.

35. Munitz and Whitrow, who noted that in Hastie's translation the Third Part of Kant's work is omitted (see *Reprint 1969*, p. xxii and *Reprint 1970*, p. xiv), did not as much as hint to Kant's concern for extraterrestrial life. As to Ley, he briefly praised Kant for his having anticipated the modern idea that intelligent beings naturally develop on any celestial body whenever the physical conditions for life are available (*Reprint 1968*, p. xx), but he did not care to mention that Hastie's translation does not contain the Third Part in question.

36. Astonishingly enough, Kant referred to his work as a "physical treatise" (see translation, p. [188]) in connection with his speculations on denizens of other planets, speculations which in his view did not exceed the limits appropriate for such a treatise.

37. The item in question is Hastie's translation of Section II in Konrad Dieterich's *Kant und Newton* (Tübingen: Verlag der H. Laupp'schen Buchhandlung, 1876, pp. 16–33). In that work, in which 155 pages of text are followed by almost as many pages of notes, there is not a single reference to Newton's works, let alone a quotation from them, although Kant's works are profusely quoted. It should be no surprise that such a strange comparison of two authors, together with other works of Dieterich, who never held academic position, is now deservedly forgotten. The translation is given in *Reprint 1970*.

38. *Kant's Cosmogony*, p. cvi.

39. Thus the "Ethics of Elfland" in Chesterton's *Orthodoxy* was partially reprinted as "The Logic of Elfland" in *Great Essays in Science*, edited by M. Gardner (New York: Pocket Books, 1957, pp. 78–83) to illustrate the point that science presupposes epistemology instead of supplying it.

40. *Heretics* (5th ed.: London: John Lane, 1908), pp. 15–16.

41. *Pragmatism* (New York: Longmans, Green & Co., 1933), p. 3.

42. Huygens' statements are quoted in full in my *Planets and Planetarians*, pp. 52–53. The labelling of Descartes' cosmogony as a novel seems to have become a byword for many years: "Conclude from this, my dear Esquire," the Jesuit Aimé Henri Paulian advised in 1763 his fictitious correspondent "that the system of vortices is essentially a novel, though very ingenious." *Traité de paix entre Descartes et Newton, précédé des vies littéraires de ces deux chefs de la physique moderne* (Avignon: chez la veuve Girard, 1763), 1:248.

43. See translation, pp. [c2r] and [6].

44. See note 33 above.

45. Euler himself seemed to be in favor of an acceleration of the earth's rotation in his letter of May 11, 1754, to Erik Pontoppidan, Bishop of Bergen between 1747 and 1755, Professor of theology at the University of Copenhagen from 1755 until his death in 1764, and member of the Academy of Sciences there since its foundation in 1742. The exchange of letters between Euler and Pontoppidan was published by the latter in 1755 in his work on the recent

origin of the universe. Kant refers to Euler's letter in an undated annotation to his lecture-notes on physical geography (AA 14:581). The two letters were also printed, with an introduction by B. Hansted in *Bulletin des sciences mathématiques et astronomiques*, 3 (1879):26–32.

46. The essay was published simultaneously in French and in Latin, in Berlin and in Pisa, respectively. I had access to the Latin version, *Pauli Frisii . . . de motu diurno terrae dissertatio quae a Regia Berolinensi Scientiarum Academia Praemium Philosophis, ac Mathematicis, primum anno 1754, tum rursus anno 1756, propositum, obtinuit.* (Pisis Anno MDCCLVI, ex nova Typographia Io: Paulli Giovanelli, & Sociorum).

47. After ascribing the apparent very small lengthening of the year to the resistance presented by the ether to the earth's orbital motion, Frisi found that the resistance in question would exceed in the ratio of 8982 to 1 the resistance which could be posed by the ether to the earth's rotation. "Which ratio," Frisi remarked, "should seem to be much too great that since the creation of the world a noticeable retardation of the daily motion may have taken place owing to the ether's resistance, even assuming that some retardation had taken place in the annual motion." (p. 104).

48. Ibid., p. 96.

49. In the German original: "Kosmogonie, oder Versuch, den Ursprung des Weltgebäudes, die Bildung der Himmelskörper und die Ursachen ihrer Bewegung aus den allgemeinen Bewegungsgesetzen der Materie der Theorie des Newtons gemäsz her zu leiten."

II. *Cosmogony before Kant*

1. They were Erhard Weigel's *Cosmologia nucleum astronomiae & geographiae, ut & usum globorum . . . succincte tradens* (Jenae: sumptibus J. Meyeri, 1680, 1695), originally published as *Pancosmus, hoc est Machina nova totius mundi superioris et inferioris phaenomena velut ad vivum exprimens. Acessit Cosmologia . . .* (Jenae: sumptibus T. M. Götzii, imprimebat S. Krebsius, 1673), Nehemiah Grew's *Cosmologia sacra* (London: printed for W. Rogers, 1701), and Christian Wolff's *Cosmologia generalis* (Frankfurt & Leipzig: Officina Libraria Rengeriana, 1731; 2d ed. 1737).

2. *A New Theory of the Earth, from its Original, to the Consummation of all Things* (London: printed by R. Roberts for Benj. Tooke, 1696), p. 312.

3. Originally published in 1687. See edition by Thomas Birch (London: Richard Priestley, 1820), 1:510. In the same context (Bk. 1, ch. 4, §xiv) Cudworth speaks of the "cosmogonia of Timaeus" (pp. 483 and 486), of cosmogonia as theogonia (pp. 491–92), of the creation of the world as "divine cosmogonia" (p. 502), of the "ancient cabala which derived the cosmogonia from Chaos and Love" (p. 511), and of "Pagan cosmogonists'" (p. 511).

4. See the English translation of Malebranche's *Recherches sur la vérité by* T. Taylor,

Father Malebranche's Treatise concerning the Search after Truth. The Whole Work Compleat (Oxford: printed by L. Lichfield, 1694), 2:61.

5. Jacques Rohault's *Traité de physique*, first published in 1671 (Paris: chez la Veuve de Charles Savreux), was in its Latin translation by Samuel Clarke the textbook even in Cambridge for some time after the publication of the *Principia*. Descartes's theory of the evolution of the planetary system was also omitted in Claude Perrault's massive *Essais de physique ou Recueil de plusieurs traitez touchant les choses naturelles* (Paris: chez Jean Baptiste Coignard, 1680).

6. Descartes' two passing references to the Milky Way are in his *Les météores* and in his posthumous *Le monde*. See my *The Milky Way*, p. 119. Concerning the pre-Galilean views of the Milky Way, see ibid., chs. 2 and 3.

7. See *Oeuvres complètes*, 21:437.

8. "Nouvelles pensées sur le système de M. Descartes, et la manière d'en déduire les orbites et les aphélies des planètes," in *Johannis Bernoulli ... opera omnia* (Lausanne and Geneva: M. M. Bousquet et Sociorum, 1742), 3:133–73.

9. *Opticks*, Query 31 (New York: Dover, 1952), p. 400.

10. See the second (1713) and the third (1726) editions of the *Principia*, pp. 481 and 525, respectively.

11. That Newton entertained the idea of not only a thoroughly evolutionary but a cyclic universe was claimed on the basis of some manuscript notes of Newton by D. Kubrin ("Newton and the Cyclical Cosmos: Providence and the Mechanical Philosophy," *Journal for the History of Ideas* 28 [1967]:325–46), but he patently minimized Newton's printed statements on behalf of a non-evolutionary world view. See my *Planets and Planetarians*, pp. 72–73.

12. He did so in his "De gravitatione et aequipondio fluidorum" (c. 1672) in A. R. Hall and M. B. Hall, *Unpublished Scientific Papers of Isaac Newton* (Cambridge: University Press, 1962), pp. 89–156. See especially pp. 139 and 142–3.

13. *Oeuvres complètes de Voltaire*, 22:403. In its original form (Amsterdam: chez Étienne Ledet et Compagnie, 1738) the *Elémens* started with a discussion of the Newtonian physics of light. There Voltaire emphasized without referring to Newton, only in ch. 17, on void and space, the finiteness of matter (pp. 212–3). The phrase, as quoted, first appeared in Voltaire's booklet, *La métaphysique de Neuton, ou parallèle des sentimens de Neuton et de Leibniz* (Amsterdam: chez Jacques Desbordes, 1740), p. 2. This booklet became the introductory part of the *Elémens* from its new edition on (Londres, 1741; for quotation see p. 6), which was republished at least two dozen times prior to the French Revolution according to the entries in the *Catalogue des Livres Imprimés de la Bibliothèque Nationale*, vol. 213, now in press. Voltaire, of course, could have become initiated to the idea of a finite universe in an infinite space by reading Addison, who while contending that "the noblest and most exalted Way of considering this infinite Space is that of Sir Isaac Newton, who calls it the Sensorium of Godhead," insisted in the same essay (#565, July 9, 1714) that "there is no Question but the Universe has certain Bounds set to it," which are, however, not within the reach of our imigination. See *The Spectator*, a new edition with introduction, notes and index by H. Morley (London: George Routledge and Sons, 1891), 3:471–73.

14. Originally the sermons were published separately. The title, "A Confutation of Atheism," was given only to sermons iii–viii, of which sermons iii–v exploited the purposiveness of human body, whereas sermons vi–viii had cosmological relevance. A facsimile reprint of the original fascicles of sermons vii and viii is given in *Isaac Newton's Papers & Letters on Natural Philosophy and Related*

Documents, edited by I. B. Cohen (Cambridge, Mass.: Harvard University Press, 1958), pp. 313–94.

15. Ibid., p. 316.
16. Ibid., p. 345.
17. Ibid., p. 320.
18. Except for a brief passage in the *Principia* (Bk. III, Prop, xli, Probl. xxi), where he used the whiteness of the Milky Way to illustrate the hue of the tail of comets. See *Principia* (Cajori), p. 525.
19. *Isaac Newton's Papers and Letters*, p. 351.
20. Ibid., p. 352.
21. By 1699 the work was already in its fourth edition. See A. T. Bartholomew, *Richard Bentley, D. D.: A Bibliography of his Works and of all the Literature Called forth by his Acts or his Writings*, with an introduction and chronological table by J. W. Clark (Cambridge: Bowes & Bowes, 1908), pp. 1–7.
22. Ibid., p. 8.
23. Ibid., p. 9.
24. See *Principia* (Cajori), pp. 543–47.
25. A facsimile reprint of the first publication of Newton's four replies is given in *Isaac Newton's Papers and Letters*, pp. 279–312. The particulars where Newton disagreed with Bentley concerned the latter's criticism of infinite mass homogeneously distribitued and his attributing to Newton the idea of gravity as an innate property of matter. Newton also took pains to note that only quasi-circular orbits, but not very elongated orbits, could not be produced by gravity alone. See pp. 286 and 298.
26. Halley came to grips with the topic in two brief communications to the Royal Society. Both are reprinted in full as Appendix I in my *The Paradox of Olbers' Paradox* (New York: Herder & Herder, 1969).
27. Chéseaux did so in a brief essay attached to his *Traité de la comète*, reprinted ibid., as Appendix II. Chéseaux may have been led to his solution of the paradox by a brief remark in Hartsoeker's posthumously published *Cours de physique accompagné de plusieurs pièces concernant la Physique qui ont déjà paru . . .* (The Hague: chez Jean Swart, 1730). In speaking of the immensity of celestial space beyond the nearest stars, Hartsoeker asserts that it must be "a mere nothing in comparison with infinite extension and that this infinite extension is without doubt strewn everywhere of great fires or fixed stars and of planets, in the same way as is the space of which I have just spoken, and that thus their number is infinite. But if such is the case, one can conclude, that the rays of light must disappear on their way, or else the entire heavens would be as luminous as the sun" (Livre IV, chap. I; p. 235).
28. A detailed discussion of it is given in my *Planets and Planetarians*, pp. 87–92.
29. For details, see ibid., pp. 92–96.
30. The expression is part of the title of a long introduction to the four books of his *A New Theory of the Earth*.
31. Facing p. 127. For its reproduction, see Illustration XVI in my *Planets and Planetarians*. A more detailed discussion of Buffon's theory is given there on pp. 96–102. Buffon's theory was in a sense revived in James Jeans' theory of the origin of planetary system. For a graphic though merely qualitative account of it by Jeans, see his *The Stars in their Courses* (Cambridge, University Press, 1931), pp. 44–47.
32. The booklet, *De mundi systemate liber Isaaci Newtoni* (1728), was immediately translated into English, which is readily available in *Principia* (Cajori), pp.

549–626. For illustration, see p. 551. Both the Latin and English versions, which carried the illustration as the first diagram in an end-foldout page, had gone through several editions by 1745 when Buffon completed the manuscript of his theory of the earth's formation.

33. *Histoire naturelle*, p. 141; *Allgemeine Historie der Natur*, pp. 82–83.

34. For their cosmogonical ideas, see my *Planets and Planetarians*, ch. 3–5, and K. B. Collier, *Cosmogonies of our Fathers: Some Theories of the Seventeenth and Eighteenth Centuries* (New York: Columbia University Press, 1934).

35. For a summary and discussion of it, together with its illustrations in Swedenborg's *Principia rerum naturalium* (1734), see my *Planets and Planetarians*, pp. 77–78.

36. See Giorgio Tonelli's Introduction to the reprint of Maupertuis' *Oeuvres* in four volumes (1756), vol. 1, p. XXIV* and pp. LXII*–LXV*.

37. *Ouvrages divers de Mr. de Maupertuis* (Amsterdam: Aux dépens de la Compagnie, 1744). In addition to the *Discours sur les différentes figures des astres*, it contained the *Eléments de géographie*, the *Discours sur la parallaxe de la lune*, and the *Lettre sur la comète*. The last two works were paginated together, the first two separately. For the review, see note 39a to the Opening Discourse.

38. The only monograph on Maupertuis, P. Brunet's *Maupertuis. L'oeuvre et sa place dans la pensée scientifique et philosophique du XVIII⁰ siècle* (Paris: Albert Blanchard, 1929), is clearly out of date. In its section (pp. 89–82) on Maupertuis' ideas on nebulae, it contains no reference to Kant.

39. Translation is from the text in *Les oeuvres de Mr. de Maupertuis* (Dresden: chez George Conrad Walther, 1752), pp. 55–94. For quotation, see pp. 84–85.

40. Ibid., pp. 85–86.

41. "An account of several *Nebulae* or lucid Spots like Clouds, lately discovered among the Fixt Stars by help of the Telescope," *Philosophical Transactions* 29 (1714–16):390–92. The second enlarged edition of the *Discours* (1742) carried a table of 16 nebulous stars (p. 109), which Maupertuis compiled from Hevelius' *Catalogus stellarum fixarum* (Gedani: typis Johannis Zachariae Stollii, 1687) in which the "nebulosae" are listed on pp. 146, 172, 190, 206–7, 218, 233, 245, 264, 310. The table was reproduced in *Ouvrages divers* (1744), but suppressed in the subsequent editions of the *Oeuvres*. See also note 35 to First Part.

42. "Observations of the Appearances among the Fix'd Stars, called Nebulous Stars," *Philosophical Transactions* 38 (1733–34):70–74.

43. *Oeuvres de Maupertuis* (1752), p. 87.

44. Ibid., p. 90.

45. Ibid., p. 93.

46. References to the fascimile reprint edition.

47. Ibid., pp. 40, 41, and 62.

48. Ibid., p. 42.

49. Ibid., pp. 83–84. Here Wright spoke of nebulae in which no stars could be distinguished: "those in all likelyhood may be external Creation, bordering upon the known one, too remote for even our Telescopes to reach."

50. Ibid., p. 79.

51. Ibid.

52. Ibid.

53. Owing to the destruction of the archives of the Académie Royale des Sciences de Montpellier during the French Revolution, the scant two pages (179–80)

in J. Castelnau's *Mémoire historique et biographique sur l'ancienne Société Royale des Sciences de Montpellier* (Montpellier: Boehm, 1858) are the primary source on Estève's life and work. Estève is not among the forty members of the Académie whose éloges were reprinted in *Éloges des Académiciens de Montpellier* (Paris: Bessange et Masson, 1811). Estève became a member of the Académie in 1746, at the age of 26, but the "Liste de MM. de la Société Royale des Sciences pour l'année 1761" (Montpellier: la Veuve de Jean Martel, 1761), a broadsheet (30 × 50 cm) in the possession of Mr. Gaston Vidal, present Secrétaire Perpétuel of the Académie, who kindly gave me access to it, classes Estève as one of the three "membres vétérans." A similar broadsheet of the list of members for 1771 (Montpellier: Jean Martel aîné, 1771) in the Bibliothèque Municipale de Montpellier has Paris after Estève's name, again among the "membres vétérans." Estève seems to have become estranged from his Académie, where apparently Rousseau's essay of 1749 debunking the arts and sciences found a favorable echo. In his booklet, *Justification de la musique françoise*, published anonymously in The Hague in 1754, Estève speaks of his Académie which until recently was worthy of being called such, but may soon become a mere bankruptcy . . . if the system of the new apostle [Rousseau] becomes established" (p. 26).

54. There are two copies of it in the *Bibliothèque Nationale* in Paris. It is not listed in the *National Catalogue of pre-1956 Imprints*, in the printed catalogue of books in the British Museum, or in the central catalogue [The Hague] of Dutch libraries. According to an information given to me by Mr. Anton van Vliet, editor at Nijhoff Publishing Company, there is a copy in the University Library of Cracow.

55. This is why he was referred to as "the honest Kant," an undue praise when seen, for instance, against the meticulous references to others' works in Christian Wolff's widely used and imitated books.

56. His best work seems to have been the *Nouvelle découverte du principe de l'harmonie, avec un examen de ce que M. Rameau a publié sous le titre Démonstration de ce principe* (Paris: chez Sebastian Jorry, 1752). His *L'Esprit des beaux-arts ou histoire raisonnée du goût* (2 vols; Paris: chez C. J. Baptiste Bauche Fils, 1753) was reprinted in 1970 (Geneva: Slatkine Reprints). His *Histoire générale et particulière de l'astronomie* (Paris: chez Ch. Ant. Jombert, 1755) in three volumes was written "avec légérité" as pointedly noted by J.-E. Montucla in his *Histoire des mathématiques* (Paris: chez Ch.-Ant. Jombert, 1757), 1:xxiii. Yet the work is not without some insightful pages, which is also true of Estève's *Histoire des anciennes révolutions du globe terrestre* (Amsterdam: Damonneville, 1752), a point which I intend to discuss elsewhere. He also wrote on rhetoric and on the philosophy of the art of living. The *Mémoires de mathématique et de physique*, a collection of papers presented by non-members to the Académie des Sciences in Paris, contains several communications by Estève, among them his observation of the lunar eclipse of July 19, 1749 (see 2 [1755]:315–16) which he made at the Observatory of Montpellier, erected in the early 18th century to provide for the astronomers at the Paris Observatory a station with more favorable atmospheric conditions. Towards the end of the 1750s Estève stopped publishing, possibly because the ten or so books which he wrote in so many years did not provoke sufficient response.

57. In that one-page-long communication, "Ein Vorläufer von Kants *Allgemeine Naturgeschichte und Theorie des Himmels*" (*Kantstudien* 28 [1923]:193), Schumann spoke of the "astonishing affinity" between the two works. The same com-

munication was also published in *Grundwissenschaft* 3 (1922):346, of which Schumann was an editor and which had for its subtitle: *Philosophische Zeitschrift der Johannes-Rehmke Gesellschaft.*

58. *Kant als Naturforscher,* 2:294–95.
59. The phrase is not listed in "The Eighteenth-Century Origins of the Concept of Scientific Revolution," by I. B. Cohen, *Journal of the History of Ideas* 37 (1976):257–88.
60. At least in a systematic way. His statement (*Origine de l'univers,* p. 97), "if men inhabit the celestial bodies immersed in the matter which is in a continual motion, they receive sensations of vision," seems to imply his belief in the existence of extraterrestrial beings.
61. Ibid., p. 3.
62. His use of the adjective "infinite" (see for instance, p. 80) is as careless as Kant's.
63. Ibid., p. 40.
64. Ibid., p. 51.
66. Ibid., p. 66.
67. Ibid., p. 84.
68. Ibid., p. 89. On the discrepancy of this figure with the data provided in Newton's *Principia,* see note 17 to Second Section of Second Part.
69. Ibid., p. 107.
70. Ibid., p. 114.
71. Ibid., p. 116.
72. Ibid., p. 137.
73. Ibid., pp. 140–41, where he quotes verbatim a passage from Maupertuis' *Discours.*
74. Ibid., p. 143.
75. Ibid., p. 146.

III. *Kant the Cosmogonist*

1. For details, see my *The Milky Way,* p. 195.
2. The silence was broken by A. De Morgan's article, "An Account of the Speculations of Thomas Wright of Durham," *Philosophical Magazine* 32 (1848):241–52.
3. In the *Freye Urtheile und Nachrichten zum Aufnehmen der Wissenschaften und der Historie überhaupt* the summary was carried in three instalments, in the January 1, 5, and 8, 1751, issues, p. 1–5, 9–14, 17–22, respectively, which in turn corresponded to the contents of Letters I–III, IV, and V–IX of the *Original Theory.* The full text of the summary is now readily available as an Appendix in F. Krafft's edition of the *Allgemeine Naturgeschichte* (Munich: Kindler, 1971), pp. 200–11. The English translation of that summary offered by Hastie in *Kant's Cosmogony* (pp. 180–91) is based on a manuscript copy of the German text which he found in the Edinburgh University Library. Having failed to compare it with the printed original, Hastie did not realize that the manuscript

was incomplete and inaccurate in several respects. Hastie's translation is reproduced in *Reprint 1970* without critical remarks. Another, much longer and hitherto unnoticed review of Wright's book appeared in 1752 in the *Hamburgisches Magazin, oder gesammlete Schriften, zum Unterricht und Vergnügen, aus der Naturforschung und den angenehmen Wissenschaften überhaupt* (Bd. 10, St. 2, pp. 151–80), which could hardly be unknown to Kant, owing to the publication there in 1749 of a paper by Martin Knutzen, whose connection with Kant will be discussed below. The reviewer, A. G. K., identified as Prof. [Abraham Gotthelf] Kästner in the *Dreyfaches Universalregister und Repertorium* of the first 26 volumes (Hamburg and Leipzig: bey Adam Heinrich Hollens Wittwe, 1767, p. 48), was Professor ordinarius of mathematics and physics in Göttingen since 1756 until his death in 1800, and next to Euler and Lambert the foremost German mathematician and physicist of the times. Kästner, whose review contained many comparisons, often unfavorable, of Wright's dicta with the best data in the astronomical literature, had real praise only for Wright's engravings. That Wright's explanation of the hue and shape of the Milky Way did not strike Kästner as something novel, may be an indication that it had indeed been in the air for some time. Kästner, who reported the book's contents Letter by Letter, explicitly noted Wright's two models of the Milky Way (p. 170), without finding one preferable to the other, and viewed Wright's proofs of the motion of stars as wholly unconvincing. The reason for this latter point was Kästner's insistence throughout the review on the difference between observational evidence and mere theorizing. The latter, according to Kästner, was not only preponderant in Wright's work but also often merging into poetical flights of fancy. Unable to appreciate the role of bold extrapolations in science, Kästner concluded: "One could only wish that this work had been devoted to real things and not, often, to representations which seem to owe their existence only to the imaginative powers of the author" (p. 180). Kästner published (anonymously) in Latin an abbreviated form of his review in *Relationes de libris novis* in 1753 (vol. V, fasc, ii, pp. 48–60). A comparison of the two reviews, in particular the special attention given in both to Wright's list of new stars, together with the ties of Kästner and of the *Relationes* with the University of Göttingen and with the Academy of Sciences there, leaves no doubt about Kästner's authorship. Kant, who could hardly derive any encouragement about the correctness of his idea of the Milky Way from Kästner's review(s), had no choice but ignore it, lest he dispose unfavourably the already well known Kästner against his book. I plan to discuss further details of Kästner's reviews elsewhere.

4. The *Gedanken von der wahren Schätzung der lebendigen Kräfte* was in part a criticism of Leibniz's ideas of *vis viva* and was published only in 1749, although the title page shows the year 1747. Kant did not seem to be aware of the fact that d'Alembert had already pointed out in 1743 that since Leibniz defined *vis viva* as mv^2 (kinetic energy), his criticism of its Cartesian definition as mv (momentum) was largely a battle of words. See in Section V the statement documented with note 53.

5. Both were written in Latin. The former, an essay of 92 large quarto handwritten pages, was printed only in 1839. The latter was printed in 1755 and ran to 38 pages.

6. Borowski, *Immanuel Kant* (p. 89), a work first printed in the year of Kant's death (1804) together with the biographical sketches of Kant by R. B. Jachmann and A. Ch. Wasianski, in one volume.

7. In the early 1920s the Auskunftsbureau of German libraries could list only the Prussian Staatsbibliothek and five universities with a copy. See Adickes, *Kant als Naturforscher* 2:207. According to the *National Catalogue of Pre-1956 Imprints* (289:283) there are seven libraries with a copy in the USA and Canada.
8. An exception is Krafft (see note 3 above, p. 193), according to whom most copies perished in fire, an information not traced to any source.
9. The printer's name is given by J. Rahts (AA 1:545) as Joh. Friedr. Driest. Borowski claimed (*Immanuel Kant*, p. 89) that the *Allgemeine Naturgeschichte* was not once put on sale.
10. See Borowski, *Immanuel Kant*, p. 27.
11. Ibid., p. 89.
12. Ibid., p. 26.
13. Stuckenberg, *The Life of Immanuel Kant*, pp. 85–91. By claiming the contrary, Jachmann was telescoping into the distant past a glory that came to the author of the *Allgemeine Naturgeschichte* only during the last ten years of his life, a point to be discussed in the next Section. According to Jachmann, "the important work, the [*Allgemeine Naturgeschichte und*] *Theorie des Himmels*, through which Kant was revealed as a great mathematician and philosopher of nature, earned him already such a fame that Frederick II [the Great] repeatedly offered him a chair in Halle, and finally with the rank of Geheimrat, which he declined out of love for his town of birth and proposed [for the post] the present professor Eberhard" (*Immanuel Kant*, p. 126). The proposal concerning the post in Halle was made in 1778 and by then the *Allgemeine Naturgeschichte* was still to emerge from an almost complete oblivion.
14. In addition to his *Discours*, discussed in the preceding section, Maupertuis also wrote the *Essai de cosmologie* (1750), a work more philosophical than scientific. Euler's cosmological ideas were embodied in his *Lettres à une Princesse d'Allemagne sur quelques sujets de physique et de philosophie* (1768–72), one of the most widely read books for the rest of the century.
15. A recent offering of that cliché is in the article "Kant" by J. W. Ellington in *Dictionary of Scientific Biography* (New York: Charles Scribner's Sons, 1970–80), 7:225.
16. *Immanuel Kant*, pp. 75–76. See also Jachmann's similar statement, ibid., p. 138.
17. As recalled by Borowski; ibid., p. 62.
18. As recalled by Jachmann; ibid., p. 147.
19. Ibid., p. 78.
20. B. Erdmann, *Martin Knutzen und seine Zeit: Ein Beitrag zur Geschichte der Wolfischen Schule und insbesondere zur Entwicklungsgeschichte Kant's* (Leipzig: Leopold Voss, 1876; reprinted, Hildesheim: Verlag Dr. H. A. Gerstenberg, 1973), p. 140.
21. Ibid.
22. Ibid., p. 139.
23. Ibid., p. 51. This course in "analysis" was most likely a course in analytical geometry rather than in infinitesimal calculus. Highly revealing in this connection is the list of courses given in mathematics in the winter semester 1781–82 at the University of Königsberg. None of the eight courses and the textbooks used in them have any connection with infinitesimal calculus. The two courses given in experimental and theoretical physics, were, if judged by the respective textbooks, also on an elementary or introductory level. For details, see J. F. Goldbeck, *Nachrichten von der Königlichen Universität zu Königsberg in Preussen und den daselbst befindlichen Lehr- Schul- und Erziehungsanstalten* (a work

published in 1782 at the expenses of Goldbeck, chaplain with the Royal
Prussian infantry regiment at Rohr). See pp. 96–97.

24. *Martin Knutzen*, p. 51 note.

25. In J. C. Poggendorff's usually very complete *Biographisch-literarisches
Handwörterbuch zur Geschichte der exacten Wissenschaften* (1863, vol. 1, p. 33), the
last publication of Buck dates from 1770! His previous publications are
biographical, historical, and descriptive, one of them being a "teleological
consideration of smoke and of its different kinds." In Goldbeck's *Nachrichten*
(p. 84) Buck is described as professor ordinarius of mathematics who "is
charged to set forth arithmetic, geometry, trigonometry, and astronomy in
his public lectures."

26. *Martin Knutzen*, p. 123. The three definitions and seven theorems "on infinite
parabolas drawn with the same parameter and around the same axis" given
under Knutzen's name in *Nova acta eruditorum* (October 1737, pp. 461–66)
contain nothing remarkable. Nor was a new page written in meteorology by
Knutzen's "instrumentum meteorognosticum, vel etiam meteorologicum
universale" which he described in the *Hamburgisches Magazin* (1749, Bd. 4, St.
3, pp. 299–306). It merely relieved the observer of the pressure, humidity,
and temperature of the air from walking from one instrument to another.
That scientific originality was also absent in Knutzen's *Historisch-mathematische
Abhandlung von den Brenn-Spiegeln des Archimedes*, which according to its subtitle
claimed to give "a few general methods to extend to great distances the
effectiveness of all burning glasses and burning mirrors" (Königsberg, 1747),
first published in short instalments in the *Königsberger Frag- und Anzeigungs-
Nachrichten*, can be gathered from its review in the *Freye Urtheile* (5[1748]:41–
44 and 49–52), a review mostly taken up by historical details.

27. The most important of these was, of course, Halley's "Astronomiae cometicae
synopsis" (1705), but even in connection with the comet of 1743 the young
Chéseaux produced in 1744, at the age of twenty-five, his *Traité de la comète*,
a work attesting both mathematical skill and originality. In 1761, J. H.
Lambert showed with his *Insigniores orbitae cometarum proprietates* (Augsburg:
E. Klett) what a self-taught man could produce if he was truly a scientific
genius.

28. *Kant als Naturforscher*, 1:12 and 15. As shown in note 23 above, the situation was
the same a generation later.

29. See translation, p. [26].

30. *Kant als Naturforscher*, 1:5 and 2:311.

31. See translation, p. [3]. A very apt remark, indeed! The explanation of the visual
shape and hue of the Milky Way would easily qualify as perhaps the most
delayed among major scientific discoveries. See chs. 4 and 5, "Galilean
Myopia" and "Newtonian Distraction" in *The Milky Way*.

32. See translation, pp. [c2v], [c5r], and [2]–[3].

33. See translation, p. [13].

34. It is well to recall that the enormous increase of optical resolution available a
generation later through Herschel's giant telescopes did not provide a definitive answer to the question whether nebulous patches were invariably due
to the fusion of starlight, let alone to the question whether some of these
patches were stellar systems on equal footing with the Milky Way. See chs.
8 and 9, "The Myth of One Island" and "The Beacon from Andromeda" in
The Milky Way.

35. See translation pp. [b8r] and [c1r]. For the Cartesian provenance of the expression, see note 26 to Opening Discourse.

36. Several of Descartes utterances to that effect are quoted in my *Relevance of Physics* (Chicago: University of Chicago Press, 1966), pp. 285–86.

37. See translation, p. [c1v].

38. Most telling in this respect is the derivation of the genesis of elements from the primordial "cosmic soup" consisting of four kinds of fundamental particles and being in thermal quasi-equilibrium during its first half million years of existence attested by the cosmic background radiation. On the basis of a few fundamental constants one can also derive the average size of mountains, of stars, the blueness of the atmosphere, and even the size of atoms and molecules.

39. See translation, p. [29].

40. Ibid., p. [28].

41. Ibid., pp. [c6v] and [c7v].

42. Ibid., p. [28].

43. Needless to say, Kant did not use the word hierarchical. Nor was it used by Lambert. The popularity of this word in cosmological literature is rather recent.

44. See translation, p. [40].

45. Ibid., pp. [109] and [117].

46. Ibid.

47. Ibid., p. [110].

48. Ibid., pp. [106] and [107]. See also notes 11 and 12 to Seventh Section of Second Part.

49. Ibid.

50. See sections 9–10 of his *Gedanken von der wahren Schätzung der lebendigen Kräfte*, AA 1:23–24.

51. As evidenced among other things, by his utterance, "Ich bin Gott!", in the *Opus postumum*. See edition by A. Buchenau (Berlin: Walter de Gruyter, 1936–38), 1:25. Equally revealing in this connection is the patheism shared by Fichte, Schelling, and Hegel, determined to unfold in full the basic presuppositions of Kantian philosophy. The point is wholly ignored by F. E. England in his *Kant's Conception of God: A Critical Exposition of Its Metaphysical Development together with a Translation of the Nova Dilucidatio* (1929; reprinted, New York: Humanities Press, 1968).

52. See translation, pp. [112] and [113].

53. Ibid., pp. [a8v] and [169]–[170].

54. Ibid., pp. [153]–[154].

55. They made Adickes exclaim that the physics of the *Opus postumum* is equivalent to Schelling's Naturphilosophie! See *Kant als Naturforscher*, 2:205.

56. Kant hardly suspected the irony as he kept telling his closest friends during those years that they could only "sarcinas colligere" from him, were he to speak to them in detail of the contents of his notes now constituting the *Opus postumum*. In describing it as "the transition of physics to metaphysics" Borowski was much closer to the heart of the matter than he could possibly suspect. See *Immanuel Kant*, p. 84.

57. A brief outline of Kant's argumentation in that essay is given in my Gifford Lectures, *The Road of Science and the Ways to God* (Chicago: University of Chicago Press; Edinburgh: Scottish Academic Press, 1978), p. 125.

IV. A Century of Silence

1. The unsigned review ran to four pages (429–32); for quotations see pp. 429 and 432. The *Allgemeine Naturgeschichte* was ascribed to an "unnamed" author in the register of the 104 issues comprising Band 12 (1755), a fact which would hardly have occured if by late 1755 the book had gained some publicity.

2. The publisher (J.J. Kanter, Königsberg) had the book out already in December, 1762. For a summary and analysis of its contents, see F. Copleston, *A History of Philosophy. Volume 6. Modern Philosophy. Part I. The French Enlightenment to Kant* (Garden City, N.Y.: Doubleday, 1964), pp. 217–19.

3. Given here in English translation as Appendix.

4. See AA 2:68–69.

5. Trescho's *Zerstreuungen auf Kosten der Natur in einigen Sommerstunden* (J. J. Kanter: Königsberg, 1763), was not available to me. A detailed and well documented discussion of its sections relevant to the *Allgemeine Naturgeschichte* is given in A. Warda, "J. Kant's 'Allgemeine Naturgeschichte und Theorie des Himmels' und Seb. Fr. Treschos 'Zerstreuungen auf Kosten der Natur'," *Altpreussische Monatschrift* 44 (1907):534–41. Especially valuable in Warda's article is the comparison in parallel columns of passages from Kant and Trescho, as the latter's work is not listed in any of the major German libraries.

6. *Bedenklichkeiten über den einzig möglichen Beweisgrund des Herrn M. Kants zu einer Demonstration des Daseyns Gottes* (Köningsberg: Johann Jacob Kanter, 1763), pp. 87–90. The preface was dated January 14, 1763, and therefore the 96 page long book must have been written in considerable haste. Weymann was one of the competitors with Kant for the Prize set in 1754 by the Academy in Berlin for the best essay on Pope's optimism.

7. See AA 10:50–51.

8. For Kant's reply, dated Dec. 31, 1765, see AA 10:51–54.

9. Passages in English translation from Lambert's letter, still unpublished in its French original, are given in *Cosmological Letters*, pp. 26 and 206.

10. *Anleitung zur Kenntniss des gestirnten Himmels* (Berlin: bey Christian Friedrich Himburg, 1777), pp. 658–59. In the 2d edition (Hamburg: bey Dieterich Anton Harmsen, 1772) only Lambert was mentioned (p. 486 note) in connection with the Milky Way.

11. *Kurzgefasste Erläuterung der Sternkunde und den* [sic] *dazu gehörigen Wissenschaften* (Berlin: bey Christian Friedrich Himburg, 1778), p. 512.

12. See, for instance, *Anleitung* (7th ed., 1801, p. 698) and *Erläuterung* (8th ed., 1806, p. 644). Similar was the pattern in Bode's last published work, the revised edition of his *Entwurf der astronomischen Wissenschaften* (Berlin: Georg Reimer, 1825) pp. 258 and 261. Bode was also the German translator of Fontenelle's famed dialogues on the plurality of worlds, *Dialogen über die Mehrheit der Welten* (Berlin: Christian Friedrich Himburg, 1780), which he enriched with many explanatory notes, so many occasions for referring to Kant, who was mentioned by Bode only twice: in connection with the Milky Way and the rise and decay of world systems (pp. 283 and 319).

13. Göttingen and Gotha: bey Johann Christian Dieterich, 1772, pp. 538–40. No change in this respect was in the second "improved" edition (Frankfurt and Leipzig, 1777), pp. 518–20.

14. See 1st ed., p. 539; 2d ed., p. 520.

15. Göttingen: Johann Christian Dieterich, 1787, p. 590.
16. Göttingen: Johann Christian Dieterich, 1794, pp. 642–43: "Actually, already six years before Lambert, Mr. Kant [proposed the same] in the book mentioned above." But the rest of the long note dealt with Herschel's discoveries and with the translation into German of his two great memoirs on the construction of the heavens.
17. See AA 13:281.
18. See, for instance, the 2d ed., pp. 612–20, and the 6th, pp. 733–55. That in the latter edition Lichtenberg still failed to refer to Kant in this connection is all the more revealing as he referred there not only to now largely forgotten works, but also to Herder's *Ideen zur Geschichte der Menschheit* (see note 32 below), which started with a brief but emphatic praise of Kant's cosmogony. Among the now largely forgotten authors often referred to by Lichtenberg was Johann Gottschalk Wallerius, professor of chemistry, metallurgy, and pharmacology at Uppsala, whose treatise on the origin of the world, originally published in Swedish in 1776, was translated from its Latin version into German by D. Christian Friedrich Keller under the title, *Physisch-chemische Betrachtungen über den Ursprung der Welt besonders der Erdwelt und ihrer Veränderung* (Erfurt: bey Georg Adam Keyser, 1782). There brief references were made to the ideas of Burnet, Leibniz and Buffon on the origin of the earth (see pp. 64–66), but Kant was wholly ignored. A French translation of Wallerius' work appeared in 1780 (Varsovie et Paris) under the title, *De l'origine du monde et de la terre en particulier.*
19. See AA 9:509 and 512. In AA the text of the *Physische Geographie* runs to almost 300 pages (9:151–436).
20. These annotations are printed in AA (14:547–635), of which about the half is taken up by explanatory notes of the editor.
21. AA 9:157–58.
22. Stuckenberg, *The Life of Immanuel Kant*, p. 140.
23. Ibid. Kant spiritedly disputed that the Catholic clergy was well educated in Bavaria, a country he never visited.
24. See Appendix to the First Part of the *Physische Geographie* in AA 9:306–08.
25. While it was certainly true that the many things one could learn through travels "were of little profit if one had not previously received training through instruction" (ibid., Introduction, p. 158), his lecturing on physical geography, uninstructed by travel, could be the target of no less pertinent comments.
26. The section has the title, "History of the great changes which the earth has already undergone and still does," AA 9:297–305. See especially, pp. 300–03. Kant failed to refer to his theory of the formation of planets as he gave an account of the planetary system in the same work (pp. 178–83).
27. He did not protest when after the publication of his *Die Religion innerhalb der Grenzen der blossen Vernunft* (1793) the Prussian government ordered him not to write again on the subject. A rather curious account of this is given by Ley in *Reprint 1968*, p. xvi.
28. Revealingly, Newtonian science (theory of colors) was mentioned only once in Reinhold's ten long letters on Kantian philosophy, originally published in the *Teutsche Merkur* in 1785–86, which assured fame to the *Critique*.
29. The book was similar in size and length to Goldbeck's report, already mentioned (see note III-23 above), on the educational institutions in Königsberg and was also published at the author's expense (Berlin, 1781). The passage on the *Allgemeine Naturgeschichte* runs as follows: "Let it be permitted to me to

adduce a remark in this connection about his *Allgemeine Naturgeschichte und Theorie des Himmels*, published in 1755. This work is one of his first writings and became known but lately. This is possibly the cause [of the fact] that some of the propositions set forth in that work, which afterwards another scholar, namely, Herr Lambert, also submitted in his *Cosmologische Briefe*, which came out in 1761, were credited to these [*Briefe*] and therefore the credit for their discovery was denied to their first proponent ... That the Kantian *Naturgeschichte des Himmels* must have been unknown to Herr Lambert when he published his *Cosmologische Briefe* is certain, because a scholar like Herr Lambert would not have left it unmentioned. Herr Lambert was himself also a discoverer—to Herr Kant belongs, however, the honor of being the discoverer before him. There are still other propositions in that *Naturgeschichte*, for instance, the hypothesis of nebulous stars, which is exclusive to Herr Kant and which Herr Lambert has never enunciated, although they were similarly ascribed to the latter by Herr Bode in Berlin. One must therefore naturally assume that this Kantian *Naturgeschichte* was occasionally, at least by some formerly, taken for a product of the Lambertian mind" (p. 248–49).

30. *Anhang zu dem sieben und dreiszigsten bis zwey und fünfzigsten Bande der allgemeinen deutschen Bibliothek. Zweyte Abtheilung*, 1783, pp. 649–54. "What the author states (p. 248f) on the agreement of Kant and Lambert in cosmological propositions and on [the fact] that Bode ascribes to the latter a hypothesis which properly belongs to the former, is not entirely correct; we know how Kant, who is too modest to take to himself anything from Lambert's fame, himself thinks in this respect and one will soon see this in connection with Lambert's letters which Bernoulli is [now] publishing" (pp. 653–54). The reference is to Lambert's German-language correspondence with scientific men, edited in five volumes by J. Bernoulli under the title, *Joh. Heinrich Lamberts deutscher gelehrter Briefwechsel* (Berlin: bey dem Herausgeber, 1781–87), of which the first volume contained the exchange of letters between Lambert and Kant in 1765 (see notes 7 and 8 above).

31. The four editions appeared in 1763, 1770, 1783, and 1794. In the latter year the book was published separately in Königsberg and Leipzig.

32. To this remark there was added a footnote which started with a reference to the *Allgemeine Naturgeschichte* as a "book which remained more unknown than deserved by its contents." See *Ideen zur Philosophie der Geschichte der Menschheit* (it went through four editions by 1807) in *Herders Sämmtliche Werke*, edited by B. Suphan (Berlin: Weidmannsche Buchhandlung, 1877–1913), 13:13–14. A few pages later Herder made another reference to Kant which is discussed in connection with the Third Part (note 23).

33. See AA 13:101–02.

34. The paper was entitled "Über die Vulkane im Monde" (AA 8:61–76; for quotations see pp. 74 and 76). The interpretation in question was proposed by Franz Aepinus, successively a member of the Academy of Sciences in Berlin and in Saint Petersburg, a prolific author, best remembered for his electrical theories. Since Kant's paper was published in the *Berliner Monatschrift*, a reference to the *Allgemeine Naturgeschichte* would have secured it considerable publicity, an outcome which Kant seemed to be intent on preventing. A confirmation of this conjecture can be gathered from Kant's passing up another and even more obvious opportunity two years later (see note 23 to Third Part) to call attention to the *Allgemeine Naturgeschichte*.

35. *Critique of Judgment*, translated with an introduction by J. H. Bernard (1892; reissued, New York: Hafner, 1951), p. 95.

36. See AA 12:205–06. The letter was dated October 13, 1797.

37. See AA 11:241.

38. The "applause," presumably Lichtenberg's reference to Kant's theory of the Milky Way in the later editions of Erxleben's *Anfangsgründe*, must appear a small matter if one thinks of Lichtenberg's failure to mention Kant (but not Lambert!) in his enthusiastic reaction to Herschel's work on the Milky Way. See my *The Milky Way*, pp. 236–37.

39. *William Herschel . . . über den Bau des Himmels. Drey Abhandlungen aus dem Englischen übersetzt. Nebst einem authentischen Auszug aus Kants allgemeiner Naturgeschichte und Theorie des Himmels* (Königsberg: Friedrich Nicolovius, 1791). The three memoirs were, "Account of some Observations tending to investigate the Construction of the Heavens" (1784), "On the Construction of the Heavens" (1785), and "Catalogue of a second Thousand of new Nebulae and Clusters of Stars; with a few introductory Remarks on the Construction of the Heavens" (1789), and covered pp. 1–160, preceded by Sommer's Introduction (pp. iii–xii). The excerpts from the *Allgemeine Naturgeschichte* covered pp. 163–200, and were followed by Gensichen's remarks (pp. 201–04). For Sommer's remark, see p. xi.

40. Ibid., p. 161.

41. Some of these corrections will be noted in connection with the translation itself.

42. Ibid., pp. 203. See also note 19 to Fifth Section of Second Part.

43. Ibid., pp. 193–95.

44. Bugge's communication, "Über die abgeplattete Gestalt und Rotationszeit der Saturnskugel . . ." was sent to Bode on Dec. 12, 1789, and was printed in 1790 in the volume indicated (pp. 95–102). Bugge based his calculation on Prop. 9 of Bk. 3 of the *Principia* in which the flattening of a celestial body is correlated with its density and period of rotation. Bugge obtained very satisfactory result with respect for Jupiter's period of rotation (already well known from observation) by using the values in question for the earth. The method did not work for Saturn (Bugge obtained 6 hours and 5 minutes), because his value for the flattening of Saturn was much larger than the one which Herschel made public in 1790 from his observations. According to Herschel the ratio of the equatorial and polar diameters of Saturn was 11 to 10. See *Collected Scientific Papers*, 1:380.

45. The title of the first article was "Prüfung der Kantischen Hypothese von dem mechanischen Ursprung des Planetensystems," *Philosophisches Archiv* (Berlin), I/2 (1792):1–36, the title of the second, "Prüfung der Kantischen Hypothese von dem Ursprunge des Ringes des Saturn, und die Berechnung der Achsendrehung dieses Planeten," I/2 (1793):1–21.

46. Ibid., p. 20 of the first article.

47. Ibid., pp. 24–25 note, where the quotation is apparently from a letter of that anonymous expert to Schwab.

48. The letter was written on July 10, 1812. For further details, see *Planets and Planetarians*, p. 128. On the successive forms of Laplace's cosmogony, see ibid., pp. 122–34.

49. See his "Anmerkung" to his "Ueber die Anordnung des Weltgebäudes," which he described as "free excerpts" from Herschel's writing on the subject, in *Astronomisches Jahrbuch für das Jahr 1794* (Berlin, 1791), pp. 226–33. "Perhaps this very exact thinker," Fischer wrote, "rejects them as being too arbitrary"

(p. 228). According to Fischer, Kant derived "with admirable facility" all phenomena in the universe (p. 227).

50. Ibid., p. 227.
51. Ibid., p. 229.
52. According to Fischer, the sole difference between Kant's and Lambert's ideas was that the latter did not admit the decay of celestial bodies and their systems into chaos (p. 229).
53. For a similar view, see note 66 below.
54. Ibid., p. 229.
55. See the volumes for 1787 (1784, pp. 211–14); for 1788 (1785, pp. 238–45); for 1789 (1786, p. 153); for 1790 (1787, pp. 173–78); for 1791 (1788, pp. 157–73); for 1792 (1789, pp. 150–55); for 1793 (1790, pp. 104–07), where Herschel's discovery of Uranus, his observations and cataloguing of nebulae, his reports about Saturn's rotation and ring—topics most relevant to the *Allgemeine Naturgeschichte*—are discussed. Kant and the *Allgemeine Naturgeschichte* were equally ignored in *Magazin für das Neueste aus der Physik und Naturgeschichte*, a quarterly published in 11 volumes between 1781 and 1796 (a 12th volume consisting of a meticulously compiled register of names, titles, and subjects, was added in 1799), first under the editorship of G. C. Lichtenberg and later under that of J. H. Voigt, professor of mathematics at Jena. Interestingly, the first publication discussed in the *Magazin* (1781, I/1:1–16) was "a new system about the sun and the fixed stars" by a certain Peyroux de la Coudrenière, who claimed that the Milky Way could not be a system of stars because the telescopes disclosed everywhere in the sky the same immensity of stars but not the whiteness of the Milky Way, which therefore must be looked upon as the place where the vapours of comets and of other celestial bodies accumulate. The *Magazin* reported (1785, III/2:35) about a cosmogonical system by F. W. Sack, which included (with no reference to Kant) a prediction of the rotation of Saturn as 11 hours and 16 minutes. Far more significant were the reports about Herschel's papers on the motion of the solar system (1785, III/2:75–81), on volcanos in the moon (1790, VII/2:173), on Saturn's period of rotation (1790, VII/3:181), on Saturn's ring (1794, IX/4:50–64), on the construction of the heavens (1797, XI/3:1–16), and on Bugge's work on the flattening of Saturn (1792, VIII/1:171–72), to mention only a few examples which could have justified a reference to the *Allgemeine Naturgeschichte*, if it had been valued outside a small circle of Kant's admirers.
56. "Etwas über die relative Bewegung der Fixsterne; nebst einem Anhange über die Aberration derselben," *Astronomisches Jahrbuch für das Jahr 1803* (Berlin, 1800), pp. 185–94. For quotation, see p. 186; for reference to translation, p. 190 note.
57. The translation by J. K. Fr. Hauff appeared under the title, *Darstellung des Weltsystems* (Frankfurt a. M.: bey Varrentrapp und Wenner, 1797), and was reviewed in *Magazin für den neuesten Zustand der Naturkunde mit Rücksicht auf die dazu gehörigen Hülfswissenschaften* (Jena), edited by Johann Heinrich Voigt, 1 (1798):173–76. This *Magazin* was a continuation of the one cited in note 55 above. Kant might have been mentioned by the reviewer, had he found reference to Kant in the *Exposition*. Laplace seems to have remained for the rest of his life unaware of Kant's cosmogony. An evidence of this is the "Notice historique" on studies on the ring of Saturn in the 5th volume of Laplace's *Traité de mécanique céleste*, published in 1825 or two years before his death

(Paris: Bachelier, pp. 319–23), in which Huygens, Maupertuis, Cassini and others are carefully recalled and a reference is made to Laplace's own calculation in 1787 of the period of rotation, of about ten hours, of a particle on the inner rim of Saturn's ring (p. 321). Laplace pointedly noted that his calculation of that value had preceded by two years Herschel's observation of it. He did not suspect that Kant preceded Herschel by forty-four years (see note 47 to Section Five of Second Part of translation). A more generic evidence of Laplace's lack of awareness of Kant's cosmogony is, of course, that Laplace's cosmogony is very different in most respects from that of Kant. For details, see *Planets and Planetarians*, pp. 122–34.

58. "Über die Durchsichtigkeit des Weltraums," *Astronomisches Jahrbuch für das Jahr 1826* (Berlin, 1823), pp. 111–12.

59. See my edition of "Drei kosmologische Vorträge von Wilhelm Olbers," in *Nachrichten der Olbers Gesellschaft* (Bremen) Nr. 79, Oktober 1970, pp. 14–28.

60. "Nachricht von merkwürdigen Beobachtungen über den Ring des Saturns," *Astronomisches Jahrbuch für das Jahr 1806* (Berlin, 1803), pp. 159–64. Kant was again ignored in Schröter's big monograph on Saturn, *Kronographische Fragmente zur genauern Kenntniss des Planeten Saturn, seines Ringes und seiner Trabanten. Erster Theil, Beobachtungen, Folgerungen and Bemerkungen über den Naturbau der festen Kreisgewölbe des Saturnringes und seiner Atmosphäre* (Göttingen: in Commission der Vandenhök Ruprechtischen Buchhandlung, 1808). In connection with each topic indicated in this long title a reference to the *Allgemeine Naturgeschichte* would have been obligatory, if its respective contents had been judged by Schröter to have scientific merit. The silence of Schröter, so famed for his observational skill as to be called the German Herschel, was matched by the silence of Gauss, even more famous as a theoretician, who in 1808 did not dignify to a comment Laplace's nebular hypothesis in his review of the third enlarged edition of the *Exposition*. See *Göttingische Anzeigen von gelehrten Sachen*, July 23, 1808 (pp. 1185–92).

61. The three separate editions were published in 1797 (Frankfurt and Leipzig; 130pp), in 1798 (Zeitz: bey Wilhelm Webel; 143pp, preceded by 18 unnumbered pages of the "Vorrede"), and in 1808 (same place and publisher with almost exactly the same pagination). The editions by Webel were unauthorized. These three editions carried explanatory notes by a certain M. F., partly based on the excerpts and notes published by Gensichen. The same annotated text appeared in 1797 in the 2d volume of *Immanuel Kants frühere noch nicht gesammelte kleine Schriften* (Frankfurt and Leipzig). The text in the first of the four volumes of *Immanuel Kants vermischte Schriften* (Halle: in der Rengerischen Buchhandlung, 1799–1807, pp. 283–520) is that of the original edition without annotations. I was unable to consult the text in vol. I of *Immaneul Kants sämmtliche kleine Schriften. Nach der Zeitfolge geordnet* (Königsberg and Leipzig, 1797), reported in *Reprint 1968*, p. 181.

62. "Sir William Herschel," in *Abhandlungen von Friedrich Wilhelm Bessel*, edited by R. Engelmann (Leipzig: W. Engelmann, 1875–76), 3:468–78.

63. "Über die physische Beschaffenheit der Himmelskörper," in *Populäre Vorlesungen über wissenschaftliche Gegenstände von F. W. Bessel*, edited by H. C. Schumacher (Hamburg: Perthes-Besser & Mauke, 1848), pp. 68–93; for quotation see p. 93.

64. *Untersuchungen über den Ursprung und die Ausbildung der gegenwärtigen Anordung des Weltgebäudes* (Gieszen und Darmstadt: bey Georg Friedrich Heyer, 1802). The two Marschall von Bieberstein brothers were high-ranking officials for the

educational system in Nassau and Baden. Their sole reference to the *Allgemeine Naturgeschichte* and Kant (p. 236) occurred in connection with the Milky Way, although they often referred to the publications of Lambert, Laplace, Bode, Schröter, Herschel, Buffon, and other well remembered authors. Of the two brothers Karl Wilhelm was the more prolific, but his contributions to von Zach's *Monatliche Correspondenz zur Beförderung der Erd-und Himmels-Kunde* between 1806 and 1810 contained no mention of Kant, although their topics were most germane to various parts of the *Allgemeine Naturgeschichte*.

65 *Über die Bildung des Erdballes und ins Besondere über das Lehrgebäude des Herrn de Luc* (Hamburg: bey Carl Ernst Bohn, 1802). De Luc, absentee professor of geology in Göttingen, set forth his views in his lengthy *Lettres sur l'histoire physique de la terre addressées à M. le Prof. Blumenbach renfermant de nouvelles preuves géologiques et historiques de la mission divine de Moyse* (Paris: chez Nyon, ainé, An VI = 1798) with no reference to the *Allgemeine Naturgeschichte*.

66. See AA 12:343. Reimarus' letter was dated August 10, 1802. No reply of Kant is extant.

67. *Über die Bildung des Erdballes*, pp. 16, 23, 26.

68. *Bibliographie astronomique; avec l'histoire de l'astronomie depuis 1781 jusqu' à 1802* (Paris: de l'Imprimerie de la République, An XI = 1803). The books published in 1755 are listed on pp. 454–58. Lalande, who was in constant exchange with German astronomers during the 1790s, did not learn from them about the excerpts published by Gensichen in 1791. The sole reference to Kant is in connection with the publication in 1782 of the first volume of Lambert's *Briefwechsel* (p. 584). According to W. Ley (see *Reprint 1968*, p. xvii), who provides no documentation, Laplace learned of Kant's work, as he was asked by someone, "whether he had taken from Kant the idea that the solar system had originated with a cloud of cosmic dust. Laplace denied it with some indignation, and there is no reason to doubt his word." This detail, the reliability of which is most doubtful, is certainly not from Adickes' references to Laplace in his *Kant als Naturforscher* (see 2:237 and 270).

69. They are listed and discussed in my introduction to Lambert's *Cosmological Letters*, pp. 26–32.

70. A reprint of that translation, *Lettres cosmologiques sur l'organisation de l'univers, écrites en 1761 par J. H. Lambert* was published in 1977 (Paris: Editions Alain Brieux) with an introduction by J. Merleau-Ponty.

71. See ibid., pp. 37, 51, 69, 99, 111, 134–35, 137, 184, 232, 242–43, 247, 254, and 279.

72. Ibid. p. 4.

73. Ibid.

74. See the painstaking researches of R. Jaquel in his *Le Savant et philosophe mulhousien Jean-Henri Lambert (1728–1777): Études critiques et documentaires* (Paris: Editions Ophrys, 1977), pp. 119–24 and 141–55, and my essay review of the French translation (see note 70 above) in *Recherches d'histoire des sciences*.

75. Herschel's sole reference in 1805 to Lambert's work as being "full of the most frantastic imaginations" was occasioned by his pageing through Merian's French abridgment of it, first published in 1770. For further details, see *Cosmological Letters*, pp. 34 and 211.

76. *Emanuel Kant: Essays and Treatises on Moral, Political, and Various Philosophical Subjects* (London: printed for the translator and sold by William Richardson, 1789–99), see vol. 2, p. 331: "Kant foretold in 1755 (in his *Universal Physiognomy and Theory of the Heavens*) from theoretical grounds what Herschel discovered

many years after by the assistance of his gigantic telescope. It cannot but be interesting to compare the structure of the heavens, which one great man has conceived according to Newtonian laws from the original *genesis* of the celestial bodies, with the construction of the heavens as another great man has exhibited it according to observations." The translator, who did not identify himself, was A. F. M. Willich.

77. *Kosmos. Entwurf einer physischen Weltbeschreibung* (Stuttgart and Tübingen: J. G. Cotta'scher Verlag), the four volumes of which appeared in 1845, 1847, 1850, and 1858, respectively. See vol. 3, p. 32.

78. Humboldt's silence on Kant was particularly telling as he discussed in that third volume such topics as the Milky Way (pp. 181–89) and the central bodies of systems of stars (pp. 280–83). Over the almost three hundred pages (371–644) of Humboldt's discussion of the solar system Kant was mentioned only in a note (pp. 551–52). According to that note, which must have cut to the quick Kant's admirers, priority over Herschel "had been ascribed with no justification to the famous philosopher Immanuel Kant" concerning the period of Saturn's rotation. Humboldt noted the four hours' difference between the value computed by Kant and the one observed by Herschel, and also noted that only the motion of the inner edge of Saturn's ring is in accord with Kant's computation but not that of the outer edge. The criticism was all the more devastating, because Humboldt also quoted Kant's words concerning the importance of his computation on behalf of the validity of his cosmogony.

79. Ibid., 1:103. In the second volume, devoted almost entirely to the history of physical world view (pp. 135–544), Leibniz's *Protogea* was the last work in a survey which was top-heavy in its references to sundry dicta of classical Greek and Roman authors.

80. Ibid., 1:90.

81. *Johann Samuel Traugott Gehler's Physikalisches Wörterbuch neu bearbeitet* von Brandes, Gmelin, Horner, Muncke, Pfaff (Leipzig: E. B. Schwickert).

82. "Weltall," 10:1371–1496.

83. Ibid., pp. 1462–83.

84. "Milchstrasse," 6:2282–83.

85. "Planeten," 7:582–89; see especially pp. 588–89 where in connection with the evolution of planets Buffon and Laplace are mentioned but not Kant!

86. "Physik-Geschichte," 7:546.

87. "Materie," 6:1393–1472, of which a large part (pp. 1409–36) is a sharp criticism of the ideas proposed by Kant and his idealist successors.

88. See note 55 to Section III of this Introduction.

89. For details, see my *Planets and Planetarians*, pp. 134–35.

90. See English translation, *Hegel's Philosophy of Nature*, by M. J. Petry, with annotations (London: George Allen and Unwin, 1969), 1:259.

91. In particular, Gauss, Ohm, and Helmholtz may be mentioned in this respect. See my *The Relevance of Physics* (Chicago: University of Chicago Press, 1966), p. 334.

92. See English translation by E. F. Payne, *Parerga and Paralipomena: Short Philosophical Essays* (Oxford: Clarendon Press, 1974), 2:134–44.

93. Ibid., p. 133.

V. *The Workshops of Glory*

1. H. von Helmholtz, *Popular Lectures on Scientific Subjects*, translated by E. Atkinson and others (New York: D. Appleton, 1873), pp. 153–96. This lecture is

reprinted in Helmholtz, *Popular Scientific Lectures*, introduced by M. Kline (New York: Dover, 1962), pp. 59–92.

2. *Popular Scientific Lectures*, pp. 70 and 77.
3. Ibid., p. 75. Here I have improved the translation on the basis of the German original.
4. *Die Wunder des Himmels, oder gemeinfassliche Darstellung des Weltsystems* (2d rev. ed.; Stuttgart: Hoffman'sche Verlagsbuchhandlung, 1842), p. 640. The *Études d'astronomie stellaire*, which F. G. W. Struve, director of the Pulkovo Observatory, published in 1847 (St. Pétersbourg: Imprimerie de l'Académie Imperiale des Sciences), could bring Kant at most to the notice of astronomers among whom, as Struve noted, "he is little known." They could only be negatively disposed toward Kant's cosmogony after reading Struve's remark (who apart from this discussed only Kant's views on the Milky Way, pp. 8–11) that Kant's program, aimed at deriving with the help of the laws of mechanics the formation of celestial bodies in their infinity and the origin of their motions from the primitive state of matter, was a "sublime enterprise, if not too difficult for the human mind."
5. *Popular Scientific Lectures*, p. 75.
6. See A. Hermann, *Max Planck in Selbstzeugnissen und Bilddokumenten* (Reinbek bei Hamburg: Rowohlt, 1973), p. 28.
7. *Popular Scientific Lectures*, pp. 75–76.
8. For documentation, see ch. 5, "The Nebulous Advance," in my *Planets and Planetarians*. The only notable exception was J. P. Nichol, professor of astronomy in Glasgow, in whose books references to Kant were notably absent.
9. Ibid., pp. 155–57.
10. Ibid., pp. 174–75.
11. "Über Kants 'Allgemeine Naturgeschichte und Theorie des Himmels'," *Altpreussische Monatschrift* 2 (1865):339–53. This periodical, which according to its subtitle served "the mirroring of the provincial life in literature, arts, science, and industry," was read far beyond the confines of the Province of Prussia.
12. Überweg merely reported the contents of the *Allgemeine Naturgeschichte* and other pre-*Critique* works of Kant on scientific topics, without discussing their merits, even in the 2d revised edition of his *Grundriss der Geschichte der Philosophie von Thales bis auf die Gegenwart. Dritter Theil. Die Neuzeit* (Berlin: Ernst Siegfried Mittler & Sohn, 1868), pp. 149–50, published three years before his death. Uncritical glowing appraisal of Kant's cosmogony was greatly strengthened by its account in Kuno Fischer's *Geschichte der neuern Philosophie*, a six-volume work, of which two volumes were entirely devoted to Kant and which went through at least ten editions between 1868 and 1914. See, for instance, the 3d revised edition (München: F. Bassermann, 1882), 3:132–52.
13. "Über Kants Allgemeine Naturgeschichte," p. 342.
14. Ibid., p. 350.
15. Ibid., p. 353.
16. "Über Kant's Kosmogonie," *Altpreussische Monatschrift* 3 (1966):312–22; for quotation, see p. 312. That Hay was a scientist, possibly a biologist, is my conjecture, based on his lecture. His name is not listed in standard lexicons, biographical dictionaries, and bibliographies.
17. Ibid., p. 318.
18. "Kant und die Naturwissenschaft, mit besonderer Rücksicht auf neuere For-

schungen," *Deutsche Vierteljahrs-Schrift* (Stuttgart) 31/2 (1868):50–102. Reuschle was professor of mathematics and physics in a gymnasium in Stuttgart and author of textbooks on mathematics, physics, geography, and astronomy.

19. Ibid., p. 94.

20. Ibid., p. 50.

21. *Popular Lectures on Scientific Subjects*. Second Series, translated by E. Atkinson (New York: D. Appleton, 1881), pp. 139–95. For quotation, given here with corrections based on the German original, see p. 184.

22. *Photometrische Untersuchungen mit besonderer Rücksicht auf die physische Beschaffenheit der Himmelskörper* (Leipzig: W. Engelmann, 1865), pp. 214–31. Zöllner did not consider the changes which Laplace's cosmogony had undergone in the various editions of the *Exposition*.

23. *Über die Natur der Cometen: Beiträge zur Geschichte und Theorie der Erkenntniss* (Leipzig: Wilhelm Engelmann, 1872), see pp. 426–82, "Immanuel Kant und seine Verdienste um die Naturwissenschaft." This second unaltered edition followed within a year the first, suggesting the attractiveness of its chauvinistic and obscurantist parts, although the book contained some scientifically very insightful though at that time unappreciated chapters, such as the one on the gravitational paradox of an infinite homogeneous universe, a paradox which, as Zöllner pointed out half a century before Einstein, could only be resolved with a four-dimensional treatment of the universe consisting of a finite amount of mass.

24. *Zur Kosmologie der Gegenwart: Bemerkungen zu J. C. F. Zöllner's Buch Über die Natur der Kometen* (Bonn: Eduard Weber's Buchhandlung, 1872). The nebular hypothesis was discussed on pp. 21–37.

25. See his review of Laplace's *Oeuvres* and of the works of the younger Herschel and other astronomers in *Westminster Review* 70 (1858):185–225.

26. "The Anniversary Address of the President," *Proceedings of the Geological Society of London* 25 (1869):xxviii–liii; for quotation see p. xlv. A slightly revised version of the part of the address bearing on geology proper is printed under the title, "Geological Reform," in T. H. Huxley, *Discourses: Biological & Geological* (London: Macmillan, 1894), pp. 304–39.

27. "Anniversary Address," p. xlv.

28. See Huxley's Romanes Lecture given in 1893 under the title, "Evolution and Ethics," reprinted in *Evolution and Ethics and Other Essays* (New York: D. Appleton, 1914), pp. 46–86; see especially pp. 48–50.

29. Ibid., pp. 62–65 and 79–80.

30. "Anniversary Address," pp. xlv and xlvi. Huxley, who also spoke highly of the significance for geology of Kant's cosmogony as set forth in the latter's *Physische Geographie*, did not wonder why Kant discussed there several cosmogonies except his own (ibid., p. xlvi).

31. "Crabbed Age and Youth" (1878), in *Essays by Robert Louis Stevenson*, with an Introduction by W. L. Phelps (New York: Charles Scribner's Sons, 1918), p. 316.

32. "Anniversary Address," p. xlix. No wonder that Huxley failed to see anything wrong in Kant's calculations of the retardation of the earth's axial rotation (ibid.)!

33. Ibid., p. xlvi.

34. "Of Geological Dynamics," an address given to the Geological Society of Glas-

gow on April 5, 1869; see its *Transactions* 3 (1871):215–40, especially p. 236.

35. "Anniversary Address," p. xlvii. English opinion of Kant's cosmogony was formed in a different sense by Agnes Clerke. While the brief reference to it in the four editions of her *Popular History of Astronomy during the Nineteenth Century* (Edinburgh Adam & Charles Black, 1885, 1887, 1893, 1902) was somewhat ambivalent (see pp. 340, 351, 374, 308 respectively), her dictum in her *Modern Cosmogonies* (London: Adam & Charles Black, 1905) was subtly devastating: "Kant is highly accommodating; one can deviate widely from, without finally quitting, the track of his conceptions; they are capacious and indefinite enough to comport with much novelty both of imagination and experience, and hence lend themselves with facility to the changing requirements of progress" (p. 62). Clerke may have been the "well known historian of astronomy" who, according to Becker ("Kant as a Natural Philosopher," *American Journal of Science* 5 [1898]:97), "stated in 1882 that Kant had put forward 'a true nebular cosmogony, though one in which the primitive reign of chaos was little likely to terminate'." Far less influential was T. E. Gore, whose *The Visible Universe* (London: Crosby Lockwood and Son, 1893) started with a detailed account of Kant's cosmogony.

36. *The History of Creation: or the Development of the Earth and Its Inhabitants by the Action of Natural Causes*, English translation revised by E. Ray Lankester (New York: D. Appleton, 1876), 1:325. The German original, *Natürliche Schöpfungsgeschichte*, was first published in 1868.

37. Ibid. Haeckel had already declared that in the *Allgemeine Naturgeschichte* "exact knowledge is coupled with the most profound speculation" and that its author deserves therefore "the honourable name of a natural philosopher in the best and purest sense of the word" (p. 101).

38. Ibid. p. 324.

39. Ibid.

40. Ibid., p. 323.

41. Ibid., p. 324. Not surprisingly, Haeckel also professed to know that Kant's theory, "which enjoys at the present day almost universal recognition," was further developed by Laplace and Herschel (p. 101). That recognition was certainly promoted by the nine editions which the German original saw in thirty years. The English translation was in its sixth edition by 1914.

42. *Outlines of Cosmic Philosophy Based on the Doctrine of Evolution with Criticisms of the Positive Philosophy* (London: Macmillan, 1874), 1:364 and 397. Both quotations are from the chapter, "Planetary Evolution."

43. Its manuscript was written between 1872 and 1882. References are to the English translation, *Dialectics of Nature*, by C. Dutt with a preface and notes by J. B. S. Haldane (New York: International Publishers, 1940).

44. Ibid., p. 11.

45. Ibid., p. 8.

46. Ibid., p. 9.

47. Ibid., p. 10.

48. *Allgemeine Naturgeschichte* (Ostwald's Klassiker der Exakten Wissenschaften, Nr. 12), edited by H. Ebert (Leipzig: Wilhelm Engelmann, 1890), p. 98.

49. In this work of 255 pages, the first 101 pages are devoted to the theories of Kant and Laplace, to objections to Laplace's theory, to the cosmogony of Faye, to the researches of G. H. Darwin, and to the question of the end of the universe. The remainder of the book is Wolf's translation of Kant's work in its entirety. For subsequent quotations, see pp. 18–19.

50. Actually, he put in mathematical form Kant's reasoning about the absence of a ring around the other planets (ibid., p. 16), without noting its fallacy.

51. Ibid. Kant could, of course, very well be familiar with Cassini's report made in 1677. See note 17 to Fifth Section of Second Part.

52. The edition was again Nr. 12 in the series (Leipzig: Wilhelm Engelmann).

53. Ibid., pp. 147–48.

54. Ibid. In that work of Kant there is only one brief reference to heat (see English translation by J. Ellington, *Metaphysical Foundations of Natural Science* [Indianapolis: Bobbs-Merrill, 1970], pp. 75–76), which is described as the source of expansive force. Had Kant submitted something remotely profound on the subject, Ellington, an admirer of Kant the scientist, might have listed "thermodynamics" in the extremely detailed subject index compiled by him.

55. Ibid., p. 148.

56. Ibid.

57. Ibid., p. 150. It was compounded inaccuracy to state, as Oettingen did, that the idea of other Milky Ways was set forth in Fontenelle's *Entretiens sur la pluralité des mondes* (1686), a work "still republished by Lalande with notes in 1819" (pp. 150–51). An edition by Lalande, who died in 1807, was still being republished in the 1820s.

58. AA 1:215–368.

59. These will be pointed out in the notes to the translation.

60. In addition to Dieterich's *Kant und Newton*, discussed in Section I above, mention may be made of *Kant oder Laplace: Kosmologische Studie* by A. Meydenbauer (Marburg: N. G. Elwert'sche Verlagsbuchhandlung, 1880) in which the introduction comes to a close with the declaration: "The [author's] reliance on Kant is in debt, I believe, to the memory of this greatest thinker of all times, who had shown, though in vain, the road to follow already more than a hundred years ago" (p. iv). In the essay a long list was given of the basic shortcomings of Laplace's theory (pp. 2–3), whereas of Kant's theory, as confirmed by Meydenbauer's study of meteorites, the latter claimed by way of a grand conclusion that it was "in harmony, in opposition to Laplace's theory, with all positive observational results, be they optical, spectral-analytical, statical, or mechanical," a conclusion worthy of a dilettante who deplored at the outset that "a crown of dilettantes tries nowadays to come grip, in some cases equipped with excellent instruments, with the cosmological problem" (p. iii).

61. *Die Cosmogonie von Kant* (Wien: K. K. Hofbuchhandlung Wilhelm Frick, 1893), p. XXVI. This study of 34 large quarto pages was a doctoral dissertation presented at the University of Munich and consisted of two parts. In the first, Eberhard considered the question of the formation of planets, of their orbits, of their rotation, and of Saturn's rings (pp. V-XXII). In the second, he discussed the value of Kant's theory for modern science and its relation to Laplace (pp. XXIII-XXVI). The remainder of the study was a conclusion and documentation. The tone of the first part was set by statements such as the one relating to orbital motion: Kant's explanation of it "is wholly defective" (p. XI) and that "it is puzzling to a high degree that Kant's theory of Saturn's ring was so greatly praised (p. XVII), because "his entire theory is generally deficient and wrong in almost all particulars" (p. XVII). In the second part Eberhard took issue with Zöllner by defending Laplace's originality and superiority with respect to Kant. The able criticism of both Kant and Laplace, which F. Pfaff published in 1883, created some echo only twenty years later (see note 100 below).

62. The orator was W. Foerster who spoke on "Die Wandlungen des astronomischen Weltbildes bis zur Gegenwart." See *Verhandlungen der Gesellschaft Deutscher Naturforscher und Ärzte. 71. Versammlung zu München. 17–23 September 1889, Erster Theil*, edited by A. Wangerin (Leipzig: F. C. W. Vogel, 1889), pp. 59–78; especially, p. 73.

63. On their papers and close collaboration, see my *Planets and Planetarians*, pp. 187–93.

64. That a motion for the inclusion of theory in the curricula was formally adopted at that meeting was claimed by Holzmüller (see p. 78 of his book cited in the following note), but the thick volume containing the proceedings of the meeting provides no clear evidence of this.

65. *Elementare kosmische Betrachtungen über das Sonnensystem und Widerlegung der von Kant und Laplace aufgestellten Hypothesen über dessen Entwicklungsgeschichte* (Leipzig: B. G. Teubner, 1906), 90–91. Holzmüller, who received his Ph. D. in 1870 at the University of Halle, was director of the industrial school in Hagen from 1874 until his retirement in 1897. The text of his book was based on lectures given to engineers and scientists in Krefeld. According to Holzmüller "the entire Kantian hypothesis is a chat in the style of Naturphilosophie which can hardly make claim to the mathematico-mechanical authority of Newton and in connection of which his famed critical sense signally abandons him" (p. 74). The basic failure of Kant's theory related to his "lively phantasy with which he tries to carry mechanical problems to exact solutions" (ibid).

66. *Das Problem der Entwicklung unseres Planetensystems* (Berlin: Julius Springer, 1908), ch. 2, entirely devoted to a critique of Kant's theory (pp. 2–12). Twenty or so years later Nölke seemed to be eager to blunt the edge of that criticism in his *Entwicklung im Weltall: Kosmogonische Probleme und Hypothesen* (Hamburg: Henri Grand, 1926), with the astonishing remark that "one has to omit only a few lines in Kant's presentation and all that remains retains its value and significance" (p. 31), a phrase which he repeated in his *Entwicklungsgang unseres Planetensystems: Eine kritische Studie* (Berlin and Bonn: Ferd. Dümmlers Verlag, 1930), p. 126. Kant, Nölke went on, should not be taken to task for not having at his disposal modern observational data, and be given full credit for his tracing the origin of Saturn's ring to radiation pressure, a most modern idea, and for calling attention to the cyclic nature of the dynamics of nature (p. 127)!

67. The German translation by L. Bamberger, *Das Werden der Welten. Neue Folge. Die Vorstellung vom Weltgebäude im Wandel der Zeiten* (1907) was already in its sixth edition by 1911 (Leipzig: Akademische Verlagsgesellschaft), p. 111.

68. *Entstehung der Welt und der Erde nach Sage und Wissenschaft* (3rd printing; Leipzig B. G. Teubner, 1919), p. 87. First published in 1911.

69. Ibid., p. 99.

70. Ibid., p. 103. Weinstein's inability to see that identity may have its explanation in his notion of cosmology as a poetical enterprise (p. 129). He indeed praised Kant for mixing poetry with cosmology. It is that mixing which prevents one from seeing differences as well as from sighting identities.

71. In the last chapter devoted to more recent theories Weinstein spoke only of Kelvin and Arrhenius.

72. Between 1900 and 1920 Chamberlin's name not once appeared in the pages of the prestigious *Bulletin astronomique*, and even Moulton was mentioned there on a few occasions only in connection with his papers that had nothing to do with the planetesimal theory.

73. For details, see *Planets and Planetarians*, pp. 202–04.

74. *Kant als Naturforscher*, see especially 2:304–10. In this almost 900-page-long book the *Allgemeine Naturgeschichte* is given more than a hundred pages (2:206–315), a sufficiently ample space for a detailed and carefully documented discussion of Kant's dependence on Newton, Bentley, Buffon, Derham, and Maupertuis, to mention only some principal names. Buffon, for instance, is mentioned only fleetingly (2:241) by Adickes, who apparently did not study the German translation of the first volume of Buffon's *Histoire naturelle*. Equally startling is Adickes' failure to look up the German translations of Derham's *Astrotheology*, a work explicitly mentioned by Kant. Most of Adickes' notes refer to the literature (mostly German) published on the *Allgemeine Naturgeschichte* during the second half of the nineteenth century, a literature wholly inadequate from the viewpoint of the history of science. Perhaps some justification is provided for all this (for those well informed about the true character of Naturphilosophie and Naturphilosophers) in Adickes's own view of Kant's achievement in the *Allgemeine Naturgeschichte*. According to him Kant's was "a feat of Naturphilosophie not of natural science" (2:310); Kant "neither wanted nor could be a natural scientist in the proper sense" (2:312); and even "in his time it would have been most natural for a real mathematician and astronomer to provide a sound basis" for one's cosmogonical theory (2:314). The relation of that theory to the history of true science can but appear of secondary importance if one is convinced with Adickes that Kant with his cosmogony "provided science with a leading hypothesis which has animated it for one and a half century and which has not even today been replaced by a better one" (2:310). Then one will not find anything contradictory in Adickes' assertions that, on the one hand, Kant's cosmogony "failed in many particular points and several times led even to conflicts with the laws of mechanics" (2:311) and, on the other, that Kant "was the first to establish and elaborate with the tools of firm, sober science [!] the idea about the unity of the universe through all spaces and times" (2:311–12). The prospects of a sober, constructive exchange with anyone ready to live with such a contradiction is hardly promising.
75. Ibid., 2:308–09.
76. Published in its third edition as Band 48a in the *Philosophische Bibliothek* (Leipzig: Verlag von Felix Meiner), 1922.
77. Quoted in Section I of this Introduction.
78. A survey and discussion of these theories is given in the concluding chapter of my *Planets and Planetarians*.
79. What Russell found was that the close encounter implied in the collisional theories was utterly incapable of providing that preponderance of angular momentum to the planets which they have with respect to the sun. See his *The Solar System and Its Origin* (New York: Macmillan, 1935), p. 114.
80. See the 2d revised edition of *Life on Other Worlds* by Sir Harold Spencer Jones (New York: Macmillan, 1951), p. 148.
81. For a summary and discussion of their theories, see *Planets and Planetarians* pp. 225–31.
82. The collection of essays, *Communication with Extraterrestrial Intelligence* (Cambridge, Mass.: The M.I.T. Press, 1973), edited by Carl Sagan, is entirely devoted to an evaluation (patently biased) of F. Drake's highly publicized estimate, cast in the form of a mathematical function, of the number of planets with a highly developed technology in our galaxy.

83. Best exemplified by the report of a study done in 1964–65 under the auspices of the Space Science Board of the National Academy of Science and published under the title, *Biology and the Exploration of Mars* by its editors, C. S. Pittendrigh, W. Vishniac, and J. P. T. Pearman (Washington, D.C.: National Academy of Science National Research Council, 1966).

84. "Astronomer's Luck," in *Quarterly Journal of the Royal Astronomical Society* 13 (1972):517–18. One wonders what McCrea thought on hearing in 1976 at a conference, of which he was a co-director, A. J. R. Prentice declare that "a modern version of the original Laplacian hypothesis is, taking into account the effects of supersonic turbulent convection and dissipative planetesimal drag, capable of providing a very satisfactory account of the formation of the solar system." See his paper, "Towards a Modern Laplacian Theory for the Formation of the Solar System," in S. F. Dermott (ed.), *The Origin of the Solar System (Proceedings of the NATO Advanced Study Institute at the University of Newcastle-Upon-Tyne in 1976 directed by W. H. McCrea and S. K. Runcorn)* (Chichester: John Wiley & Sons, 1978), p. 159. Was it not only three short years earlier that Prentice took the view that "today . . . hardly a single feature of the solar system is properly understood"? See his paper, "Formation of Planetary Systems," in J. P. Wild (ed.), *In the Beginning: Symposium on the Origin of Planets and Life Held as Part of the Copernicus 500th Birthday Celebration at Canberra on 27 April 1973* (Canberra: Australia Academy of Schence, 1974), p. 19. Prentice certainly misunderstood, or rather revealed his failure to study, the history of his topic by declaring in the same breath that "the German philosopher, Immanuel Kant, proposed in 1755 that at one time the sun was surrounded by a great gaseous nebula which became flattened into a disc-like structure as a result of rotation. Centres of conglomeration soon appeared in the gaseous disc where the gas density exceeded the average and these became the protoplanets from which the present planets were later derived." Of course, a scientist's ignorance of scientific history does not necessarily vitiate his theory, but one wonders how Prentice's ring-theory fares after Voyager I flashed back in early March a series of astonishing data about Jupiter. The data, of which the most startling provided evidence of the existence of a ring around Jupiter consisting of boulder-size debris, made Carl Sagan remark: "This is almost beyond interpretation. There's different chemistry, different physics, different forces at work out there" (TIME, March 19, 1979, p. 86). Different physics and the like are readily postulated by those who have previously taken for an open book the solar system, indeed all solar systems and life on each of them.

85. Most conspicuous in this respect was the *Festschrift* published by the University of Königsberg (Leipzig, 1924), which contained eleven contributions, the last of them being a long study (pp. 239–69) by R. Unger of the historical background of Kant's famous words on the awe which the contemplation of the starry sky always produced in him. Absence of reference to Kant the scientist was not wholly understandable in the *Festschrift* published in the same year by the International Union for the Philosophy of Law and Economics (Berlin-Grünewald: W. Rotschild) under the editorship of F. von Wieser, as it contained a study of the infinite in the works of Novalis (pp. 29–39).

86. "Kant as a Student of Natural Science," in *Immanuel Kant: Papers Read at Northwestern University on the Bicentenary of Kant's Birth* (Chicago: Open Court, 1925), pp. 101–111.

87. "Science," in *Immanuel Kant 1724–1924*, edited by E. C. Wilm (New Haven:

Yale University Press, 1925), pp. 51 and 61–62. Misleading wit set the tone of Shapley's lecture from the outset: "Before he degenerated into the major philosopher of this minor planet, Immanuel Kant was a scientist. Before he began his speculations concerning speculation, he speculated adroitly concerning physical fact" (p. 51). To this the editor added the equally misleading footnote: "Kant was throughout his life a conscientious student of science." Shapley certainly had no excuse for ignoring that many of the writings of Euler and d'Alembert, older contemporaries of Kant, were beyond his ken.

88. Ibid., pp. 57 and 60. Later Shapley remarked that "Kant's nebular hypothesis cannot well withstand present-day criticism" (p. 65).

89. Ibid., pp. 60–61. Certainly an absurd claim.

90. Ibid., p. 67. A classic case of a scientist reading his own research into old documents the contents of which he knows only from second-hand information or through hearsay.

91. Ibid., p. 66.

92. Ibid.

93. Ibid., p. 56.

94. Ibid., p. 54. Similarly uncritical were the long introduction and the many notes by A. Lampa (best remembered as a champion of Ernst Mach's positivism in physics) to his edition of the *Allgemeine Naturgeschichte*, published as Bd. 152–53 in *Deutsche Hausbücherei*, under the title, *Die Kant-Laplacesche Theorie* (Vienna: Österreichischer Bundesverlag, 1925), which included Lampa's translation of the concluding cosmogonical section of Laplace's *Exposition du système du monde*. According to Lampa, Kant's "inventive phantasy never once overstepped the boundaries drawn by sober, scientific and critical consideration" (p. 25). Lampa claimed that Kant was the first founder of scientific cosmogony (ibid), that his style is never unclear (p. 28), 2nd that his exactness is borne out by the numerically computed details in his work (ibid). Lampa's failure to study the historical background was in evidence by his exculpating Kant's wholly erroneous value for the moon's density by claiming that the true value could not be known at that time (p. 25). For Lampa even the Third Part "retained a great value and lasting significance" (p. 31), a claim which must be seen against Lampa's glowing endorsement of the Kantian notion of the "phoenix of nature" ever existing and ever rejuvenating itself from its ashes (pp. 29–30).

95. New York: Macmillan, 1926, pp. 199 and 225.

96. "Natural Science and the Critical Philosophy of Kant," in *The Heritage of Kant*, edited by G. T. Whitney and D. F. Bowers (Princeton: Princeton University Press, 1939), p. 42.

97. *Metaphysics and the Philosophy of Science* (Oxford: Basil Blackwell, 1969), pp. 471 and 480.

98. *Conjectures and Refutations* (New York: Harper and Row, 1968), pp. 175–77. A few among Popper's listeners may have recalled that a decade earlier Bertrand Russell, started his outline of Kant's philosophy by expressing his disagreement with the general estimate that Kant was "the greatest of modern philosophers," and summed up the *Allgemeine Naturgeschichte* as a work which "anticipates Laplace's nebular hypothesis, and sets forth a possible origin of the solar system. Parts of this work have a remarkable Miltonic sublimity. It has the merit of inventing what proved a fruitful hypothesis, but it does not, as Laplace did, advance serious arguments in its favour. In parts it is purely fanciful, for instance in the doctrine that all planets are inhabited, and

that the most distant planets have the best inhabitants—a view to be praised for its terrestrial modesty, but not supported by any scientific grounds." *A History of Modern Philosophy* (New York: Simon and Schuster, 1945), p. 705.

99. The manner in which this is done often has the veneer of impeccable scholarship, which on closer inspection turns out to be a clever throwing of a red herring. Thus E. Cassirer introduced his presentation of the *Allgemeine Naturgeschichte* in his *Kants Leben und Lehre* (Berlin: Bruno Cassirer, 1918) with a recall of the story that Kant once astounded a visitor from London with his most accurate description of Westminster Bridge (p. 45). Cassirer's readers, whom he kept in the dark about the context of eighteenth-century science and about the true measure of Kant's familiarity with it, were thus led to believe that Kant's discourse about the universe was just as accurate. Needless to say, Cassirer had to resort to the tactics of "scholarly evasiveness" by claiming that in his perspective the merits of the Kant-Laplace theory did not need to be discussed (p. 48).

100. *Das Problem der Entwicklung unseres Planetensystems*, pp. 215–16. Revealingly, Nölke offered this conclusion in rebuttal of the final remark in *Entwicklung der Welt auf atomistischer Grundlage: Ein Beitrag zur Charakteristik des Materialismus* (Heidelberg: Carl Winter's Universitätsbuchhandlung, 1883) by Friedrich Pfaff, professor of geology at the University of Erlangen, who in addition to a thorough criticism of both Kant's and Laplace's theories also listed the essential differences between the two (see pp. 155–62). In view of the current abuses of cosmogonical theories on behalf of materialistic philosophies, Pfaff emphasized that since it was illogical to assume an infinite regress in the chain of causation, the ultimate origin of the universe had to be sought in the Creator's *fiat*. Nölke, a devoté of the agnostic perspective of the *Critique*, could only be repulsed by that theistic viewpoint and would have no doubt agreed that the sundry references to the Creator in the *Allgemeine Naturgeschichte* were just as superfluous and unconvincing as was the case with the cosmogony of Descartes who, to recall Pascal's famous remark, "in all his philosophy would have been quite willing to dispense with God." It is the resolve to evade the rationality of the perspective of creation that turns the *Critique of Pure Reason* into a work aptly characterized by Pierre Duhem as "the longest, most obscure, most confused, and most pedantic commentary of these words of Pascal: 'We have an incapacity of proof, insurmountable by all dogmatism'." According to Duhem, the *Critique of Practical Reason* was a commentary, not much more successful, of the continuation of Pascal's statement: "We have an idea of truth, invincible to all scepticism." See Duhem, *La science allemande* (Paris: Hermann, 1915), pp. 17–18.

101. Scientific views of the cosmos have undergone during the last half a century, and especially since the discovery in 1964 of the 3°K cosmic background radiation, a radical shift from the markedly nebulous toward the extremely specific, so as to cast a pallor on the prospects of any a priori cosmological theorizing. A similar shift came overpoweringly into evidence with respect to the solar system exactly at a time, mid-November 1980, when a typesetting mishap—fortunate in retrospect—made room for a last-minute addition. At that time, or November 14 to be specific, the distinguished French daily, *Le Monde*, carried at the center-top of its front page the headline: VOYAGER-1 A BOULEVERSÉ TOUTES LES THÉORIES SUR LE SYSTÈME SATURNIEN. The headline was followed by a seven-line caption in Italics: "In less than twenty-four hours, between its close passage around Saturn's

Titan and its second crossing of the rings' plane, the space probe Voyager-1 has multiplied by a factor of a hundred or a thousand our knowledge of Saturn's system and has completely upset conjectures that had been worked out by the best theoreticians. There will be in history a Saturn before the 12th of November and a Saturn after that date. And few connections between the two."

A month or two before Voyager-1, launched on September 5, 1977, reached its closest approach to Saturn, the data transmitted by the two television cameras of that tiny one-ton spacecraft began to intimate that major scientific news were in the making. In August a red spot, similar to the one that had for long been an exclusive mark of Jupiter, was noted on the southern hemisphere of Saturn, indicative of huge storms on its gaseous surface. Soon afterwards a similar spot was detected on its northern hemisphere. Winds stirred up by these spots may have a speed of 1,300 km per hour, far exceeding the violence of the worst storms on earth. Then came the sighting of more and more rings. On October 21, Dr. Edward C. Stone, of the California Institute of Technology and the project's chief scientist, made the following entry in his notebook: "Too many divisions. They're in the wrong places to agree with the classical resonance theory. We need more satellites. Need to find some embedded large particles" (*The New York Times*, Nov. 18, 1980, p. C8, col. 1). They came as flood rushes in. And so did the rings.

Until August 1980 four rings around Saturn had been known with certainty. By October the number of rings was almost a hundred, and by mid-November, half a thousand, a figure which on further analysis of data may reach a thousand. Six rings were found in the Cassini division alone which, according to generally shared belief, should have been completely empty. One of those rings is not less than 500 miles in width. No less a surprise was the detection of the E ring extending far beyond the outer edge of the A ring, until now the outermost ring. The B ring, lying on the inner side of the Cassini division, was found to have radial spokes, a result which made Bradford Smith, a University of Arizona astronomer and chief of the Voyager's photointerpretation team, exclaim: "Those spokes are giving us nightmares" (TIME, Nov. 24, 1980, p. 40). Equally if not more nightmarish appeared the newly discovered very narrow F ring, just outside the A ring. Unlike the outer rings, the F ring is in an undulating motion with occasional "braids" appearing on it. Its stability may seem to be provided by small satellites, of which two were spotted, straddling on its outer and inner edge respectively. Gazing at the picture of those "braids", Smith mused: "It boggles the mind that it even exists" (NEWSWEEK, November 24, 1980, p. 61). Much the same applies to the system of rings as a whole. To quote Smith again, "The mystery of the rings keeps getting deeper and deeper" (ibid, p. 62).

The rings are not, however, so mysterious as to foreclose any speculation about their origin. In fact, the observation at close of Saturn's satellites suggests the very opposite of Kant's idea that the rings are the product of Saturn's ascending atmosphere. The rings seem to have originated from the breakup of some of Saturn's protosatellites as they collided with some large comets. The only comfort for Kant's theory from the new findings, namely, that the sunlight is indeed reflected on Saturn's dark side by its inner rings, is partly offset by their casting a shade on it during "daylight." Compared with this slight support on behalf of Kant's discourse about the genesis of Saturn's system, the findings about the surfaces of Saturn's satellites should seem to deal a death blow not only to Kant's but to anyone's speculation about living beings there. Not only are those satellites, with the exception of Titan, void of any atmosphere; their surface is pockmarked with craters, caused by devastating impacts from the outside, so as to make the soil, which is mostly ice, even more inhospitable for life. Ironically, the worst blow to dreamers, old and new, about extraterrestrial intelligence, comes from the findings about the atmosphere of Titan, a planet twice the size of the earth, and a much touted candidate as a possible abode of life. While observations from the earth indicated that most of Titan's atmosphere was composed of methane, suggesting the presence of organic molecules, and perhaps some forms of life there, Voyager's ultraviolet spectrometer revealed that Titan's atmosphere was mostly molecular nitrogen, along with atomic and ionised nitrogen. Methane in Titan's atmosphere amounts to a mere 1 percent. The probability of life, however primitive, is practically nil there.

Future speculations about the origin of Saturn's system must therefore forego hallowed clichés, good only for journalistic sensationalism, about extraterrestrial life within the solar system. Speculation must center on the extraordinary complicatedness of the system, a feature which must make one wary of hasty conclusions, even when reached by experts in celestial dynamics and magnetohydrodynamics. The latter discipline is required by the obvious ionization of some rings of Saturn, especially of the B ring with its spokes. Apart from magnetohydrodynamics, Saturn's system now calls for such an expertise in celestial dynamics as to make one gasp at the boldness of Kant to try his hand at the problem with no expertise of that kind whatever at his disposal. He certainly did not suspect that the system of Saturn, the genesis of which appeared to him an open book, would more than two hundred years later make one NASA scientist gasp: "It is the unthinkable that we're looking for—the unimaginable" (*New Scientist*, November 20, 1980, p. 491).

VI. *Translator's Travails*

1. *Germany*, translated by C. G. Leland (New York: John W. Lovell, 1892), 1:139.
2. Ibid. See also note 7 below.
3. Ibid., p. 140. Only a genius can do this, according to Heine, for whom "Immanuel Kant was no genius; and being conscious of this defect, Kant became . . . more distrustful of genius, and in his critique of the faculty of judgment he even declared that genius has nothing to do with science, as its sphere of action lies in that of art." Heine refers to Kant's work quoted in note 29 to Opening Discourse.
4. *Immanuel Kant's Critique of Pure Reason* (1929; New York: St Martin's Press, 1965), pp. vi–vii.
5. See Section I of this Introduction.
6. W. H. Walsh, *Kant's Criticism of Metaphysics* (Edinburgh: University Press, 1975), p. viii.
7. According to Heine, "Kant did much harm by the unwieldy, stiff-buckram style of his work, for imitators without intellect or vivacity aped him in his external form, and so there sprang up the superstition that a man could not be a philosopher and write well" (*Germany*, 1:140).

8. See N. K. Smith's remark (*Immanuel Kant's Critique of Pure Reason*, p. vii) on Kant's feverish insertion of clauses into sentences unsuited for their reception during the last four or five months of preparing the *Critique* for the printer. "Kant's syntax contains some sentence constructions which from the point of view of today's grammar are syntactically wrong," is stated in *Untersuchungen zur Sprache Kants* by L. Fischer *et al.*, (Hamburg: Helmut Buske Verlag, 1970), p. 10.

9. *Kant's Cosmogony*, p. cvii.

10. Ibid., p. cvi.

11. *Les hypothèses cosmogoniques. Examen des théories scientifiques modernes sur l'origine des mondes, suivi de la traduction de la Théorie du Ciel de Kant* (Paris: Gauthier-Villars, 1886), p. ix.

12. Ibid.

13. Ibid. Revealingly, Wolf specified those pages as the ones in which "Kant sets forth his ideas on the successive formation of worlds in the indefinite expanse of chaos, their decay and their resurrection." That Wolf, member of the French Academy of Sciences, failed even to hint that such pages, in view of the law of entropy, may only be philosophical in an unscientific way, seems strange indeed.

14. See Oettingen's edition of the *Allgemeine Naturgeschichte* in Ostwald's *Klassiker der Exakten Wissenschaften* (Leipzig: W. Engelmann, 1898), p. 153. The phrase in question runs through p. [33] of the text.

15. Berthold Heinrich Brockes (1680–1747), city councilor in Hamburg, and founder of the "Teutsch Übenden [Germanizing] Gesellschaft", published his translation of Pope's *Essay on Man* under the title, *Versuch vom Menschen des Herrn Alexander Pope, Esq, nebst verschiedenen andern Übersetzungen und einigen eigener Gedichten* (Hamburg: verlegts Christian Herold, 1740), a volume which contained not only some of Brockes' own poems and other translations, but also the translation by B. J. Zinck of a rebuttal from the "History of the Works of the Learned" of objections against Pope's *Essay*. Although Kant indicates only once (p. [121]) that he used Brockes' translation, it was the source of his two previous (pp. [d5r] and [21]) and three subsequent (pp. [171], [188], and [196]) quotations of Pope.

16. *Essay on Man. Der Mensch. Ein philosophisches Gedichte von Alexander Pope*, Deutsche Übersetzung mit der englischen Urschrift nach der letzten vermehrten Ausgabe. Heinrich Christian Kretsch (Altenburg: in der Richterischen Buchhandlung, 1759).

17. See Immanuel Kant, *Dreams of a Spirit-Seer illustrated by Dreams of Metaphysics*, translated by E. F. Goerwitz and edited with an introduction and notes by F. Sewall (London: Swan Sonnenschein, 1900), p. 84.

TRANSLATION

Opening Discourse

1. An obvious play on the pride which Frederick the Great took in the Academy of Sciences in Berlin, founded by his grandfather, Frederick I, in 1700 along with an organizational plan drawn up by Leibniz, but closed by the parsimonious Frederick William I. One of the first acts of Frederick upon ascending the throne in 1740 was to reopen the Academy. In 1744 he reorganized it into four classes (philosophy, mathematics, sciences, literature) and filled its roster. The latter, as is clear from the glowing and detailed report in the *Freye Urtheile* (1 [1744]:275–79 and 284–88; May 1 and 5, issues respectively) did not yet include Maupertuis and Euler. Maupertuis was secured as President of the Academy in 1746 and served in that capacity for the next decade. Euler came to Berlin from St. Petersburg, a move indicative of Frederick's rivalry with Catherine the Great in the business of importing foreign talent. Far more available than the reports in the *Freye Urtheile* are the often heavy pages in *Geschichte der Königlich Preussischen Akademie der Wissenschaften* by A. Harnack (Berlin: Reichsdruckerei, 1900), 1:247–58, 293–304 (on the re-establishment of the Academy), and 1:471–72 (on its members). Less documentary but more entertaining is the chapter, "Frederick and the Academy," by W. Dilthey in P. Paret (ed.), *Frederick the Great: A Profile* (New York: Hill and Wang, 1972), pp. 177–97. The new Berlin Academy, which even from Paris looked as a first-class institution, could but appear an Eldorado of learning from Königsberg, where a professor lamented in 1736: "As is well known, I live where books and periodicals from other places are seen only after long years." See Stuckenberg, *The Life of Immanuel Kant*, p. 38.

2. The anonymous publication was on Kant's part a calculated move to enhance the effect of his being eventually noted by members of the Berlin Academy. Kant seems to have privately spoken to that effect, otherwise Borowski, whose name appears as one of the three student-objectors on the title page of Kant's dissertation on physical monadology for the degree of magister (1756; see AA 1:473), and was one of Kant's first students, would not have described four decades later in his *Immanuel Kant* (p. 26) the publication of the *Allgemeine Naturgeschichte* with a pointed reference to the Berlin Academy. However, the anonymous publication most likely reminded many in Königsberg of the publication there in 1743 of an almost 800-page long book, *Vernünftige Gedanken von der Natur*, which had for its subtitle the questions: "What is Nature? Is she powerless without God and His all-wise ordering? And how is the only indivisible divine power alone making active all in this world in and through intermediate causes, according to the measure of efficiency and fitness loaned to them?" The author, who identified himself in the title page as a "Christian

245

friend of God" who published his work "for the glorification of Divine Majesty and for the promotion of important truths" was Christian Gabriel Fischer, professor of physics in Königsberg from 1715 until 1725. In that year he was dismissed from his post and exiled from Prussia because of his published views on the origin of the soul and its status after death. Fischer was permitted to live in Königsberg after 1736 (he died there in 1751) and stirred a major controversy with the publication of his *Vernünftige Gedanken*, in which nature, such as the laws of motion treated rather primitively in Bk 6 (pp. 272–355), was reached only after purely metaphysical and theological topics, including the unity of divine and human natures in Christ (pp. 178–88). Compared with Fischer's unorthodoxy in matters theological, his laborious endorsement of a more or less mechanistic explanation of plants and animals in Bk 8 (pp. 395–698) could appear but a trifle to representatives of Lutheran orthodoxy in Königsberg.

3. One of the few atheists in mid-eighteenth-century Prussia was Frederick the Great himself. Another was de la Mettrie, a member of the Berlin Academy, who in 1748 claimed that his thoroughly materialistic *L'homme machine* was the logical implementation of Descartes' mechanistic philosophy.

4. The reference is to the biblical fundamentalism characterizing the powerful Pietistic branch of the Lutheran Church in Prussia at that time. Their leader, in Königsberg was Franz Albert Schulz, occupant of many important posts, including the chair of theology, who persuaded Kant to matriculate as a student of theology in the hope that he would eventually choose the ministry. The prospect must have been odious for Kant who for many years declined to keep in touch with his brother, a Lutheran minister.

5. Epicurus lived, indeed he flourished, in Christendom from the moment of the first printing in 1473 of Lucretius' *De rerum natura*, a celebrated exposition of Epicurus' doctrines. In the mid-seventeenth century Epicurus' ethics and atomism found a sympathetic and influential account in Gassendi's *De vita et moribus Epicuri* (1747) and *Philosophiae Epicuri syntagma* (1758).

6. While Kant made protestations of his religious orthodoxy, he clearly expressed in the *Allgemeine Naturgeschichte* his dislike of the prospect of God's supernatural interventions in Nature. Schulz may have had this in mind, when in 1758 he confronted Kant, who sought his support for obtaining the chair in logic and metaphysics, with the question: "Do you in your heart fear God?". Something of the uneasiness which the question provoked in Kant can be gathered from the fact that he spoke about it to Borowski, who many years later found it significant to report the incident. (See his *Immanuel Kant*, pp. 18–19). Schulz, not only a Pietist but also a leading Wolffian, who claimed that all divine truths can be demonstrated in a logically rigorous manner, was as much interested in Kant's religious sentiments, as in his theological views. Schulz's suspicions were fully justified by the publication of the *Critique* and the *Religion within the Limits of Reason Alone* (1793).

7. The word "Naturalisten" as used here by Kant has no exact equivalent in English. Kant means neither a "naturalist" or a student of nature, especially of plants and animals, nor a "natural philosopher," but an advocate of naturalism, that is, one for whom nature is the ultimate entity and therefore excludes a theistic interpretation. Later (see p. [b2r]) Kant designates the "naturalist" as a "freethinker."

8. By the time Kant came to the scene, the inference from the apparently purposeful arrangements of nature had produced (with English authors in the lead) a

vast literature to which German scholars contributed with customary zeal and thoroughness. The general approach set by Christian Wolff in his *Vernünftige Gedancken von der Absichten der natürlichen Dinge* (five editions between 1723 and 1752) was soon implemented in studies of particular aspects of nature. Particularly prolific were Johann Albert Fabricius (1668–1736), professor of the Gymnasium in Hamburg and also author of books on the history of classical literature, and Friedrich Christian Lesser (1692–1754), pastor in Nordhausen, near Erfurt, and member of the Berlin Academy. Fabricius prefaced in 1728 his translation of Derham's *Astrotheology* (see note 30 to First Part) with a list of well over 200 works useful for leading to the recognition of a provident God from the contemplation of nature. In 1730 Fabricius published his *Hydrotheologie* (a booklet of 32 pages republished in an enlarged form in 1734), which came to a close with his promise of eventually publishing a list of a thousand works relating to the subject. In 1732 there followed Fabricius' *Pyrotheologie*, a booklet of 119 pages consisting of the titles of four-hundred-and-fifty-one chapters distributed in ten Books, a project never completed. Of far greater value was Lesser's *Insecto-theologia* (three editions between 1738 and 1758; a French translation in two editions between 1742 and 1745, which on account of its being enlarged by Peter Lyonet's notes was published in English translation in 1799), which shows Lesser a meticulous observer of insects. His other works included a *Lithotheologie* (two editions between 1735 and 1751) and a *Testaceo-theologie* (four editions between 1741 and 1770). While these works of Lesser had considerable scientific merit, his *Versuch einer Heliotheologia, oder einer natürlichen und geistlichen Betrachtung der Sonne* (Nordhausen: Verlegts Johann August Cöler, 1753), a booklet of 76 pages, was largely devotional and contained no "natural" considerations worthy of mention about the sun. In view of the enormous popularity of this type of literature, there was certainly some daring on Kant's part in his departing from it, both on account of the Fischer affair in Königsberg and in view of Lesser's presence in the Berlin Academy. While nothing is easier than to find fault with that kind of teleological literature (see, for instance, K. Barth, *Church Dogmatics.* Vol. III, *The Doctrine of Creation*, Part I, [Edinburgh: T. & T. Clark, 1958], pp. 193–205), teleology, as I argued in my Gifford Lectures (*The Road of Science and the Ways to God* [Chicago: University of Chicago Press; Edinburgh: Scottish Academic Press], ch. 18), remains unexorcized from natural science and begs an answer, both philosophical and theological.

9. According to Adickes (*Kant als Naturforscher*, 2:213), this purposeful character of the daily variation of winds over Jamaica was the "parade-horse" of contemporary teleology, a statement not documented by him. The rise of sea-breeze over Jamaica around nine in the morning and its dying out by late afternoon was noted in widely read books such as *Britannia: or, a Geographical Description of the Kingdoms of England, Scotland, and Ireland, with the Isles and Territories thereto belonging* (London: printed by Tho. Roycroft, 1670) by Richard Bloome, who after noting the absence of hurricanes over Jamaica wrote that the island "hath gentle and refreshing winds, which constantly blow all the day from nine in the morning easternly, and become more fresh as the Sun mounteth higher, by reason of which *travel* and *labour* is sufferable; but from about eight at night to about eight in the morning, it frequently blows westernly; and with these *winds* or *breezes* the *Vessels* get out of the *Harbotrs*, and ply to Windward" (p. 333). This passage is reproduced almost verbatim in Bloome's *A Description of the Island of Jamaica* (London: printed by T.

Milbourn, 1672), pp. 7–8. The rise of seabreeze around nine in the morning was also pointedly noted by William Dampier in his "A Discourse of Trade Winds, Breezes, Storms, Seasons of the Year, Tides and Currents of the Torrid Zone . . ." (pp. 27–28), an appendix in the second volume of Dampier's *A New Voyage round the World* (London: printed for James Knapton, 1703–05). But this apparent gem from Jamaica was not seized upon in connection with the usefulness of winds in such classics of teleology as Nehemiah Grew's *Cosmologia sacra* (London: W. Rogers, 1701, p. 9), W. Derham's *Physico-theology* (London: W. Innys, 1714; see especially the long note [pp. 18–19] on sea breezes), B. Nieuwentijdt's *The Christian Philosopher* (translated from the Dutch original by J. Chamberlayne; London: J. Senex, 1718–19; 2:439–43), and last but not least in C. Wolff's *Vernünftige Gedancken von den Absichten der natürlichen Dinge* (see preceding note), or in the chapter on winds (pp. 291–307) in Wolff's *Vernünftige Gedancken von der Würckungen der Natur* (3d ed.; Halle in Magdeburg in der Rengerischen Buchhandlung, 1737) a work no less teleologically oriented. In view of this Kant must therefore, have had in mind authors of secondary importanace, if the interpretation he disputed had appeared in print at all!—Kant's discussion of the weather in Jamaica was not mentioned when there appeared in the *Hamburgisches Magazin* (Bd. 25, Stück 6, 1761, pp. 624–39) a German summary of an account of the British colonies in Jamaica and in the West Indies published a year earlier in the *Journal oeconomique*, in which the regular variation of winds was given in detail. That the climatic conditions were anything but pleasant in Jamaica was argued in "A Letter of that curious Naturalist Mr. Henry Barham, R.S.S. to the Publisher, giving a Relation of a fiery Meteor seen by him, in Jamaica, to strike into the Earth; with Remarks on the Weather, Earthquakes, etc. of that Island," *Philosophical Transactions* 29–30 (1718–1720):837–38.

10. Kant's interest in winds was further evidenced by his publication, next year, of a booklet with the title: "M. [agister] Immanuel Kant's comments on the clarification of the theory of winds, whereby he also invites to his lectures" the reader. The lectures were on physical geography (see note 19 to Section IV of Introduction) in which a treatise on winds formed the third section of Part I.

11. In the monumental *Grosses vollständiges Universal-Lexicon aller Wissenschaften und Künste* several authors, especially Christian Wolff, are cited on the usefulness of winds. See vol. 57 (Leipzig und Halle: Verlegts Johann Heinrich Zeidler, 1748), col. 622. The article on winds covers 58 folio-columns. In connection with trade-winds the remark is made that although they are useful they may have natural causes (cols. 613–14)! Clearly, Kant was not original.

12. Kant means the aforementioned winds, clouds, rain, storms, etc, or in general the various elements of nature about which he later (p. [28]) states that they are of many, indeed of infinitely many kinds, according to their densities.

13. That is, existing necessarily.

14. This "perfect chaos" is an echo of Descartes' starting his own cosmogony with as perfect a chaos as the poets (Lucretius) could ever imagine. Kant's chaos, as will be seen later, is anything but a chaos taken for complete homogeneity, that is for a thorough mixing of all its components.

15. This dependence is later pre-empted by Kant's insistence (in a truly Leibnizian and Wolffian fashion) that Newtonian laws of attraction (and repulsion), the composition of chaos as conceived by him, and the infinity of matter are of that highest degree of perfection which alone is worthy of the Creator, who

16. Possibly an echo of Bacon's statement in his essay "Of Atheism" that "a little philosophy inclineth man's mind to atheism; but depth in philosophy bringeth men's minds about to religion."

17. On Lucretius, see note 5 above.

18. The earliest of them was Leucippus who flourished in the second half of the 5th century B.C.

19. These deviations were in Epicurus' account wholly arbitrary, as Kant points out shortly afterwards (pp. [b5v–b6r]).

20. Here Descartes and Newton's relentless criticism of Cartesian vortices come instinctively to mind. In the cosmogony of Kant, who wants to appear as Newtonian as possible, vortices exist only prior to the full formation of the planetary system, a phase which Newton did not consider. Later (pp. b7r-v) Kant acknowledges the affinity of his ideas with those of Descartes.

21. See notes 13 and 15 above.

22. Kant seems to imply the perfectly valid point that no chaos is conceivably without some order in it. But his inference from an orderly chaos to the existence of God is vitiated by his failure to state that the orderliness of chaos can be of infinitely different kinds, none of which is the Creator bound to produce, let alone is he bound to create one specific chaos. The freedom of God to create, and to create any kind of world, was overlooked by Kant already in 1747 when he argued that not only worlds with any number of dimensions were possible, but that God was bound to produce all of them (see AA 1:24).

23. See note 6 above.

24. Actually, Descartes was so apprehensive on that score that after learning about Galileo's condemnation in 1632, he stopped writing his *Le monde*. As to the cosmogony set forth in his *Les Principes de la philosophie*, it was systematically ignored not only by his critics, but also by his disciples. See Section II of this Introduction.

25. Kant quoted from *Uebersetzung der Algemeinen Welthistorie* [etc.] *genau durchgesehen und mit häufigen Anmerkungen vermeret* von Siegmund Jacob Baumgarten (Halle: bey J. J. Gebauer, 1744), 1:80. The italics are by Kant. Here the passage is quoted according to the English original, *An Universal History from the Earliest Time to the Present compiled from Original Authors and Illustrated with Maps, Cuts, Notes, Chronological and Other Tables* (London: Printed for J. Batley in Paternoster Row, 1736), 1:35. The work was started by George Sale whose collaborators were mostly from Oxford and Cambridge. It represented, together with Dom A. Calmet's eight-volume *Histoire universelle, sacrée et profane, depuis le commencement du monde jusqu'à nos jours* (Strasbourg: J. Renauld Doulssecker, 1735–47), the last major attempt to pigeonhole history, geological and political, into biblical chronology (see R. W. Southern, "Aspects of the European Tradition of Historical Writing: 2. Hugh of St. Victor and the Idea of Historical Development," *Transactions of the Royal Historical Society* 21 [1971]: 159–79). In the *Universal History* the Mosaic account of genesis served as the framework for an account of cosmogonical theories (pp. 1–52), followed by a section on the creation of man and the location of the Garden of Eden (pp. 53–58). The philosopher is Descartes, whose cosmogony is followed by those of Burnet and Whiston (pp. 36–39).

26. Kant most likely echoed here Maupertuis who in his *Essai de cosmologie* took to

task "some philosophers, who were brazen enough to explain by these sole laws [of mechanics] all the mechanism and even the first formation [of the world]: give us, they have said, matter and movement, and we shall form a world such as this. An enterprise truly extravagant." Maupertuis in turn may have echoed Voltaire who in his *Elémens de la philosophie de Neuton* (1738) deplored the atheistic implication of Cartesian philosophy as unfolded by Spinoza: "It is since then that one has convinced himself with Descartes that it is impossible that the world should be finite, that motion is always of the same amount; it is since then that one dares to say: give me motion and matter, and I will make a world; and thus it must be admitted that these ideas seem to exclude, by very just consequences, the idea of the sole infinite being, only author of movement, sole author of the organisation of substances" (*Oeuvres complètes*, 22:404). Maupertuis and Voltaire had, of course, in view Descartes' claim made both in the *Principes* and in the *Le Monde*, that his laws would inevitably lead to the formation of the present world. See *Oeuvres de Descartes* (Paris: L. Cerf, 1897–1913), 8:322 and 11:34–35.

27. Kant's confident reference to the law of gravitational attraction as making clear the "inner driving mechanism" of planetary motions reminds one of E. Mach's remark that the law in question turned (unknown to most of those who like Kant gloried in it) from an "uncommon intelligiblity" into a "common unintelligiblity." About the same time Maxwell said that men of science would gladly devote the "whole remainder of their lives" to the study of a mechanical theory of gravitation if a promising one were available. See my *The Relevance of Physics* (Chicago: University of Chicago Press, 1966), p. 77.

28. The Kantian notion of matter as essentially endowed with the force of attraction was most un-Newtonian. No passage in the *Principia* and in the *Opticks* encouraged that notion which was expressly disavowed by Newton in his second letter to Bentley: "You sometimes speak of Gravity as essential and inherent to Matter. Pray do not ascribe that Notion to me; for the Cause of Gravity is what I do not pretend to know." See *Isaac Newton's Papers and Letters on Natural Philosophy*, edited by I. B. Cohen (Cambridge, Mass.: Harvard University Press, 1958), p. 298. See also note 35 to First Part.

29. The statement, especially when taken in connection with Kant's entrusting to necessary mechanical laws the implementation of purpose, implies that a mechanical explanation of plants and animals is in itself possible. He made no reference to his statement of his when thirty-five years later he published the *Kritik des Urtheils* (1790), a work which he considered the capping stone of his philosophical system and in which he took a very different view: "We can say boldly it is alike certain that is absurd for men to ... hope that another Newton will arise in the future who shall make comprehensible by us the production of a blade of grass according to natural laws which no design has ordered." See *Critique of Judgement*, translated with an introduction by J. H. Bernard (1892; reissued, New York: Hafner, 1951), p. 248. Reference to a blade of grass in that sense occurs also on pp. 225 and 258.

30. Thomas Wright (1711–1786) of Durham was a skilled mechanic, engraver, and author of books on astronomy and antiques. His life and work are portrayed with extensive documentation by M. A. Hoskin in his Introduction to the reprint edition of the *Original Theory* (see note 46 to Section II of this Introduction). This book became soon after its publication a rarity and remained largely unknown until recently. There was, however, no justification for Rahts' remark (AA 1:547) that on Wright's life "no precise informations

are available to us. His literary activity should be placed in the period 1740–60." On the availabilty of information prior to 1900 on Wright's life and work, see my *The Milky Way*, p. 206–07.

31. Kant's failure to mention the essay by its title is strange to say the least.

32. See note 3 of Section III of this Introduction.

33. Contrary to the impression given by Kant, he was not original in attributing a common motion to the stars. The summary of Wright's work in the *Freye Urtheile* (as well as in the *Hamburgisches Magazin* and the *Relationes de libris novis*) contained this idea.

34. James Bradley (1692–1762) was from 1721 professor of astronomy in Oxford and, following Halley's death in 1742, Astronomer Royal. The long passage is given here from his classic paper, "A Letter to the Right Honourable George Earl of Macclesfield concerning an apparent Motion observed in some of the fixed Stars" (*Philosophical Transactions* 45 [1748]: 1–41; for quotation see pp. 39–40), which is very accurately rendered in German by C. Mylius (*Hamburgisches Magazin*, Bd. 3, Stück 6 [1748]: 571–620; for quotation see pp. 616–17) and which was used by Kant verbatim, though not without some omissions and errors. Kant's failure to refer to this translation may perhaps be excused by the standards prevailing at that time, but the same cannot be said of Rahts' handling of this point (AA 1:547). His reference to the *Hamburgisches Magazin* does not state that the pages indicated contain the passage quoted by Kant. Rahts failed to note that the words within ⟨ ⟩ are missing in Kant's quotation of the German text. Kant's reliance on the volume 1748 of the *Hamburgisches Magazin* makes it most likely that he was familiar with its volume from 1752 which contained Kästner's lengthy German recension of Wright's *Original Theory*, a point already discussed in Section II of the Introduction. As to Hastie's handling of the quotation (*Kant's Cosmogony*, p. 32), it could easily create the impression that Kant was a reader of the *Philosophical Transactions*. This is also true of the editors of the three *Reprints*, of Wolf, the French translator, and of Oettingen. Kant most likely derived his basic information on the subject from Maupertuis' *Eléments de géographie* as printed in his *Ouvrages divers*, in which Article XVI is on the motion of stars (pp. 50–54) with a full reference to Bradley's paper.

35. The reference is most likely to the *Historia coelestis ex observationibus Tychonis Brahe ab Anno 1582 usque ad Annum 1601*, compiled by L. Baratti in two volumes (Vienna, 1656–66).

36. The reference is to the works, *Historia coelestis Britannica* (1725) and *Atlas coelestis* (1729), of John Flamsteed (1646–1719), first Astronomer Royal, published posthumously by Halley.

37. In the German translation, which is most likely by Kant himself, "absolute space" is rendered as "Weltraum."

38. The passage in brackets is left out in the German translation.

39. See Section II of the Introduction.
    a. Reference is to the recension in Latin of *Ouvrages divers* in the *Nova acta eruditorum, anno MDCCXL publicata* (Leipzig: literis Langenheimianis, 1745), pp. 221–29. See pp. 224–26 for the section quoted by Kant, who put in quotation marks the second half of the passage, a procedure all the more baffling because it is precisely there that he took considerable liberties with the text. Hastie, who obviously did not look up the Latin recension, gave a passage from the *Discours sur les différentes figures des astres* which differs even more from the Latin recension than does Kant's

"translation" of it. In the Akademie Ausgabe the sole comment on this long footnote rich in historical material is a reference to the *Nova acta* and to the *Discours* as if the two had contained the same text!

b. "which Mr. de Maupertuis explains after these" is missing in Kant's text.

c. Huygens reported his finding in his *Systema Saturnium* (1659); see *Oeuvres complètes*, 15:239.

d. See note 41 to Section II of the Introduction.

e. Ibid., p. 390.

f. See note 42 to Section II of the Introduction and note 30 to First Part.

g. "Empyrean heavens," according to the Latin recension.

h. See note 41 to Section II of the Introduction.

i. Here the following lines are missing from the Latin recension as translated by Kant: "of spherical form due to attraction, which became spheroidical through rotation around the axis [and], which, if they differ little from the sphere, would always represent circles, and, if [they differed from the sphere] very much, would represent, according to their various positions to the ecliptic, [either] circles, or ellipses, or plainly irregular figures, if several of such masses, viewed by the eye from afar, would coalesce into one and cover in part each other mutually." The omission of these lines is all the more revealing as on p. [c6v] Kant is not at all explicit in crediting Maupertuis with the explanation of the various shapes of nebulae.

j. The passage is quoted in Section II of the Introduction.

k. The Latin recension continues: "but in that case one should rather gather that these [luminous] masses are more distant from us than are the stars, because of weaker light."

l. This subclause is added by Kant.

m. Kant's parenthetical remark.

n. The rest of this sentence should read, according to the Latin recension: "seen to be projected unto the disc of those areas [spots], or if they are more distant, they transpire through those [luminous] masses as through the tails of comets."

40. Here Kant should have given credit to Maupertuis.

41. Hastie was hardly doing justice to Kant by omitting this Section.

42. Newton speaks of repulsive forces only in the hypothetical Queries added to the *Opticks*.

43. Christian Früchtegott Gellert (1715–69) took Germany by storm with the publication between 1746 and 1748 of his *Fabeln und Erzählungen*, a collection of short poems and stories written in an unaffected style in support of a reasoned piety and morality. One of the poems was about Hans Nord who announced through broadsheets to Londoners that any one of them could, upon the advance payment of eight pennies, see him enter a large flask with a narrow neck. A great crowd gathered but only to learn that Hans Nord took to the road with the entry fees in his pocket. See *Gellerts Dichtungen*, edited by A. Schullerns (Leipzig: Bibliographisches Institut, 1891), pp. 146–47.

44. These and similar reservations of Kant about the validity of his cosmogony are in flagrant conflict with his repeated assertions of its exclusive truth.

45. A most reasonable remark, but also a most unreasonable excuse for not subjecting to mathematical treatment the basic features of one's cosmogony, let alone for one's talking away qualitatively its crucial quantitative difficulties.

46. Revealingly, Kant did not recall the fate of Descartes' cosmogony when subjected to the "mathematical rigor" of Newtonian physics.

First Part

1. In Brockes' translation (pp. 4–5; see note 15 to Section VI of the Introduction) the German counterpart of these lines faces lines 32–34 of Epistle One of *Essay on Man*, lines which are a question:

   "Is the great chain, that draws all to agree
   And drawn supports, upheld by God, or thee?"

   Hastie, who did not consult Brockes' translation, took the lines quoted by Kant for lines 7–8 of Epistle Three, rendered by Brockes (pp. 58–59) as follows:
   "Betrachte dieses ganze Rund, und sieh mit ernstem Ueberlegen,
   Die grosse Liebes-Kette an, die das, was in der Unterwelt,
   So wohl als das, was in der Obern verbindet und zusammen hält."

2. Reference to the differential and integral calculus given in Newton's *Principia* in a geometrical formalism which had, however, been transposed by 1755 into the modern algebraic notation in Euler's numerous works.

3. This is Kepler's Second Law.

4. This is Kepler's Third Law.

5. Again, differential and integral calculus in a geometrical form.

6. A rather clumsy wording for radius.

7. In other words, the "systematic constitution" must resemble a flattened ellipsoid.

8. Long before Kant the astronomical literature had as one of its staple features the count 10 of "companions," that is, the moon, the four satellites of Jupiter discovered by Galileo in 1610, the first satellite of Saturn discovered by Huygens in 1655, and four further satellites of Saturn discovered by G. D. Cassini between 1671 and 1684. It would therfore have been more appropriate on Kant's part to write "since Cassini's time." No further increase in the number of known members of the planetary system came until the discovery of Uranus by Herschel in 1781.

9. The German "ewige" (eternal) is obviously an erroneously printed version of "einzige" (few). Kant later (p. [7]) gives the number of comets as being between 28 and 30, and speaks (p. [45]) of the "few cometary bodies" that were formed beyond Saturn's orbit.

10. The limit was set not so much by deliberation as by default or lack of courage. At any rate, Kepler certainly recognized a systematic constitution of the starry realm insofar as he viewed the Milky Way as a belt of small and densely packed stars enclosing a finite universe. Kepler did so in his *Epitome astronomiae copernicanae* (1618). See my *The Milky Way*, p. 108.

11. This remark of Kant on Wright's ideas (see Section II of Introduction) was rather unjustified in view of Kant's own purpose which used a "mechanical" cosmogony in support of a rather unconvincing teleology and of a distinctly bizarre reasoning about the moral and physical characteristics of denizens of other planets. Wright's taking other galaxies as so many abodes of eternal reward and punishment did not serve a much less "reasonable" purpose.

12. A happy remark indeed, and amply illustrated by the brevity of dicta on the Milky Way even after its first telescopic observation by Galileo in 1610. For

253

details, see chapters 4 and 5, "Galilean Myopia" and "Newtonian Distraction," in my *The Milky Way.*

13. The traditionally accepted number was 1022, given in Ptolemy's *Almagest.* The number greatly increased after Halley's survey in 1676 of the southern sky from Saint Helena. In Hevelius' *Prodromus astronomiae exhibens fundamenta . . . quibus additus est . . . Catalogus stellarum fixarum* (Gedani: typis J.-Z. Stollii, 1690), the number of fixed stars observed by the naked eye is given as 1888 (p. 111).

14. The absence of any qualification on Kant's part of this "imperishable" duration should seem strange in view of his emphatic assertion in Seventh Section of Second Part that all systems are subject to decay and rebirth.

15. Kant here uses "Centerfliehkraft," whereas on the preceding page he used "den Mittelpunkt fliehende Kräfte."

16. Here Kant changed in his own hand "Kraft" (force) to "Schwung" (thrust) in the manuscript of excerpts prepared by Gensichen (see AA 1:548).

17. Kant obviously took that number from Buffon's *Histoire naturelle* (1:149), or from its German translation (1:87). Like Buffon, Kant too failed to note that the number in question referred to comets with computed orbits. Buffon may have relied on the *Traité de la comète* of Chéseaux, who remarked (p. 42) that there are at least 30 comets with computed orbits. The estimate of Chéseaux, an expert on comets both in respect to observation and theory, was presumably an updating of the 24 (21) comets with computed orbits listed in Halley's "Astronomiae cometicae synopsis," *Philosophical Transaction* 21 (1705):1882–1904. Halley's Table was reported without additions in Pierre Charles Le Monnier's *La théorie des comètes où l'on traite du progrès de cette partie de l'astronomie* (Paris: chez Gab. Martin, J. B. Coignard, & les Frères Guerin, 1743), foldout facing p. 15. Halley's list of comets was enlarged by 12 in *Leçons élémentaires d'astronomie géometrique et physique* (Paris: chez les Frères Guerin, 1746, p. 243) by Nicholas de Lacaille, whose Table was reproduced in the "Éclaircissements" added by de Mairan to the second edition (1754) of his *Traité physique et historique de l'aurore boréale* (p. 345; see note 1 to Sixth Section of Second Part). The number in question rose to 51 in the first edition of Lalande's *Astronomie* (Paris: chez Desaint & Saillant, 1764) and to 80 in the second enlarged edition of Bode's *Erläuterung der Sternkunde und der dazu gehörigen Wissenschaften* (Berlin: bey Christian Friedrich Himburg, 1793), pp. 682–83. That the number of comets sighted was much larger had for long been a generally shared view when Lambert set forth in his *Cosmologische Briefe* (p. 72) his estimate that there may be as many as five million comets in the solar system.

18. A phrasing which misleadingly suggests that stars, which stand apart from the Milky Way, had been previously looked upon as being analogous to comets.

19. As with the case with the explanation of the Milky Way, the idea of a systematic motion of stars was also in the air. It was emphatically voiced in Wright's *Original Theory* (p. 63), a fact reported in all its three reviews published in Germany between 1751 and 1753. Tobias Mayer, professor of astronomy in Göttingen, conceived about that time of his plan to establish the motion of stars on the basis of comparing ancient and recent star catalogues, a plan of which Lambert may have first learned during his visit in Göttingen in 1756. See *Cosmological Letters*, pp. 5 and 216–17.

20. Huygens gave the value 27664 in his *Cosmotheoros* (see *Oeuvres complètes*, 21:814–16). The actual distance is 18 times greater than the one estimated

by Huygens who was fully aware of the uncertainties of his method. Huygens' value was exactly reproduced in Derham's *Astrotheology*, a chief source for Kant on astronomical lore. See note 30 below and pp. 21–22 in the four editions of its German translation listed there.

21. Since the square root of the cube of 21000 is about twice as great as the value calculated by Kant, an error corrected in Gensichen's excerpts, one should have half a degree instead of one.

22. Distant in time.

23. See Opening Discourse, pp. [c3v–c4v].

24. A view entertained by prominent astronomers, such as Tobias Mayer. See note 18 above.

25. Another view often voiced before Kant. See, for instance, Hevelius, *Cometographia, totam naturam cometarum exhibens* . . . (Gedani [Danzig]: auctoris typis et sumptibus, imprimebat Simon Reiniger, 1668), p. 424. and chapters 4 and 5 of my *Milky Way*. The view was reported in Derham's *Astrotheology*. See note 30 below and pp. cxx, cxxxiv, clx, and cxl (misprint for clx) respectively in the four editions of its German translation.

26. Philippe de la Hire (1640–1718) himself found a much too great difference between his observations of some stars made twenty years apart. See the concluding paragraph of his "Observation faite à l'Observatoire Royal du passage de la lune par les Pleiades, le 12 Mars au soir," *Mémoires de l'Académie Royale des Sciences depuis 1666 jusqu'à 1699*. Tome X (Paris: par la Compagnie des Librairies, 1730), pp. 275–78. According to de la Hire, Riccioli's observations recorded in his *Almagestum novum* (Bologna, 1651) were made with the greatest care.

27. Part of the idea was proposed by Maupertuis.

28. These "miraculous" notions, whatever they were, were not to be found in the representative astronomical literature. The "probable" opinion related those nebulous stars to the Milky Way, which was often thought of as a mixture of very small stars and of some ethereal material.

29. This passage, given by Kant as a verbatim quote, does not occur in ch. 6 on nebulous patches in the various editions of the *Discours*. Only the various ideas expressed in that quote about those patches can be found in that chapter in widely separate sentences. According to Hastie's erroneous claim (*Kant's Cosmogony*, p. 62), the passage is from the 1742 edition of the *Discours*, which he wrongly quotes as *Discours sur la figure des astres*.

30. The author of *Astrotheology* is William Derham (see note 42 to Section II of the Introduction. Concerning his opinion reported here by Kant, who had already given it in Halley's wording, see p. [c5v]. Kant's reference to the *Astrotheology* shows that he was familiar with it, a fact about which he will later provide (p. [99]) an indirect though revealing evidence. Derham's *Astrotheology, or a Demonstration of the Being and Attributes of God, from a Survey of the Heavens* went through six editions between 1715 and 1731, and was available from 1728 in German translation by J. A. Fabricius, under the title, *Astrotheologie, oder himmlisches Vergnügen in Gott* (Hamburg: bey Theodor Christoph Felginers Wittwe), which saw three more editions in 1732, 1739, and 1745. A thoroughly revised form of that translation, with a different subtitle, was published in 1765 (Hamburg: bey Johann Carl Bohn). The great popularity of Derham's work is also attested by its translations into Dutch, *Godgeleerde Starrekunde* (1728), and French, *Théologie astronomique* (1729). See also note 8 to the Opening Discourse.

31. See Section II of the Introduction.
32. Kant's overconfident rebuttal of Maupertuis' view of nebulae is best seen against the words of Herschel who in 1791, after almost ten years' of observations, reached the conclusion (which he was unable to discard for the rest of his life) that "perhaps it has been too hastily surmised that all milky nebulosity, of which there is so much in the heavens, is owing to starlight only . . . If therefore this matter is self-luminous, it seems more fit to produce a star by its condensation than to depend on the star for its existence" (*Collected Scientific Papers*, 1:422–23).
33. While this kind of reasoning proved itself very valuable, it could also be very misleading, as amply illustrated in the history of science.
34. One is reminded here of the saying that "logic is the art of going wrong with confidence."
35. Here Kant relies on Maupertuis' compilation (see note 41 of Section II of the Introduction) from Hevelius' data on nebulous stars of which, ironically enough, only two could be verified by subsequent observations. See K. G. Jones, *Messier's Nebulae and Star Clusters* (New York: American Elsevier, 1969), p. 357. Yet apart from this, the list's data did not justify Kant's generalization from them.
36. A similar eagerness to systematize observations misled many an astronomer more the a century later into believing that nebulae were co-ordinated around the galactic poles. Interestingly enough, it was an observation, namely, Herschel's discovery of Uranus, whose orbit is less eccentric than that of Saturn, which forced Kant to instruct Gensichen to leave out in the excerpts the rest of the material of this First Part.
37. Uranus' eccentricity is not 1/14 or so, as suggested by the series, but 1/21.
38. The approximate values for Mercury and Mars are 1/5 and 1/11 respectively.
39. See note 37 above.
40. Actually, their vaporous constitution is the cause of their great eccentricity and of their tails.
41. The discovery of Uranus, Neptune, and Pluto made this prediction wholly vacuous.
42. An idea which reveals something of Kant's amateurism in celestial mechanics, or more specifically of his oversight of the significant perturbation which such a situation would have long entailed for Saturn's orbit.

Second Part

First Section

1. These lines correspond to lines 9–14 of Epistle Three of *Essay on Man*:

> See plastic Nature working to this end,
> The single atoms each to other tend,
> Attract, attracted to, the next in place
> Formed and impelled its neighbor to embrace
> See Matter next, with various life endued,
> Press to one centre still, the gener'l Good.

Kant quoted only the first half of the last line, which in Brockes' translation ends with "ihr allgemeines Gut" (their universal good).

2. It is rather unlikely that a printer should set 9 instead of 10, the correct number

given on pp. [1] and [150]. The wrong number on this page seems to have its cause rather in Kant's haste or carelessness of which the *Allgemeine Naturgeschichte* provides not a few examples.

3. Here Kant, who later repeatedly refers to some data of Buffon as a confirmation of his own theory, should have given credit to Buffon, because the entire paragraph is a paraphrase of Buffon's statement: "The planets all turn in the same sense around the sun, and almost in the same plane . . . This conformity of the position and direction in the motion of planets necessarily presupposes something common in their motion of impulsion and must make [us] suspect that it was imparted to them by one single and same cause" (*Histoire naturelle*, 1:133; *Allg. Historie der Natur*, 1:79). The same holds true of Kant's criticism of Newton in the next paragraph, a criticism at least implicitly formulated by Buffon in the same context.

4. A rather inordinate reasoning on the part of one who three years later wanted to obtain the chair of "ordinary logic" at Königsberg. Kant contrasts an interpretation of the uniformity of planetary motions, with a plainly observed fact, the more or less complete emptiness of interplanetary space. Of course, Kant had in mind the interpretation which Newton attached to that emptiness, a point which could have been stated with no difficulty.

5. A figure of speech, widely used in the cosmogonical literature between 1690 and 1750, to denote God's direct role in the formation of the planetary system, the topic of ch. 3, "Gravity and God's Arm," in *Planets and Planetarians*. For its use by Buffon, see *Histoire naturelle*, 1:131, or *Allg. Historie der Natur*, 1:78.

6. By probability Kant means the first of the two interpretations or hypotheses.

7. Kant, who did not know enough celestial mechanics to realize that Buffon's theory was gravely defective, a point not yet aired in print, had no right to state that his and Newton's interpretations pre-empted all other possibilities.

8. One of the many instances contradicting Kant's repeated assertions that he merely submits a theory or hypothesis.

9. The phrase contradicts Kant's statement that the working out of the physical part of cosmogony is easier than giving its mathematical part, a task achieved by Newton (see p. [c2v]), and that in physical cosmogony one cannot aim at mathematical exactness (pp. [c8v], [d1v], and [37]).

10. The pretentious demonstration would have been a mathematical treatment which as Kant implies, he could have given if he wanted to. After all, he wanted to take in 1756 the post of extraordinary professor of mathematics vacant since Knutzen's death in 1751. According to Adickes (*Kant als Naturforscher*, 2:218). Kant had in mind in the foregoing context not himself but that "experienced surveyor" to which he referred on p. [c2v].

11. As will be seen shortly, this exclusively highest degree of simplicity was a very contrived construct.

12. Kant, as Descartes before him, is fully confident in the manner of an a priori thinker about knowing the form of creation which alone is compatible with the mind of the Creator, a way of thinking which inevitably makes the Creator unnecessary.

13. Kant here should have said something about the compatibility of difference with simplicity.

14. Once more Kant fails to sense the pitfalls of his blithe cavorting with infinity, such as implied, say, in the notion of an infinitely dense particle.

15. A mere look into his own backyard would have made it clear to Kant that far

from being inexhaustible in every respect, nature displayed strong limitations when seen under any angle. But certain philosophical presuppositions, such as the principle of plenitude, can easily conceal the obvious.

16. Kant should have unambiguously stated the latter, if he had a rigorous mathematical mind, as he clearly tried to reconcile the homogeneous distribution of matter with the variations of density.

17. A phrase befitting a novelist, and perhaps certain philosophers, but certainly not a "Newtonian" cosmogonist.

18. A unit of width equal to 1/12th of an inch, used for instance by Huygens in his carrying out his experiment of estimating the distance of Sirius. See note 19 to First Part. There are other definitions of a line, such as the one used by buttonmakers for whom 1 line is equal to 1/40th of an inch. See *Random House Dictionary of the English Language* under "line".

19. See note 28 to the Opening Discourse.

20. Kant fails to realize that there would have been perfect equilibrium in the distribution of particles of different kinds of densities as pictured by him.

21. Clearly, if this final lumping of matter into distinct units would have been gravitationally stable without the intervention of "repulsive" force, then the original distribution of particles too would have been stable. Furthermore, Kant does not consider the attractive force of "infinitely dense" particles, that is, the inevitable coalescence of all matter into one single lump at the "physical center" of the infinite universe, a center which he later (p. [110]) postulates and tries to justify with affectation of profundity.

22. This repulsive force was not only a rather mysterious and most questionable entity but also wholly unnecessary in Kant's system, as he later relies, in the manner of a good disciple of Epicurus, on the process of collision between particles of the primordial chaos.

23. Rarely in the history of cosmology was so much asserted about all on the basis of so little. At any rate, the hierarchical distribution in which elementary particles were the starting condition implied "in a single doctrine" the future hierarchical correlation of all celestial bodies.

24. Kant's very reasoning should have made it clear to him that he did not need a centrifugal force any more than he needed a repulsive force.

25. Let the German original "seitwärts gelenkte Umwendungskraft" be the justification of this phrasing.

26. This is the state of least resistance, which, precisely because it still implies resistance, is not a stable condition. Kant may have been influenced here by Maupertuis' formulation a few years earlier of the law of least action, which created quite a stir in Berlin and elsewhere, because Voltaire rushed with his acid pen to the aid of König, a chief critique of Maupertuis.

27. This smallest reciprocal action is obviously not a *free*, that is, wholly unimpeded circular motion. Once more Kant is oblivious to the implications of resistance, however small.

28. It should seem revealing that Kant offered no illustration of this "natural result."

29. Kant relies on the process of collisions, which, however, would not produce a uniform circular motion in one direction, because the original distribution of particles was symmetrical by implication and therefore the collisions of particles rushing toward the center would have also been symmetrical.

30. As Nölke notes (*Das Problem der Entwicklung unseres Planetensystems* [Berlin: Julius Springer, 1098], p. 5), there is no ground for this distinction in Kant's theory.

31. Kant here himself spells out the very process of resistance which, if consistently

considered, destroys his cosmogony. Kant again makes it unwittingly clear that his cosmogony rests, in addition to attractive force, not on repulsive force, but on resistance caused by collisions.

32. Not only is this phase patently self-contradictory, but also void of any value concerning the casual relation expressed in it.

33. Kant seems to forget that whatever the fineness of the primordial particles, they greatly varied in densities. Therefore, the formation of planets around some denser particles must have started long before the formation of a rotating "dust-cloud" around the sun. The sun itself, which as he put it before (p. [30]) started from an "infinitely small seed in quick steps," triggered the cosmogonical process around it because of that seed's particularly large density. The planets would have started their formation right at the outset from their "infinitely small seed" of sufficiently large density.

34. This unexpected ushering in, as if through a back door, of another law or a circumstance conveniently needed, is characteristic of Kant's entire cosmogonical discourse. Kant's failure of specifying these "customary" laws speaks for itself.

35. By the time of Kant it had become natural to refer to Newtonian attraction with no hint at the problems involved in its action-at-a-distance. Newton made it clear in the *Opticks* (Qu. 31) that action-at-a-distance must have a mechanism, such as impulse. In his third letter to Bentley, he declared that the opinion that "Action and Force may be conveyed from one [body] to another, is to me so great an Absurdity, that I believe no Man who has in philosophical Matters a competent Faculty of thinking, can ever fall into it." *Isaac Newton's Papers and Letters on Natural Philosophy*, edited by I. B. Cohen (Cambridge, Mass.: Harvard University Press, 1958), pp. 302–03. See also notes 27 and 28 to the Opening Discourse.

36. Instead of "possible" Kant should have written "proposed so far", but the facile conceptualizer once more got the best of him.

37. Bodies, mostly comets, which have very eccentric orbits. Needless to say, the reasoning is at loggerheads with Kant's original assumptions. In spaces very far from the sun, the particles, though their acceleration toward the sun is much weaker, are much closer to one another owing to their "hierarchical distribution," and therefore their mutual collisions are much more frequent.

38. It is such expressions that helped so many readers and interpreters of the *Allgemeine Naturgeschichte* to overlook that the stuff in question was an agglomerate of particles highly differentiated on the scale of density, an entity very different from that diffuse homogeneous nebulous matter which Laplace assumed as the initial condition of his cosmogony.

39. Such and similar passages remind one of Wolfgang Pauli's comment on a paper which he was asked to evaluate. "It is not right," he said with some reluctance as he gave the paper back. "Is it wrong then?" "No," Pauli went on, "it is not even wrong."

40. Kant's derision of the slight "fortuitous" deviations of atoms from their courses in Epicurus' system was not much different from the kettle calling the pot black.

41. "Bestehungsplane" instead of "Beziehungsplane."

42. Kant here confused the inability to treat with perfect mathematical exactitude so many factors with the alleged absence of such an exactitude in nature. Laplace's "omniscient spirit", who could foresee from the initial conditions all future events however trivial, expressed far better the scientific rigor of

mechanistic philosophy or, at least, was not guilty of so elementary error in logic.

Second Section

1. Needless to say, Kant failed in that endeavor.

2. This equal and homogeneous distribution of particles is at variance with their hierarchical distribution, as originally presupposed by Kant, and which he again assumes in the next paragraph.

3. By "statical law" Kant obviously means a state of equilibrium which undoubtedly obtains in his original chaos, a hierarchical and symmetrical distribution of particles according to their densities. But even assuming that such a distribution is not a state of equilibrium, it can only lead, contrary to Kant's next statement, to a situation in which a "given height" will be occupied by particles of the same specific weight.

4. This entire paragraph is a classic example of the "qualitative" reasoning on the basis of which the desired result can be made appear plausible to any amateur in physics.

5. This overconfident view of future possibilities is strongly suggestive of the a priori aspect in Kant's approach to cosmogony, an approach far more reminiscent of Descartes than of Newton.

6. This statement contradicts not only Kant's subsequent admission that the densities of Mercury and Venus are not yet known, but also the *Principia* in which only the relative densities of the sun, Jupiter, Saturn and earth are calculated as 100, $94\frac{1}{2}$, 67, and 400, values which Kant later (p. [161]) quotes though with an error. These values given in the third edition of the *Principia* (Bk. III, Prop. viii. Theor. viii, Cor. 3) differ but slightly from the values given in the first and second editions. See Var. Ed. 2:582. In addition, Newton calculated the ratio of the earth's and moon's densities as 9 to 11 (Bk. III, Prop. xxxvii, Prob. xviii, Cor. 3; ibid., 2:670).

7. In all three editions of the *Principia* Newton states (Bk. III, Prop. viii, Theor. viii, Cor. 4; Var. Ed. 2:583) that "other things being equal" the smaller planets are denser and so are the planets closer to the sun, but he mentions as examples only Jupiter with respect to Saturn and the earth with respect to Jupiter. Newton's immediately following statement in the first edition— "God placed the planets at different distances from the sun, so that each may profit according to its grade of density of a greater or smaller [measure of the] heat of the sun"—was omitted in the second and third editions (Var. Ed. 2:583), but found its way in a slightly different form into Newton's posthumously published *De systemate mundi* (in *Principia* [Cajori] p. 566). Kant could not, of course, be unaware of the discussion of this topic in Derham's *Astrotheology* (Bk. VII, ch. 2, "Of the due Position and Distance of the Sun and its Planets"; pp. 168–73 in the 4th edition of its German translation). See also I. B. Cohen, *Introduction to Newton's Principia* (Cambridge: University Press, 1971), pp. 153–55.

8. In the corollary cited in the preceding note, Newton stated this only of the water on earth and not of the earth itself, and he did not refer to comets. This further discrepancy between the contents of the *Principia* and Kant's reporting suggests that his information about it was based more on hearsay than on careful study.

9. In obvious disagreement with the *Principia*; see note 6 above.

10. A strange criticism of Newton on the part of a Kant who was becoming involved in contradictions in the measure in which he was unfolding his cosmogony.

11. Of these two examples the first was defective. Had Kant not been dominated by his bent on cosmogonical system-making, he would have mentioned the satellite-systems of Jupiter and Saturn where the respective relation of densities was unknown at that time.

12. The entire reasoning is too arbitrary to deserve criticism.

13. See note 6 above.

14. See notes 6 and 9 above.

15. Here Kant unwittingly reveals the inaccuracy of his foregoing statement that Newton calculated the masses of each planet and also his tacit reliance on Buffon, who estimated that the densitites of Venus and Mercury exceeded the density of the sun 8 and 28 times, and the density of the earth twice and 7 times, respectively. See Buffon, *Histoire naturelle* (1:144–45; *Allg. Historie der Natur*, 1:84–85).

16. One of the few correct (elementary) calculations in the *Allgemeine Naturgeschichte*. It is obtained, as J. Rahts pointed out (AA 1:551), by taking the sine of $3\frac{3}{4}$ degrees (on half of $7\frac{1}{2}$), or 0.06, which is in the ratio of 1:17 to sin 90, or 1.

17. Unfortunately for Kant, he uncritically accepted (and without acknowledgment) the reference to Newton's *Principia*, third edition, p. 405, in Buffon's *Histoire naturelle* (1:136; *Allg. Historie der Natur*, 1:81) as the source of this value. In all three editions of the *Principia* only the relative values of the masses of the sun, Jupiter, Saturn, and earth are given with very slight variations as 1, 1/1067, 1/3021, and 1/169,282 (Var. Ed. 2:579–82). In this sequence the last ratio is negligble even when written as 4/169,282, that is, by taking into consideration the masses of Mercury, Venus and Mars, and taking each of them to be equal to the mass of the earth. Multiplying the first three members of the sequence by 10,000 gives the series of 10,000 9.3 and 3.4. This gives the ratio 10,000:12.7 which is equal to 790:1, a value in gross discrepancy with the value given (and probably computed) by Buffon, but a value close to modern estimates which include the ultra-Saturnian planets, all the satellites, and all the asteroids. The erronous value ascribed by Buffon and by Kant to Newton has not so far been noted in the many commentaries to the *Allgemeine Naturgeschichte*. Buffon gives the ratio 650:1 six times on four successive pages, more than enough to give full confidence to an amateur like Kant.

18. See notes 9 and 17 to First Part.

19. The estimate is not so much easy as arbitrary.

20. This speculation of Kant is at variance not only with the originally hierarchical (and implicity homogeneous) and symmetrical distribution of mass, but also with his insistence that the greater accumulation of denser particles is a more important factor in the process than the availability of more mass at greater distance from the sun, which again contradicts his original assumption.

21. It was easy for Kant to speculate on the origin on planetary system on the basis of very few data. The accumulation of more data made similar speculations more and more precarious, although hardly ever in the eyes of their proponents. The havoc which some new data can play with such speculations is well illustrated by the finding on Venus, through the Pioneer 2, of argon-36 and argon-38 in concentrations larger than expected. If the explanation of this is a larger abundance of argon on Venus from its early formation on, then, as Dr. Michael McElroy of Harvard University remarked, "a great

change in our thinking of the origin of the planets" would be necessary. See *The New York Times*, Dec. 11, 1978, p. A16, col. 8.

22. A confident self-appraisal, pre-empting the credibility of Kant's protestations of diffidence.

23. Kant uses here a round figure (the true value is about 95,000) to facilitate the ensuing calculation which, though elementary, will contain an error.

24. The bimillion stands for an English billion or 10^{12}. In computing the ratio of the two volumes Kant should have taken 200,000 earth radii and have obtained the result of 8000 bimillion.

25. Consequently, this figure too is wrong. The correct figure would have been 8 times 50 bimillion or 400 bimillion.

26. See note 17 above.

27. Once more an elementary calculation performed by Kant is erroneous. The correct ratio is $1:260\frac{1}{2}$ implying a discrepancy which can hardly be assigned to printing error. The error is noted by Rahts (AA 1:551) with the benevolent though lame remark that Kant's "oversight has no significant effect on the numbers derived from it subsequently."

28. This discrepancy with the immediately foregoing figure is suggestive either of Kant's carelessness with figures, or of his not having proofread his work.

29. Underlying this reasoning, which has only the semblance of being scientific, is the idea that the small flattening of the earth is an indication of its solidity throughout.

30. Such an estimate had been a commonplace since Boyle's experiments.

31. Once more Kant uses a round figure, rather different from the value 860 as given in the third edition of the *Principia* (Bk. III, Prop. x, Theor. x; Var. Ed. 2:585).

32. The actual product is 1,382,500, which indicates that this time Kant performed correctly an elementary multiplication.

33. Hardly an approximate result, as the dividing of 50 bimillion (50×10^{12}) by 1.4×10^6 yields about 36 million.

34. In view of the great variety of cometary tails, this generalization is hardly reliable and is not to be taken for an opinion voiced by astronomers prior to Kant. Perhaps Kant was influenced by Chéseaux whose estimates of the base and height of the triangular tail of the great comet of 1743 yielded values that exceeded the diameter of the earth by a factor of over ten thousand. See Chéseaux, *Traité de la comète*, pp. 26–27.

35. The sight of stars through the tail of comets is mentioned in the *Principia* (Bk. III, Prop. xli, Probl. xxi; Var. Ed. 2:741).

36. No calculation whatsoever seems to underly this statement.

37. Another case of Kant's contradicting his statements that he merely offers hypotheses and conjectures.

38. Kant should have already given credit on more than one occasion to Buffron who by 1755 was a household word all over Europe. As Buffon himself noted with satisfaction on February 14, 1750, with reference to the first three volumes of his *Histoire naturelle*: "The first edition, large as it was, sold out in six weeks [in August of the previous year], a second and a third impressions are in preparation and will shortly appear. The book has been translated into German, English, and Dutch." See P. Hazard, *European Thought in the Eighteenth Century*, translated by J. Lewis May (1954; Harmondsworth: Pelican Books, 1965), p. 156, with an impressive portrayal of Buffon's fame, ibid., pp. 159–60.

39. A classic example of one error (see note 17 above) supporting an erroneous conclusion, and of its unobtrusive spread into another theory.

40. Not a mere chance, but a mere oversight of an elementary error in calculation.

Third Section

1. Kant gives the impression that the view he combats is something to be reckoned with. Actually, already in the cosmogony of Descartes comets were not at all a species different from planets, and Newton repeatedly insisted in all three editions of the *Principia* (Bk. III, Prop. xxxix, Probl. xx, Lemma iv, Cor. 3 and Prop. xli, Probl. xxi, exemplum; Var. Ed. 2:603 and 741) that comets were bodies similar to planets and anything but meteors, that is, sublunary phenomena, a view certainly outmoded by Kant's time. The prevalence of the Newtonian view is evident in Buffon's *Histoire naturelle*, (1:132–33; *Allg. Historie der Natur*, 1:78–79) and in Lambert's *Cosmologische Briefe*. Kant wants to make the comets a species of planets in such a way as to fit the pattern of gradualness of his cosmogony. As a result he would have to dispute the Newtonian view of the solidity of the comets' bodies and to assume a fairly circular orbit for at least the nearer comets. That comets were not only dissimilar to planets, but so many intruders into the solar system was a view advocated years later in Laplace's *Exposition du système du monde*.

2. Here Kant simply echoes the principle of gradualness and plenitude, which had been brought into prominence by Leibniz, and the imagery of Pope about the vast chain of being.

3. See pp. [19] and [20] above.

4. Although the discovery by John Dollond in 1758 of the art of making achromatic lenses greatly increased the resolving power of telescopes, only the telescopes constructed by Herschel and Fraunhofer made possible the search for members of the solar system beyond Saturn. The findings did not confirm some pivotal aspects of Kant's expectations.

5. Jupiter and Saturn, beyond which Kant envisaged the existence of further and smaller planets.

6. An eccentricity about twice as large as that of Jupiter and Saturn, which, though not helpful for Kant's theory, had already made it possible for Kepler to ascertain the elliptical orbit of Mars and formulate his Three Laws, each an indispensable foundation-stone for Newton's celestial dynamics.

7. A typically cumbersome phrasing which could have been easily avoided by writing "the equality of central force with the sidewise thrust."

8. The claim that the accumulation of mass was less nearer the sun than farther from it was one of the weakest points of Kantian cosmogony.

9. Denser particles would certainly be deviated more effectively though only if the resisting material would still be denser, but in that case the sun's density too would be much larger. Kant's error in this connection is worse than the error of those toying with the idea of perpetuum mobile. Kant wants to get more out of his mechanical process than it contains.

10. Obviously, when no mathematics is employed, a very complex process can be seen in such a light as to yield the desired result.

11. Did Kant wish to convey the notion that the tail, or rather hair (*kóme*), of some celestial bodies had nothing to do with their name, comets (*kométes*)?

12. A bizarre phrase unfit even for a popular cosmogony.

13. A curious oversight on Kant's part of the proportionality of central force (gravitational attraction) to the amount of mass.

14. Indeed, the disproportionality between the two is tremendous, a fact which had already trapped Descartes in sheer verbalizations. That a point on the sun's equatorial belt takes almost a month to complete a full revolution, whereas Mercury, whose orbit has a radius about sixty times larger than the radius of the sun, completes its revolution in only three months, is part of the lopsided distribution of angular momentum in the solar system in favor of the planets, a perennial stumbling block to any form of nebular hypotheses of its origin.

15. Apart from the distinct muddle implied in this reasoning, it is a mere evasion of the problem of the relatively very great orbital velocity of Mercury.

16. A point further elaborated by Kant on p. [60].

17. That Newton's work had effectively disposed of such fears was a point made by Halley in the ode which he prefixed to the first edition of the *Principia*, a work published largely at his behest.

18. Most planetary motions take place within the belt of zodiac, which is a region less exactly defined than the width of $7\frac{1}{2}$ degrees mentioned above on p. [44].

19. The German original, "von den Schranken ihrer Laufbahne," is somewhat mysterious.

20. Typically, Kant makes no effort to reconcile his predictions with data on cometary orbits, such as contained in Halley's Table of comets (see note 17 to First Part), which was given a thorough mathematical analysis in 1761 in Lambert's *Cosmologische Briefe*, a feat of which Kant was wholly incapable.

21. Again, the absence of a comparison with data is glaring, and in particular in connection with a point, the orbiting of the nearest comets in the same direction as the planets, which is rather crucial for the truth of Kant's theory.

22. An evasiveness unlikely to impress a judicious reader.

23. Kant's failure to refer to any source, and his eagerness to talk away the fact that of the 30 comets 19 appear to contradict his presupposition, speak for themselves. In Halley's Table 13 our of 24 comets were listed with retrograde motion. Actually, as the number of comets listed in such Tables (see note 17 to First Part) had increased, the respective number of comets with forward and retrograde motion came closer to equality.

24. Even if Kant was familiar with Chéseaux's *Traité de la comète*, he was certainly not influenced by the wise remark there that the course of comets, the shape and the size of their tails are all susceptible of exact demonstrations, "but one is reduced to mere conjectures as soon as one wants to go farther and discover the nature of these stars" (pp. 35–36).

25. Here Kant should have noted that this idea is the very opposite to the one advocated by Newton (see note 1 above). Kant's contention that the bodies of comets are composed of very light material has some resemblance to the modern view. He would, however, have given proof of scientific insight only if he had followed Chéseaux, who had already argued in his *Traité de la comète* (p. 42) that the bodies of comets ought to be very light or else their passage through the orbits of planets would have resulted in noticeable perturbations of these orbits.

26. Kant now obviously has in mind many more comets than 30, let alone the 21 in Halley's Table, of which no less than 17 had their perihelia within the orbit of Venus. See Lambert, *Cosmological Letters*, pp. 66–67 and 70.

27. An exaggeration and generalization typical of a dilettante.

28. The translation of this footnote follows the grammatically incorrect original,

which Hastie not only "corrected" but also moved into the text itself with the additional words "or Aurora Borealis."

29. The equatorial zone.
30. Needless to say, in this case the northern light would be a fairly steady phenomenon, which is hardly the case. Satisfactory explanation of that light did not come until the discovery of cosmic rays. The passage shows Kant's deep attachment to a teleology (anchored in the habitable character of Nature everywhere), which was as naive as the one he had opposed. More than ten years after he had written the *Critique*, he argued in his *Perpetual Peace* that the northward drift of timber in some rivers and oceanic currents proved Nature's providence ("in a manner not well known") for people living there. See English translation with an introduction by N. M. Butler (New York: Columbia University Press, 1939), p. 29.

Fourth Section

1. To this terse statement Rahts attached a long note (AA 1:551–53) to defend the correctness of Kant's explanation of the non-retrograde orbiting of satellites. He should rather have noted that Kant no longer makes use of such factors as the slight dissymmetry in the collision of particles, the interaction of repulsive and attractive forces, and the state of least resistance, factors which played an indispensable role in his theory of the formation of planets and of the uniformity of their sense of orbiting in much the same plane.
2. Kant assumes the planets to be already fully formed and yet he also pictures the interplanetary spaces as still sufficiently full of particles to permit the further formation of satellites. With a similar inconsistency he does not consider why these particles, moving along as they do with the planets, have not already coalesced with them.
3. The importance of this word cannot be emphasized enough. Kant should have written "farther" in order to obtain the desired result, namely, a forward rotation for the satellites. Such admiring an interpreter of Kant's cosmogony as Zöllner admitted in his *Photometrische Untersuchungen mit besonderer Rücksicht auf die physische Beschaffenheit der Himmelskörper* (Leipzig: W. Engelmann, 1865, p. 225) that it leads to a retrograde rotation of satellites, although Zöllner, who characterized Kant's explanation as "unclear," should have rather written that it does not lead to anything. Wolf, Kant's French translator, also spoke of his inability (*Les hypothèses cosmogoniques*, p. 12) to make himself a clear meaning of Kant's statement. Rahts' lengthy defense of Kant's explanation (AA 1:551–53) comes to an end, revealingly enough, with the remark that whereas the process as imagined by Kant can easily be visualised, it cannot readily be cast into a mathematical form.
4. The sentence, distinctly obscure, gives no clue as to how small particles would, while being swung in front of the planet, coalesce into a moon, instead of coalescing with the planet itself.
5. Although the subsequent discoveries of satellites around Uranus and Neptune with retrograde motion do not present insurmountable problems for celestial dynamics, the more is known about satellite systems, the less convincing should appear the explanation of their genesis in so few phrases.
6. The manifold data obtained about the moon since man first landed on it make it ever more likely that its origin is not to be sought in the coalescence of dust around the earth, but either in a process of capture, or in a tidal action

sufficiently strong to detach a considerable part of the already quasi-solid earth.

7. Had it been known in Kant's time that Mars has two satellites (discovered by Asaph Hall in August 1877), he would have found in their smallness a confirmation of his theory. What would he have said, had he known that one of them orbited faster than Mars rotated, is another question. Undoubtedly, the five satellites of Uranus (the existence of a sixth is now being suspected) and the two satellites of Neptune (see note 61 to the next Section) would have appeared to Kant as clear proofs of the truth of his cosmogony.

8. To explain the rotation of planets Kant assumes that much of their mass accrued to them only after they had obtained their final orbits, an assumption laden for his theory with complications which he does not consider.

9. He does not consider why those, which maintain themselves in *freely* floating circular motion around the planet, would finally coalesce into a satellite.

10. In the German, "fliehende Kraft," translated by Hastie (*Kant's Cosmogony*, p. 106) as "centripetal [!] force." Kant obviously meant to write "zenterfliehende Kraft" or centrifugal force, as demanded by the context. His "Zenterfliehkraft" in the second line of p. [89] is rendered by Hastie (ibid., p. 125) with "centripetal power," again in patent disregard of the context.

11. Following the observations of D. J. Cassini between 1665 and 1692, a rotation period of 9 hours and 50 minutes had become a commonly accepted value. See J. J. L. de Lalande, *Astronomie*, p. 1255. The more exact value of 9 hours 55 minutes and 40 seconds was obtained by Herschel in 1781. See *Collected Scientific Papers*, 1:19–22.

12. A rather unconvincing generalisation as the rotation period of Mars (24 hours and 40 minutes), a value commonly accepted since 1666 (see Lalande, *Astronomie*, p. 1253), could not be considered an increase over that of the earth, and the rotation periods of Mercury, Venus, and Saturn were still unknown.

13. A calculation obscure enough to be left alone by Kant's commentators. If Kant had assumed a linear increase of rotational velocity, then, in view of Jupiter's distance from the sun being five times the earth-sun distance, he should have ascribed a rotation for Jupiter five times faster than that of the earth.

14. Newton had already pointed out in the *Principia* (Bk. III, Prop. xxxvii, Probl. xix, Cor. 6; Var. Ed. 2:670) that the great axis of the moon was pointing toward the earth and that the moon's center of weight was farther from the earth than its geometrical center. Newton did not, however, ascribe to this fact the equality of the moon's orbital and rotational periods.

15. See Section I of the Introduction. Strangely enough, Kant did not spell out the essence of that solution, namely, the tidal friction caused by gravitation, which he had already set forth in a small essay. Needless to say, the proper articulation of that solution far exceeded Kant's scientific attainments. In Harnack's massive history of the Berlin Academy (see note 1 to the Opening Discourse) Kant is given only a fleeting mention in connection with that prize (1:399), perhaps an indication that his lucky surmise of the essence of that solution was not common knowledge there around 1900.

16. Contrary to Kant, the two problems are not correlated.

17. This general plane of reference is the plane perpendicular to the sun's axial rotation, which deviates by 7 degrees from the ecliptic.

18. Actually, the inclination of Jupiter's axis had been well known for at least half a century to be about 3 degrees (see Lalande, *Astronomie*, p. 1255).

19. The correct value of Mars' axial inclination, or 25 degrees, was first given by Herschel in 1784. Prior to him the astronomical literature contained occasional references to Cassini's memoir on Mars (1666) in which it was stated that the axis of Mars is oriented almost perpendicularly to the plane of its orbit as far as this could be judged from the spots on its surface, indices hardly reliable for establishing the period in question. (see Lalande, *Astronomie*, p. 1253).

20. Here again Herschel provided the accurate value of 26 degrees and 45 minutes. Prior to him, Maraldi's value of 31 degrees and 23 minutes was generally accepted. The slightly different value of 31 degrees and 20 minutes was given in 1745 by G. Heinsius in what Lalande called a "very good dissertation" on the appearance of Saturn's ring (*Astronomie*, p. 1259). It may be noted here that the axial inclinations of Uranus and Neptune are about 90 and 40 degrees respectively. About Pluto one can note only the inclination of its orbit, which is 17 degrees or almost three times larger than the maximum of such inclinations found among the other planets.

21. The then known four satellites of Jupiter certainly were remarkable for their orbiting in a plane exactly coinciding with Jupiter's plane of rotation. The then known five satellites of Saturn were also good illustrations of the point made by Kant. Whereas the five satellites of Uranus also orbit closely parallel to their planet's rotational plane, the latter is inclined at almost 90 degrees to the ecliptic and so are its satellites' orbital planes. The inclination of Neptune's axis is less closely paralleled by the orbits of its satellites.

22. Here Kant would have done well by qualifying his statement with "presumably" or "probably." As an armchair geologist and geographer he had his own mental field trips. Needless to say the explanation offered by him flies in the face of some basic principles of dynamics.

23. Another scientific promise which Kant failed to fulfill.

24. Kant could have saved himself from a blunder had he recalled Newton's third law of motion on reaction which is always equal to action. He would have derived similar profit from reflecting on the minuteness of mass implied in any such a process compared with the total mass of the earth.

25. In all likelihood Kant refrained from following Buffon, who conjured up tens of thousands of years, lest he should suffer in the hands of Lutheran divines in Königsberg the treatment given to Buffon by the theologians of the Sorbonne. See also p. [175].

26. Markings on Jupiter were first noted in 1630 and their variability was established by Cassini in the latter half of the century. The great red spot, which appeared in 1878 on Jupiter, certainly evidenced the cataclismic conditions on its surface. What had taken place on Mars was dramatically suggested by the sighting of a huge extinct volcano, called Olympus Mons, which towers 15 miles above a base that stretches almost 400 miles and has a crater of about 50 miles in diameter. See *Time*, Jan. 22, 1979, p. 75.

27. Investigation of Venus with artificial satellites proved all too well its stormy surface conditions. Kant himself was pleased to report, many years later, on Herschel's spotting a volcano in the moon, though without referring to the *Allgemeine Naturgeschichte*.

28. A gross and elementary error. In Newton's *Principia* (Var. Ed. 2:582) the ratio of the diameters of Jupiter and of the earth is given as 997:109, which even a cursory inspection yields somewhat less than 1000 for the ratio in question. The value on the basis of modern data is about 1400.

29. See note 6 to Second Section of Second Part.
30. Once more Kant shies away from conjuring up long geological epochs.
31. Kant obviously means mass not volume. See note 17 to Second Section of Second Part.
32. This alleged shift is incompatible with the principle of the conservation of angular momentum, sufficiently specified by then.
33. Kant clearly implies that the foregoing parts of his cosmogony were fit to be subjected to mathematical treatment.
34. Actually, the great cover-up of fallacies consisted in his giving a physical cosmogony without mathematics.

Fifth Section

1. See note 1 to Fourth Section of Second Part.
2. Kant should have written: "to its previously much greater eccentricity." That the increase of eccentricity from Jupiter to Saturn was much smaller than demanded by their respective distances from the sun, did not apparently perturb Kant, a feature typical of zealous system-makers.
3. The cooling should have resulted in precipitation and not in further evaporation.
4. Here Kant borrows from Maupertuis. See Section II of Introduction.
5. The fact that the secret is still unsolved after having been probed by many a scientist far better equipped for the task than Kant, should give a glimpse of the measure of his self-confidence.
6. This *free* orbiting would hardly permit the subsequent stages outlined by Kant.
7. Here Kant seems to imply that evaporation can give some particles a speed exceeding the so-called escape velocity on a massive planet such as Saturn.
8. He had, however, already spoken of those particles as being in *free*, that is, unimpeded and stable orbital motions and therefore no "central laws," and certainly not their kinds left unspecified by Kant, would force them toward the extended equatorial plane of the planet.
9. If such is the case, the entire ring of Saturn would have long ago been dissipated.
10. The statement is noteworthy for two reasons. One is the alleged correlation of cometary tails with Saturn's ring (see note 4 above). The other is its arbitrary factuality.
11. The relation, as will be stated by Kant, is an exact equality, which is implied in Kepler's Third Law, on the basis of which he will calculate the rotational period of the inner edge of Saturn's ring.
12. But, according to Kant, they had already crashed back to the planet's surface.
13. Protrusions on two opposite sides of Saturn had been noted by Galileo, Hevelius, and others. It was Huygens who in his *Systema saturnium* (1659) openly stated the existence of a ring around Saturn which he had already intimated in 1656 in the form of an anagram. Saturn's ring gave ample opportunity to such popularizers of astronomy as Fontenelle to stir up the astonishment of their readers at the spectacles of the heavens, although even professional astronomers were wont to register their wonderment in their technical communications on Saturn. Thus Jacques Cassini started in 1715 in his "Observations nouvelles sur Saturne," with the remark that "the system of Saturn is so admirable through the singular shape of this planet, through the variety of its appearances and through the number of satellites which accompany it, that one can hardly imagine an object more appropriate to excite the curiosity of philosophers and of all those who are engaged in the contemplation of celestial bodies" (*Histoire de l'Académie Royale des Sciences. Année MDCCXV. Avec*

les *Mémoires de Mathématiques et de Physique pour cette Année* [Paris: de l'Imprimerie Royale, 1718], p. 41). Almost a hundred years later, Herschel introduced his "Observations on the Singular Figure of the Planet Saturn" as follows: "There is not perhaps another object in the heavens that presents us with such a variety of extraordinary phenomena as the planet Saturn; a magnificent globe, encompassed by a stupendous double ring: attended by seven satellites: ornamented with equatorial belts: compressed at the poles: turning upon its axis: mutually eclipsing its ring and satellites, and eclipsed by them: . . . all the parts of the system of Saturn occasionally reflecting light to each other: the rings and moons illuminating the nights of the Saturnian: the globe and satellites enlightening the dark parts of the rings . . ." (*Collected Scientific Papers*, 2:332). Even a prosaic writer as Lalande felt impelled to note that Saturn's ring was the most spectacular feature of the sky (*Astronomie*, p. 1257).

14. Kant here tries to bask in the glory of Newton who succeeded in creating the belief that he did not "feign" hypotheses. Actually, Newton denied only to his opponents the right to rely on hypotheses, as was convincingly argued by A. Koyré, *Newtonian Studies* (Cambridge, Mass.: Harvard University Press, 1965), pp. 46–52. As to Kant, his postulating of a hierarchically structured chaos and the equality of repulsive and attractive forces was equivalent to making hypotheses. The sentence itself is much too carelessly constructed.

15. See note 29 to Third Section of Second Part.

16. This is an echo of Leibniz's optimism and of his insistence that the actual world was the best of all possible worlds. Kant was still a Leibnizian when writing the *Allgemeine Naturgeschichte*.

17. Although Cassini noted in 1677 a narrow dark line divided the ring into two concentric parts, the ring remained for long taken for a single unit. In referring to its interior rim, Kant, a diligent student of Derham's *Astrotheology*, could not help thinking about a note in it which deserves to be quoted in full: "Mr. Huygens in his *Systema Saturn.* p. 47. and *Cosmotheor.* p. 109. determines the Diameter of Saturn's Ring to the Diameter of Saturn, to be as 9 to 4; and the Breadth of the Ring, and Distance of the Ring from Saturn's body, to be nearly equal . . ." See 1st ed. (1715), p. 198; 4th ed. (1721). p. 206; German transl. 1st ed. (1728), p. 201; 4th ed. (1745), p. 201. These data (see note 19 below) were at the basis of Kant's calculation of the period of Saturn's rotation. The ratio of the diameter of the so-called crape ring of Saturn, discovered in 1850 by G. P. Bond, to that of Saturn is 7 to 4.

18. This statement of Kant, immediately leading to what he considered to be the touchstone of the truth of his cosmogony, calls for three remarks: 1. In view of the patent inefficiency of even the most powerful volcanos to propel dust-like and vaporous material much farther from the surface of the earth than a mere fraction of its radius, Kant, who prided himself to be an expert on volcanos, should have given some idea about a far more powerful upward-propelling mechanism in activity on Saturn. 2. In this age of artificial satellites it has become a popularly known fact that no satellite or missile can be put into orbit by simply shooting it upward, carefully specified as may be its initial velocity, which is in essence the mechanism underlying Kant's idea of the formation of Saturn's ring from vaporous particles propelled upward by heat with largely varying velocities. In addition, the missile, once it has reached a certain height, must be given a thrust at right angle to its originally vertical motion. The first diagram in Newton's *De mundi systemate*, to which reference was already made, graphically conveys the substance of this remark,

set forth, needless to say, already in the *Principia*, though in propositions hardly within the grasp of Kant. 3. Had Kant been truly "honest" in acknowledging his sources, he should have referred to Maupertuis' *Discours sur les différentes figures des astres* with which he was familiar through its edition of 1744 in Maupertuis' *Ouvrages divers*. There the non-mathematical *Discours* is followed by a "Calcul" of the flattening of rotating bodies in which Proposition I relates the centrifugal force at the equator of a planet whose period of rotation is known (Maupertuis expressly warns that the theorem is therefore inapplicable to Mercury, Venus, Mars, and Saturn, pp. 87–88) to the centrifugal force at the orbit of any of its satellites. Preceding the Scholion added to that Proposition, Maupertuis states that the centrifugal force of a body on the equator of a rotating stars (planet) is directly proportional to its distance from the center of that planet and inversely to the square of its period of rotation. It was this proportion, given explicitly together with Maupertuis' warning about Saturn in the review of the *Discours* in the *Acta eruditorum* used by Kant while writing the *Allgemeine Naturgeschichte* (see p. [c4v]), that was simply rewritten by him as a sort of equivalent to Kepler's Third Law, compounding thereby the basic inadequacy of his theory of the formation of Saturn's ring.

19. The steps by which Kant arrived at this value were first reconstructed by Gensichen in 1791 in a note attached to his shortened edition of the *Allgemeine Naturgeschichte* (pp. 193–94; see note 39 to Section IV of the Introduction) which he published with Kant's approval. Gensichen, however, complained that he could not ascertain the data used by Kant, who apparently no longer had his notes. Relying on data of Cassini for Saturn's ring and for its first satellite, data which he found in Wolff's *Elementa matheseos* (2:554, edition of 1715), Gensichen obtained a value which fell short only by 11 seconds of the value computed by Kant. The equations underlying the computation are elementary. By using capital letters for the parameters of any satellite of Saturn (C = velocity, P = length of orbit, R = its radius, T = time of one orbiting), small letters (c and r) and Greek letters (ρ, π, τ) for the corresponding parameters of the inner edge of the ring and of Saturn's equatorial belt, respectively, Gensichen wrote:

$$\sqrt{r}/\sqrt{R} = C/c, c = C\sqrt{\frac{R}{r}},$$

therefore

$$T/\tau = \frac{P/\tau}{c/C}, \text{ or } T/\tau = \frac{R/\rho}{c/C} = cR/C\rho = CR\sqrt{\frac{R}{r}}/C\rho = R\sqrt{\frac{R}{r}}/\rho;$$

or $\tau = \dfrac{\rho\sqrt{r}}{R\sqrt{R}}. \, T$ (a final form not given by Gensichen).

According to Rahts (AA 1:555), Kant's value can be obtained exactly if one relied on data in Huygens' *Cosmotheoros* and in Newton's *Principia*. A very popular and widely read work, the *Cosmotheoros* was certainly a good suggestion, although precisely because of the round figures used there by Huygens, it could not form the basis of the "exact" calculation Kant claimed to give, a point to which Rahts did not call attention. He also failed to note the availability of those figures in Derham's *Astrotheology*. Contrary to Rahts, none of the three editions of the *Principia* contained 15 days, 22 hours, 40 minutes for the orbital period of the fourth satellite of Saturn, but either 41 minutes or 41 minutes and 14 seconds (see Var. Ed. 2:590). It is, of course, possible, as Rahts suggested, that Kant took 40 minutes as the median value between the one in *Cosmotheoros* (41 minutes) and the other (39 minutes) in *Systema saturnium*, which Rahts referred to pp. 702 and 501, respectively, of the 1751 edition of Huygens' *Opera varia*. At any rate, in view of Kant's carelessness with numerical data and calculations, Rahts' reconstruction of Kant's steps has interest only inasmuch as it shows the arithmetic simplicity of the procedure which certainly required no scientific genius for its formulation and execution, especially if one keeps in mind Kant's indebtedness to Maupertuis as explained in the preceding note. According to Rahts, Kant took from *Cosmotheoros* the ratio $4:6\frac{1}{2}:9$ for the ratio $\rho:r:r^1$, where ρ is the radius of Saturn, r the radius of the inner edge of Saturn's ring, and r^1 is the radius of its outer edge. In the *Cosmotheoros* the radius of the orbit of the fourth satellite of Saturn is given as 4 times the diameter of the outer edge of the ring, which is 144 ($4 \times 2' \times 18$), if the foregoing ratio is written in integers, that is, $8:13:18$. Thus the time of Saturn's rotation will be equal to

$$\frac{\rho\sqrt{r}}{R\sqrt{R}} . T$$ (Rahts clearly uses the notation of Gensichen whom he does not credit), where R is the radius of the orbit of the fourth satellite and T is its

period of orbiting. The value of the ratio $\dfrac{8\sqrt{13}}{144\sqrt{144}} . 1377600$ or $\dfrac{\sqrt{13}}{216} 1377600$

will, by taking $\sqrt{13}$ as 3.61, and $\dfrac{3.61}{216}$ as 0.01672, lead to the product 0.01672 × 1377600, or 23033 seconds, that is, 6 hours 23 minutes and 53 seconds. But, as R. Wolf pointed out in his *Handbuch der Astronomie* (Zürich: F. Schulthess, 1892; 2:476), the even less correct value of 4 hours 19 minutes is obtained when Huygens' more accurate data about Saturn are used. This is, of course, a further evidence of the basic fallacy of Kant's theory, which Wolf, strangely enough, failed to notice. In 1763 Kant gave a very different value, discussed in note 8 to Appendix.

20. Possibly Kant meant to say that this was the only kind of prediction proper in physical science. The phrase as it stands will appear a hollow boast if one recalls Halley's prediction of the return of the comet of 1682 (later known as Halley's comet) in 1758, a prediction the truth of which was anticipated with growing interest when Kant was writing the *Allgemeine Naturgeschichte*.

21. In a paper read on January 23, 1794, and published immediately in the *Philosophical Transactions*, Herschel announced that he had found that period to be 10 hours 16 minutes and 15 seconds (see *Collected Scientific Papers*, 1:465), a value very different from the one derived by Kant. Interestingly, when in the *Astronomisches Jahrbuch für das Jahr 1793* (1790, p. 238) Herschel's discovery was reported, no reference was made to Kant, who himself did not care to comment, nor did his circle of admirers. Undoubtedly, Herschel would have learned about Kant's work if Count Brühl, (the Saxon ambassador in London, who eagerly reported Herschel's latest discoveries and was in close contact with Herschel) had been familiar with, let alone if he had some admiration for it.

22. The markings which made possible for Herschel his calculations were not spots but multiple belts (see *Collected Scientific Papers*, 1:459).

271

23. A vain hope indeed, both in respect to Saturn's rotational period and its derivation by Kant. Happily for the *Allgemeine Naturgeschichte*, a few parts of it, such as the explanation of the hue and shape of the Milky Way, were not based on those "similar reasons." The latter, however, directly affected (and in an adverse way) Kant's explanation of the formation of Saturn's ring and of the zodiacal light, and indirectly the rest of his entire cosmogony.

24. This ratio equivalent to 0.69 and not commented upon either by Rahts, or by Adickes (let alone other less important interpreters of the *Allgemeine Natur-geschichte*), calls for several remarks. First, in view of the too speedy rotation derived by Kant for Saturn, the ratio can but be at variance with its true value, or about 0.17. Second, since Kant was familiar with Derham's *Astro-theology* and most likely borrowed from it the value of that ratio for the sun (see note 5 to Sixth Section of Second Part), Kant probably computed the ratio for Saturn on the basis of a communication of Halley to Derham which the latter gave as part of the following note: "The Proportion of Jupiter's or any other Planets [sic], or the Sun's Gravity, to their Centrifugal Force may be computed from the most sagacious Sir Isaac Newton's *Princip.* L. 3. Prop. 8. & 19. But the before commended Savilian Professor [Halley], suggested to me this easier, and quicker Rule, for such Planets as have Satellites, viz. *The Proportion of the Centrifugal to the Centripetal Force, or Gravity of any Planet at its Surface, is compounded of the Ratio which the Cubi of the Semidiameter of the Planet hath to the Cube of the Distance of any of its Satellites from the Center of that Planet; and the Ratio which the Square of the Satellites Periodick time hath to the Square of the Periodick time of the Planets Revolution.* Thus for instance, the distance of Jupiter's outermost Satellite being 253 [25.3] Semidiameters of Jupiter, and its Period 16 days, 16 hours, 32 minutes, or 24032 minutes, and Jupiter's Revolution 526 minutes; we shall find the Gravity in Jupiter's Surface to be to his Centrifugal Force in his Equator as 1 to 9.96" (1st ed. [1715], p. 144; 4th ed. [1721], pp. 151–52; German transl., 1st ed. [1728], pp. 150–51; 2nd ed. [1732], pp. 150–51; 3d. [1739], pp. 150–51; 4th ed. [1745], pp. 151–52). Clearly, and this is the third remark, Kant once more was not as "honest" as he could have been. He should have acknowledged his indebtedness either to Derham, or to Maupertuis whose Proposition I (see not 18 above) sets forth the same compounding of ratios. Fourth, by using, say, the data of Titan, Saturn's largest satellite (distance = 20 semidiameters of Saturn, period of orbiting = 15.9 days or almost exactly 23000 minutes, data all too well known long before Kant), he should have obtained the ratio 0.43. Had this been the case, and this is the fifth remark, Kant not only would have spared his book from another inaccurate elementary calculation, but, since the latter ratio is smaller than the one computed by him, he may not have felt necessary to enter into a specious interpretation of the differences between Huygens' and Newton's theories of the flattening of the earth and to face up later to the possibility of a much too conspicuous flattening of Saturn.

25. No sooner had Herschel found the flattening of Saturn, or the ratio of its equatorial and polar diameters, to be 11 to 10 (*Collected Scientific Papers*, 1 : 380), than Bugge (see Section III of Introduction) calculated on its basis a value for Saturn's rotational period which was only 25 minutes shorter than the value calculated by Kant, a circumstance which Gensichen noticed with unconcealed satisfaction in his abbreviated edition of the *Allgemeine Naturges-chichte* (pp. 193–94). Gensichen was not, of course, enough of a mathematician to see the true source of discrepancy between the two values.

26. Whatever "thoroughness" there is in the subsequent scrutiny, the credit for it belongs entirely to Maupertuis as the rest of the paragraph is merely a paraphrase, and in places more confusing than enlightening, of the second half of Article V, entitled "Comment les expériences sur la pesanteur pouvoient faire croire que la Terre n'étoit pas sphérique," in Maupertuis' *Eléments de géographie* (1742). This was the first of the four works of his printed in the 1744 edition of his *Ouvrages divers* which, in view of Kant's remark on p. [c4v], most likely provided him with the text of Maupertuis' *Discours*. Since the review of the *Ouvrages divers* in the *Acta eruditorum* gives no details about that Article, Kant must have become familiar with it through direct reading, which most likely led him to Bradley's paper on the apparent motion of some stars (see note 34 to Opening Discourse). The first half of the Article is an account of Richer's pendulum experiments at Cayenne in 1672 which provided evidence that the centrifugal force becomes greater towards the equator, because there the circles described by the bodies are greater and the direction of the centrifugal force is more in direct opposition to the force of gravity. Maupertuis then continues: "The centrifugal force therefore diminishes the gravity at each place all the more, the closer that place is to the equator; and the gravity thus altered must appear smaller at the equator than toward the poles, and smaller at the places which are closer to the equator than at those places which are most distant from it. This is what was observed after the pendulum had been transported from Paris to Cayenne. The calculations of Newton and of Huygens went as far as to compare the quantity of centrifugal force with gravity and they found that at the equator the former was the 289th part of the latter. In considering afterwards that the waters of the sea maintain themselves in equilibrium all over the earth (because one must not regard the ebb and flow as contrary to that equilibrium) and in viewing the earth as having been formed of homogeneous and fluid matter, or that it was such previously, they undertook to determine on such a basis the figure [of the earth] through the laws of hydrostatics. In order that this fluid matter, which composes the earth, be in a state of rest and that the waters be not flowing from this or that side, it was necessary that the weight of the column, which goes from the [earth's] center to the equator, be equal to the weight of that column which goes from the center to the pole; [so that] these two columns, which one may suppose to be inclosed in tubes that communicate at the center of the earth, support one another and remain in equilibrium. But since the column, which goes to the equator, is formed of a matter which the centrifugal force made lighter than the matter [of the tube] which goes to the pole, it was necessary that the column of the equator be longer than that of the pole: this is what made the earth flattened. Each of these two great mathematicians made his calculation, and they did not differ but in the more or less of the flattening. This difference came from the [respective] system which each followed concerning gravity; because they were in agreement on the centrifugal force. But Huygens assumed that, apart from the alteration, which the centrifugal force causes to gravity, the gravity would be the same in all places of the earth, on the surface as well as in the interior; and [that it] tended everywhere exactly toward the center [of the earth]. He found, in following that hypothesis, that the diameter of the equator must exceed the axis of the earth by 1/578th part of its length. By attributing gravity to the mutual attraction of all parts of the matter which forms the earth, according to the inverse square of their distances [from one another],

273

Newton no longer viewed gravity as having to be the same everywhere. If the figure of the earth depended on gravity, gravity itself depended on the figure which the earth had; and the earth once being flattened by the centrifugal force, this [flattened] figure alone made the gravity smaller at the equator than at the pole[s], independently of the centrifugal force. Newton did his calculation according to that subtle theory and found that the diameter of the equator had to exceed the axis of the earth by 1/230th part of its length" (pp. 22–24). Kant's repeated failure to refer to Maupertuis is difficult to explain, as conscientious references to him, still President of the Berlin Academy, would have enhanced the chances of a favorable reaction there to the *Allgemeine Naturgeschichte*. It seems that Kant did not wish to give the impression that he was not enough of an expert to handle this topic on his own. Indeed, he gave at best an indirect credit to Newton, as the author of the *Principia*, when in the ensuing paragraph he extended the topic to Jupiter. The question of the flattening of the earth had by then enjoying added publicity through the literary activity of Voltaire.

27. Somewhat before the publication of Newton's *Principia* Huygens had already formulated his theory of gravitation (including a calculation of the ratio of the equatorial and polar diameters of the earth, but the theory first saw print only in 1690 in his *Discours sur la cause de la pesanteur* (*Oeuvres complètes*, especially, pp. 468, 471, and 476–77, also for his criticism of Newton). Huygens' theory and calculation of the flattening of the earth is the topic of ch. 2. in I. Todhunter's still classic *History of Mathematical Theories of Attraction and the Figure of the Earth from the Time of Newton to that of Laplace* (London: Macmillan, 1873).

28. The rather abrupt and obscure manner in which Kant brings in the idea of fluid column is best seen when compared with Maupertuis' handling of the same detail.

29. The hypothesis of Newton is set forth in Probl. iii, of Prop. xix of Book III of the *Principia* on the method of finding "the proportion [ratio] of the axis of a planet to the diameter perpendicular thereto" (Var. Ed. 2:593–600).

30. A phrase typical of an amateur. The centrifugal force does not give rise to rotation but is rather a manifestation of it.

31. Kant should have rather stated with Newton that the ratio of the two diameters will be as 230 to 229 (see *Principia*, Var. Ed 2:598).

32. See note 25 above.

33. Kant here confuses average density with equal density. Even in his time it was abundantly clear that the average density of surface materials (including rocks) was only one half of the average density of the earth which exceeded by a factor of about 5 that of water and that of the sun, a value well known to Kant (see note 6 to Second Section of Second Part). Today the density of the earth's inner core extending to about 1000 miles from the center is estimated to be about 11 times greater than that of water. This corresponds to the density of silver; iron having a density of about 8.

34. Kant here confuses specific density with state of fluidity.

35. The ratio is specified in the following footnote, which would have gained in clarity if Kant had simply quoted the opening phrase of Theor. ix of Prop. ix in Book III of the *Principia* (Var. Ed. 2:584), that the force of gravity, considered downwards from the surface of the planets, decreases, on the assumption of uniform density, nearly in the ratio of the distances from the center.

36. Again a case of inconsistency or imprecision. The foregoing 3/5 now becomes 2/3.
37. The actual ratio turned out be much less. See note 25 above.
38. See note 20 to Fourth Section of Second Part.
39. The third part is the result of dividing 90 degrees by 31 degrees.
40. Indeed, he flattered himself too much.
41. The calculation, which is indeed exact, was made by Derham (see note 24 above) whose work is once more left unacknowledged by Kant.
42. Kant should rather have referred explicitly to the *Principia* (Probl. iii of Theor. xix of Book III) which he was now copying out almost verbatim. He should also have mentioned that after concluding his discussion of the differences of the theories of Huygens and Newton, Maupertuis offered a chapter (Article VI) on Jupiter's flattening as a phenomenon which proves the flattening of the earth.
43. Contrary to Kant, Cassini gave the ratio 1/15, the value also reported by Newton. Gian Domenico (Jean-Dominique) Cassini (1625–1712), first director of the Paris Observatory, reported his finding to the French Academy on June 9, 1691. See *Histoire de l'Académie Royale des Sciences. Depuis 1686 jusqu'à son Renouvellement en 1699* (Paris: chez Gabriel Martin [etc], 1733), 2:130.
44. These findings by the Rev. James Pound, rector of the parish church in Wansted (Essex) since 1712, and member of the Royal Society since 1713, who communicated them to Newton to be inserted in the third edition of the *Principia*, are not part of Pound's papers (several of them on Jupiter) published in the *Philosophical Transactions* between 1715 and 1723. He is equally well remembered as the uncle and first mentor of James Bradley, future Astronomer Royal.
45. From this reference to "Newton's system" no reader unacquainted with the *Principia* (and were not such most readers of the *Allgemeine Naturgeschichte*?) could surmise that this conclusion had been explicitly stated by Newton, immediately after reporting the values obtained by Cassini and Pound.
46. Kepler's Third Law. That this law could be very useful in studying Saturn's system was noted in the chapter on Saturn's globe and ring in *Elémens d'astronomie* (Paris: De l'Impremerie Royale, 1740; see especially pp. 338–39) by Jacques Cassini. There he referred to a communication of his in 1715 (see note 13 above) to the Académie des Sciences in which he had argued that the satellites forming the ring must be not only very small but also of so large a number as to allow for many satellites to be moving along each of a great number of concentric circles within the ring. Otherwise the ring would not maintain its visual shape, because the satellites, which obey Kepler's Laws, would be seen in much larger numbers now in this, now in that, direction.
47. Needless to say, in order to calculate this approximately correct value, Kant did not have to know the rotational period of Saturn, but only the period of orbiting of any of its satellites in addition to its distance and that of the ring from the planet. After Herschel's observation in 1789 (see *Collected Scientific Papers*, 1:380) had been reported in 1790 in the *Astronomisches Jahrbuch für das Jahr 1793* (p. 238), Gensichen hastened to derive that value from the proportion discussed in note 19 above, but it yielded him a value of almost twenty minutes less. He discussed that discrepancy in his abbreviated edition of the *Allgemeine Naturgeschichte* (pp. 194–95 note), obviously because it cast a doubt on Kant's calculation of the rotation period of Saturn. Gensichen tried to explain away the discrepancy by suggesting that Herschel's observations did

not possibly relate to the inner edge of the ring but to a point inside it. Gensichen was unaware of the fact that the *Histoire de l'Académie Royale des Sciences. Année 1787. Avec les Mémoires de Mathématiques et de Physique* (Paris: de l'Imprimerie Royale, 1789) carried Laplace's "Mémoire sur la Théorie de l'anneau de Saturne" (pp. 249–67) in which the value of "about ten hours" was calculated. A more exact value was given in 1798 by Laplace (again with no reference to Kant) in the 2d volume of his *Traité de mécanique céleste* (Paris: de l'Imprimerie de Crapelet, An VII), p. 163. See also note 57 to Section IV of Introduction.

48. Another instance of Kant's carelessness with calculations. Gensichen calculated 16 hours.

49. Regardless of the sequence implied in his cosmogony, Kant now concentrates on a phase which appears to be more favorable to his explanation.

50. An error not noticed by Rahts (or by Hastie), but noticed by Bueck.

51. Apart from the absence of sound physics in the entire paragraph, the calculation in question could in no way be carried out by Kant, who once more wants to appear an expert in mathematical physics by interjecting a studiedly vague remark about casting his theory into a mathematical form.

52. A sufficiently vague report which Rahts chose to leave without a comment. There is no mention of it in *Saturn and Its System* (London: Longman, 1865) by R. A. Proctor, who reported no observation of Saturn between Maraldi (1714) and Herschel (1789), and in *The Planet Saturn; A History of Observation, Theory and Discovery* (New York: Macmillan, 1962)by A. F. O'D. Alexander, a work much more detailed and accurate than the former.

53. One can only wish that Kant had referred in at least such a relatively complete form to all works he had quoted and utilized. The translation in question was done by Wolf Balthasar Adolf von Steinwehr (1704–1771), member of the Berlin Academy, who in two multivolume series offered to the German public the memoirs of the French Academy dealing respectively with the physical and physiological sciences. The former series, which comprised the translation of memoirs published between 1692 and 1741, appeared in 13 volumes between 1748 and 1759. The title page of the second volume reads as follows: *Der königl. Akademie der Wissenschaften in Paris Physische Abhandlungen. Zweyter Theil, welcher die Jahre, 1703, 1704, 1705, 1706, in sich hält.* Aus dem Französischen übersetzet, von Wolf Balth. Adolph von Steinwehr, der Königl. Akademie der Wissenschaften in Berlin Mitgliede (Breslau: Verlegts Johann Jacob Korn, 1748). For the memoir of (Jean-Dominique) Cassini, of which only the title, "Betrachtungen über die Observationen der Trabanten und des Ringes des Saturns," is reported by Rahts (AA 1:556), see pp. 566–78. As Kant indicates, the subsequent quotation is on p. 571. Cassini's somewhat diffident remark that the ring, which is "possibly formed as a swarm of small satellites that could make for Saturn an appearance analogous to that which the Milky Way makes for the earth by an infinity of small stars of which it is formed; though with the difference that the Milky Way makes no parallax for the earth, whereas this trace [ring] makes a very large one for Saturn," occurs a page earlier. Kant's parenthetical insistence on the vaporous constitution of the ring and on the "equal motion" of particles in it, is of interest not so much as a mistaken disagreement with Cassini, but because of Cassini's view on nebulous stars stated in the same context: "the appearance of the ring is caused by a heap of very small satellites of different motions which one does not at all see separately, in the manner in which one does not see

distinctly with one's eyes the small stars which compose the nebulous stars, but which appear all together in the form of a small clear cloud" (p. 571). Long before the nebulous stars were seen by Kant as systems of stars comparable to the Milky Way, they had been looked upon as much smaller systems of very small stars (see *The Milky Way*, ch. 4 and 5). For the original of Cassini's memoir "Réflexions sur les observations des satellites de Saturne et de son Anneau," see *Histoire de l'Académie Royale des Sciences. Année MDCCV. Avec les Mémoires de Mathématiques & et de Physique pour la même Année* (Paris: chez Jean Boudot, 1706), pp. 14–24. The view that Saturn's ring consists "of an infinity of small planets very close to one another," was again put forward by Jacques Cassini (who did not refer to his father's paper) in 1715 in his "Observations nouvelles sur Saturne" (see note 13 above, p. 48). Thomas Wright too spoke of Saturn's ring as a congeries of "infinite number of smaller planets" moving around Saturn (*An Original Theory and New Hypothesis of the Universe*, p. 65), but this detail was not reported in the book's summary in the *Freye Urtheile*. Maraldi's view that Saturn's ring was solid was later endorsed by Laplace, who in 1785 argued that the ring was composed of many solid subrings, a view which Herschel put to acid observational test (see note 55 below). That dynamical considerations exclude both solidity and fluidity was shown by Maxwell in his Adams Prize winning essay (1857), in which he also argued conclusively on behalf of the composition of the ring as a multitude of disconnected particles.

54. Typically, this brief quotation too is incorrect in two places with respect to the translation used and also to the original.

55. Herschel, who prior to 1791 doubted the reality of the Cassini-division, was dismayed by the idea that Saturn's ring may periodically be broken into subrings and reunited again. We must not, he wrote, "indulge a suspicion of this being a reality, unless repeated and well-confirmed observations had proved beyond doubt that this ring was actually in so fluctuating condition" (*Collected Scientific Papers*, 1:429–30).

56. This view, obviously a commonplace, also appeared in Lambert's *Cosmologische Briefe*.

57. What makes this statement, correct in itself insofar as it is an aspect of the "compounded ratio" stated by Halley and Maupertuis, wholly misleading is its being connected by Kant with his theory of the formation of Saturn's ring. That connection is the basis of Kant's immediately following explanation of the absence of a ring around Jupiter and the earth.

58. See p. [81] where the sequence of the ratio is given in the reverse order.

59. See p. [85] where the value $9\frac{1}{4}:1$ is given.

60. Kant is clearly carried away in the manner of a zealous system-maker to the point, where Oettingen, until then not too critical of Kant's theory of the formation of Saturn's ring, begins to wonder. As Oettingen notes, at this distance, which is about five times the earth-moon distance, the gravitational acceleration of a body toward the earth is only one tenth of a millimeter per second^2. See his edition of the *Allgemeine Naturgeschichte* (Ostwald's Klassiker der Naturwissenschaften), p. 156.

61. Kant is astonishingly oblivious to the fact, all two well known in his time, that Saturn's satellites orbit in the same plane as does Saturn's ring, that is, inclined at about 30 degrees to Saturn's orbital plane! The same pattern is in evidence around Uranus whose axis is inclined at 98 degrees to its plane of orbiting. Its two satellites and its recently found set of 8 faint rings have

an orbital plane with the same inclination. But even a mere recall of the earth-moon system should have given Kant second thoughts. That all satellites orbit in the main plane of the solar system is the unequivocal meaning of the German original in which the orientation of the plane of Saturn's ring is contrasted through the words "nicht so wie" with that of the plane of orbiting of satellites. Kant's blunder was registered, though fleetingly, by Adickes, *Kant als Naturforscher*, 2:313.

62. While shortly beforehand Kant was only "almost assured," he now speaks of "certain proof," a discrepancy indicative of the major and minor inconsistencies that run through the *Allgemeine Naturgeschichte*. As was mentioned in Section III of Introduction, Kant was all too delighted to inform Gensichen about Lichtenberg's approval in this connection. Kant's words to Gensichen are fully quoted by Oettingen (*Allgemeine Naturgeschichte*, Ostwald's Klassiker der Naturwissenschaften, pp. 156–57), who, like most other commentators of Kant, failed to notice the anomaly registered in the preceding note.

63. Kant is most serious about those "arbitrary notions." By characterizing them as such, he clearly tries to forestall criticism and recrimination on the part of orthodox theologians.

64. Beneath this personification of nature there lies a train of thought which Kant many years later formulated with stark bluntness in his *Perpetual Peace:* "Since reason cannot apply the relations of causes and effects, to any other objects than such as experience has made known to us, it is more modest, and conformable to the limits of the human understanding, to employ the word *nature*, when theory and not religion is the question, preferably to that of *Providence*, which intimates a pretended knowledge of its mysteries, and a flight as temerarious as that of Icarus, towards the sanctuary of its impenetrable designs" (New York: Columbia University Press, 1939, p. 28).

65. The sarcasm of the phrase, aimed at the divines busy with the history of creation (Genesis), clearly shows that the notions which Kant is now developing are far from being arbitrary to him.

66. Under the impact which was given by the Reformation to the literal interpretation of the Bible, the cosmogony of Genesis could but give unnecessary headaches to Protestant divines and also to their Catholic counterparts who were quickly drawn into the strategy of confronting the former on their own ground. A good sample of both sides' inept grappling with the waters of firmament is given in article "Wasser" published in the 53rd volume (1747, cols. 73–74) of *Groszes vollständiges Universal-Lexicon* (63 vols; Halle und Leipzig: Verlegts Johann Heinrich Zedler, 1732–1750).

67. A reference to Whiston's theory of deluge.

68. The comet touching off the deluge in Whiston's theory.

69. Reference to Noah.

70. Kant wants to discredit any future use by theologians of his theory of ring formation.

Sixth Section

1. The Mr. de Mairan, mentioned by Kant, is Jean Jacques d'Ortous de Mairan (1678–1771), Fontenelle's successor as perpetual secretary of the Académie des Sciences (1741–43). Assuming that Kant had proper information on the subject, he should have informed his readers that de Mairan was the author of a massive and still classic work, *Traité physique et historique de l'aurore boréale*, first published in 1732. Already in that first edition the *Traité* contained much

more on the zodiacal light than Kant's generic dicta on it could even suggest. While leaving the text of that first edition practically unchanged in its second edition (Paris: de l'Imprimerie Royale, 1754), the latter contained also twenty-one "Eclaircissements" (p. 301–570), of which the first nine had already been published in *Histoire de l'Académie Royale des Sciences. Année MDCCXLVII. Avec les Mémoires de Mathématiques et de Physique pour la même Année* (Paris: de l'Imprimerie Royale, 1752), pp. 363–435. To a great extent these nine "clarifications" deal with a dispute that arose between de Mairan and Euler, after the latter disagreed with de Marian who took the zodiacal light for a phenomenon of the solar atmosphere. According to Euler, who developed his ideas in a memoir read before the Académie des Sciences in Berlin in 1746 ("Recherches physiques sur la cause de la queüe des comètes, de la lumière boréale, et de la lumière zodiacale," *Histoire de l'Académie Royale des Sciences et Belles Lettres. Année MDCCXLVI* [Berlin: chez Ambroise Haude, 1748], pp. 117–40), the zodiacal light was made up of particles emanating from the sun: "In fact the sun is surrounded along its equator by a light which extends to a prodigious distance, and which one calls zodiacal" (p. 119). Euler also stated that the sun's light, undulatory though it be, can push those luminous particles to very great distances from the sun. Furthermore, Euler analyzed the case of stable orbits for those particles, an analysis demanding the solution of a cubic equation, with the result that "it can happen that the atmosphere of the sun may change into a ring and surround the sun, as the ring of Saturn surrounds that planet. Observations do not permit to decide whether the zodiacal light is contiguous with the sun or is placed at some distance from that star in the form of a ring. Therefore it should suffice to propose these conjectures until observation permits the determination of something more certain" (p. 140). This memoir of Euler could hardly be unknown to Kant, whose failure to refer to it is all the more difficult to explain because his ideas were closer to Euler's position than to that of de Mairan. Possibly here too, as was the case in the preceding Section with his tacit reliance on Maupertuis' *Eléments de géographie*, Kant became the victim of his strategy to appear more of a scientist than he was, a strategy hardly useful in respect to the Berlin Academy, with Maupertuis its president and Euler its most distinguished member. The lenticular shape (de Mairan does not use the expression *figura lenticulari*) of the zodiacal light is mentioned time and again in the *Traité* (2d ed., pp. 21, 27, 29, etc). The only detail about the zodiacal light mentioned by Kant, which is not found in Mairan's work, is the mechanism which Kant had already used in connection with the accumulation of most chaotic matter in the equatorial plane of the sun and of that of Saturn. Rahts' respective notes (AA 1:525 and 557) provide no information about Mairan's *Traité* or any of his publications relating to the zodiacal light.

2. That the sun's rays exert pressure on particles upon which they impinge, had long been entertained in connection with the bending of comets' tails away from the sun.

3. The expression is glaringly inaccurate in terms of Kant's cosmogony in which the non-central forces of repulsion play an essential role in the process in question.

4. Kant has in mind the approximately 25 days, or the sun's period of rotation. Whereas in terms of angular velocity the sun's rotation is very slow in comparison with the rotation of the earth, Jupiter, and Saturn, in terms of

equatorial velocity it exceeds more than twice that of the earth which is about half a kilometer per second.

5. The manner in which Kant gives that value can in itself suggest that he calculated it. In all likelihood he found it in the German translation of Derham's *Astrotheology*, a work he mentioned above (p. [13]). There, in chapter ii of Book VI, a chapter devoted to "the guard which gravity affords against the centrifugal force of the several globes," Derham registers his gratitude to Halley who calculated for him the ratio in question as 47000 to 1 (first edition, London: W. Innys, 1715, p. 142), a value which appeared unchanged in the subsequent editions (see, for instance, the 4th "much corrected" edition, 1721, p. 150), and was reproduced exactly (p. 149) in the four editions of the German translation (see note 30 to First Part and note 24 to Fifth Section of Second Part). Kant's phrase, "not even 1/40000th," evasive as it is of the value as given by Halley (a value also in close agreement with calculation based on modern data), may be ascribed either to Kant's often cavalier attitude toward numerical data, or to his affectation of originality. The expression "not even" was justifiable only if he himself calculated the ratio, although in this case he was not only in error, but also in disagreement with "the very acute and learned Dr. Halley," as Derham spoke of his friend in the same context.

6. Since Kant discusses the zodiacal light in reference to Saturn's ring, he might just as well have mentioned that the distance in question exceeded about twenty times the sun-Saturn distance.

Seventh Section

1. This view had been widely entertained before Kant owing to the great popularity of Fontenelle's *Entretiens* and Huygens' *Cosmotheoros*.

2. This statement as it stands is most vulnerable, as no observation whatever indicated that the stars of the Milky Way were in motion, that they were in motion around a center, and that this center was an enormously massive body. Lambert, who in his *Cosmologische Briefe* also postulated such a large (though opaque) body to secure the stability of the system of stars, was fully aware of the fact that the orbiting of stars around such a body would be much faster than around a purely geometrical center. This problem, as was noted in Section IV of the Introduction, was skilfully analysed in 1800 by Soldner who referred to both Kant and Lambert.

3. Kant either did not know or simply ignored the bafflement of many an astronomer who had found that better telescopes did not only resolve those nebulous patches into stars, but unveiled more and more of the nebulous material as well. This situation did not change when Herschel greatly increased the resolving power of telescopes. See chs. 5 and 7 in my *The Milky Way* and note 55 to Section IV of the Introduction.

4. One of the many cases of Kant's imprecise, often rhapsodical use of the words infinite and infinity.

5. Pope's phrase obviously found favor with Kant. See also p. [122].

6. Among those whom Kant could have cited was Henry More, author of *Democritus Platonissans* (1647), who in his *Apology* (1664) rightly traced such a position to the influence of Descartes. More's disciple, Joseph Glanvill, claimed in his *Lux orientalis* (1682) not only on philosophical but also on biblical grounds that God's infinity demanded an infinite universe (see Lovejoy, *The Great Chain of Being*, pp. 125–26). Kant could not, however, have cited Derham,

one of his chief sources, who stopped short of endorsing strict infinity for the universe. The type of universe, which for Derham was "most worthy of an infinite Creator, whose Power and Wisdom . . . are without measure," was extending but "to an indefinite Space" (*Astrotheology*, 4th ed. pp. xxxviii and xlii). The rush to infinity proved to be irresistible in a number of cases, some of them now almost entirely forgotten. Kant may very well have been familiar with the reasoning of a certain Freymund, whose *Drey Gespräche über wichtige Wahrheiten*, a booklet of two signatures in 4°, was given a lengthy account in the *Freye Urtheile* 2(1745):83–86. The first two "Gespräche" had for their topics the infinity and eternity of the universe, both of which were claimed to be unquestionable verities on the basis of God's infinity and eternity. A generation later Voltaire endorsed the eternity of the universe on the same grounds, but not its spatial infinity, as the latter conflicted, according to him, with the impossibility of an actually realized infinite number. See his *Il faut prendre un parti ou le principe d'action* (1772) in *Oeuvres complètes de Voltaire*, 28:521–23.

7. Instead of this exceedingly clumsy phrase, Kant could have easily stated that it would be senseless to imagine God as being in activity with only an infinitely small part of his creative ability engaged, although this phrasing, clear in itself, would have remained fraught with grave philosophical difficulties.

8. That God is inactive unless He is creating is a naive misconception of those who "following Descartes" had no use for the Scholastics' insight that God was *actus purus*, or very act of existence. This insight of theirs was a fruit of their meditation on that passage in Exodus in which God reveals his most special name, (I AM—HE WHO IS, or Yahweh), a passage which E. Gilson aptly called the "metaphysics of Exodus" (see *The Spirit of Medieval Philosophy: Gifford Lectures, 1931–1932*, translated by A. H. C. Downes [New York: Charles Scribner's Sons, 1940], p. 433). The extent to which Descartes succeeded in discrediting the medieval philosophical heritage can be seen, for instance, from the fact that such a dedicated churchman and incisive thinker as Samuel Clarke poured ridicule on the expression *actus purus* in 1704 in his Boyle lectures, *A Demonstration of the Being and Attributes of God* (7th ed.; London: James and John Kapton, 1728), p. 40.

9. A clear instance of Kant's instinctive reliance on the a priori approach, which with the same logic lands him in erroneous conclusions about Creator and creation. For a further analysis of this point in Kant's intellectual development, see ch. 8, "Arch without Keystone," in my *The Road of Science and the Ways to God* (Chicago: University of Chicago Press, 1978).

10. Opponents of the idea of infinite physical extension should have come above all from among scientists, who, however, had by then repeatedly taken lightly its optical and gravitational paradoxes. (see Section II of Introduction). As to metaphysicians, even those among them, such as Descartes and Henry More, whose premises strongly implied the infinity of the universe, remained ambivalent on more than one occasion. That the assertion of the infinity of the universe could readily lead to pantheism had already been examplified in the writings of Bruno and Spinoza. A most notable warning against this inner logic came only ten years after the publication of the *Allgemeine Naturgeschichte* in the article "Infini" of the *Encyclopédie* (vol. 8, 1765, p. 702) with the insistence that infinity in the strict sense must be reserved for the Supreme Being.

11. Johann Friederich Weitenkampf (?–1758), designated by Kant as M[agister of

281

philosophy], was privatdozent at the University of Helmstedt before he took the post of deacon in Braunschweig. He submitted his defense of the finiteness of the universe in his *Gedanken über wichtige Wahrheiten aus der Vernunft und Religion* (3 vols; Braunschweig und Hildesheim: Verlegts seel. Ludolph Schröders Erben, 1753–55), of which the second volume (Zweiter Theil) was published in 1754 and contained the essay, "Gedanken über die Frage: Ob das Weltgebäude Grenzen habe?" (pp. 3–60). The essay consists of 40 paragraphs of which 1–8 are devoted to the greatness of the observable universe, 9–26 to the proposition that the universe cannot be infinite in extent, because its parts would then be infinite in number, a consequence fraught with the contradiction implied in the notion of an actually realized infinite quantity. Paragraphs 27–36 answer the objection that God's infinite desire to impart happiness demands an infinite number of creatures and therefore an infinitely large world. In the remaining four paragraphs the enormity of the finite observable universe is again portrayed. According to Rahts (AA 1:557), Weitenkampf's rebuttal of the infinity of the universe was contained in his *Lehrgebäude vom Untergange der Erden*, about which Rahts gives only its year of publication, 1754, possibly because, if his inaccurate rendering of the title is an indication, he had no access to it. In the *Lehrgebäude*, a book of 330 pages (plus 12 pages of Index) brought out by the same publisher, Weitenkampf battles the idea of the eternity of the world and not of its infinite extent. Concerning this latter point, he explicitly refers (p. 26) to his essay on it in the *Gedanken*. Weitenkampf, who shares the contemporary belief that God must create intelligent beings (souls) in order to fulfill the purpose of material creation, rejects physical eternity, because the number of souls created in endless times would be infinite, but such an actually realized infinite number is impossible (pp. 60–63). Behind this reasoning of Weitenkampf there is also his fear (fomented by his Lutheran pessimism concerning the respective number of the elect and damned) that in an eternal universe the number of damned would be infinitely larger than the number of the elect. While this motivation of Weitenkampf is without philosophical merit, he was, unlike Kant, good enough a philosopher and theologian not to take God's eternity and the eternity of souls for a sum of an infinite number of time elements. At any rate, less than ten years before the publication of the *Allgemeine Naturgeschichte* the effort to present eternity as the sum of time elements provoked a well-deserved derision. The occasion was the defense on July 23, 1746, by Johann Augustin Köselitz at the University of Leipzig of his *Dissertatio de successione momentorum in ipsa aeternitate* (Breitkopfen, 48pp) which was given in the *Freye Urtheile* (3[1746]:481–83; Aug. 9, 1746) a review that came to a close with a warning against "metaphysische Wörtergrübeleyen." As to Köselitz's definition of elementary units of time, the reviewer gave it in its original Latin and added that translating it into German would leave it just as incomprehensible.—The use of the impossibility of an actually realized infinite quantity as an argument against the infinity and eternity of the universe, seems to have been in high regard in German academic circles in the decades preceding the publication of the *Allgemeine Naturgeschichte*. The argument is the backbone of two dissertations: one by A. J. J. von Sieden, *Dissertatio mathematico-metaphysica de mundo finito et infinito* (Rostoch: typis Johann Jacobi Adleri, 1738, 36pp) in which both the eternity and the infinity of the universe are rejected (see esp. pp. 25–28), the other by Ph. Magnus, *Dissertatio metaphysica de impossibilitate mundi aeterni*, defended in Wittenberg but published in Jena (litteris Schillianis, 1741, 30pp), which consists of three parts: historical, dogmatical, and polemical. Weitenkampf's insistence on the impossibility of an actually realized infinite quantity is ignored in "Selbsterhaltung und Beharrung: Zur Konstitution der neuzeitlichen Rationalität" (*Akademie der Wissenschaften und der Literatur. Mainz. Abhandlungen der Geistes- und Sozialwissenschaftlichen Klasse.* Jahrgang 1969. Nr. 11. 51pp) by H. Blumenberg, who uses Weitenkampf's *Lehrgebäude* as an example (pp. 45–49) of modern rationality which aims at dissipating the prospects of a finite cosmic existence. Weitenkampf is not mentioned by Lovejoy in his *The Great Chain of Being* as he quotes (p. 140) Kant's rebuttal of the argument in question. See also note 49 below.

12. As was pointed out in Section II of the Introduction, already in 1720 Halley reported this objection against the infinity of the universe in a generic manner which seems to indicate that the objection was in the air. Whereas Halley's remark was most likely unknown to Kant, who, of course, could not yet know that Leibniz had already declared in his *Nouveaux essais sur l'entendement humain* (written in 1704 but first published in 1765) that "we deceive ourselves by wishing to imagine an absolute space, which would be an infinite whole, composed of parts. There is no such thing. It is a notion which involves contradiction, and these infinite wholes, and their opposites, the infinitesimals, are only admissible in the calculations of geometers, just like the imaginary roots of algebra" (Bk. II, ch. xvii; see *Leibniz Selections*, edited by Philip P. Wiener [New York: Charles Scribner's Sons, 1951], p. 424). Again, Leibniz's letter of March 17, 1706, to Father Des Bosses, in which he admitted that the notion of physical infinity was fraught with difficulties (it could not, according to Leibniz, form a coherent whole), first saw print only in 1768. See *Philosophischen Schriften von Gottfried Wilhelm Leibniz*, edited by C. J. Gerhardt, (Hildesheim: Georg Olms, 1960), 2:305. Kant, however, could be familiar with a much earlier and very different view of Leibniz, who in 1671 endorsed the idea of "worlds in worlds in infinitum" in his *Hypothesis physica nova* (*Philosophischen Schriften*, 4:201).

13. A perfect opportunity for any uncritical admirer of Kant the scientist to present him as a prophetic forerunner of special relativity.

14. This brave promise could but make Kant appear to the uninitiated a very profound scientist. Actually, he was too much of a dilettante in calculus to cope with the project even if it had been a sound one. In 1755 the strictures, which Berkeley had voiced against the notion of infinitesimally small quantities in *The Analyst* (1734) and *A Defence of Free Thinking in Mathematics* (1735), were still fully valid and much too well known. Until Cauchy gave in 1821 a satisfactory formulation to the theory of limit, the cornerstone of calculus, students had to take it "on faith," a point acknowledged by no less a mathematician than Lagrange.

15. The expression, consequence (Folge), was hardly expressive of the utter contingency of the universe, awareness of which had been steadily eroding among admirers of Descartes, Leibniz, and Wolff. The latter two were especially taken to task in this respect by Joachim Lange, professor of theology in Halle, in his *Modesta disquisitio novi philosophiae systematis de Deo, mundo et homine* . . . (Halle: prostat in Officina Orphanotrophei, 1723).

16. In this connection it is appropriate to recall that in his first publication (the one on the living forces, 1747) Kant argued on the same basis that worlds of all possible numbers of dimensions could and had to exist (he did not explain

how they related to one another); that in his inaugural dissertation (1770) he upheld reason's ability to ascertain the quantitative limitedness of the universe; and that in the *Kritik* he presented spatial and quantitative infinity as aspects of one of the antinomies which barred reason from ascertaining the existence of God.

17. A rather clumsily constructed contrast between the infinity of space and that of matter, which hardly makes a favorable reflection either on Kant the stylist, or on Kant the philosopher.

18. Here Kant should have referred to Bentley, who had discussed this point in his Boyle lectures.

19. This is an echoing of Leibniz's position against Newton, or rather against Samuel Clarke, Newton's mouthpiece in the famed dispute which had been all too well known since the first publication in 1717 of the Clarke-Leibniz correspondence.

20. Kant failed to realize that this physical center should have a mass of infinite quantity, a consequence obviously disastrous for his cosmogony.

21. The idea of the organic interconnectedness of all parts of the universe had already received a memorable expression in 1710 in the *Theodicée* of Leibniz, who lets Pallas Athene present to Theodorus the variety of worlds as culminating in the apex of a pyramid. See *Theodicy: Essays on the Goodness of God, the Freedom of Man, and the Origin of Evil*, translated by E. M. Huggard (New Haven: Yale University Press, 1952), pp. 371–72.

22. What has been stated (see note 20 above) about the mass of that central body, applies also to its density.

23. This reasoning shows Kant a most uncritical thinker, though neither the first or the last of those who, being infatuated with infinity, lose their critical faculties.

24. Actually, in view of Kant's subsequent statements, his cosmogony presents one not so much with a successive completion of creation, but with endless repetitions of that alleged completion.

25. Kant had no justification whatever to state that we are anywhere near that center. Within the context of his cosmogony he could merely state that we are in one of the infinite number of spherical shells which correspond to states of full development.

26. Whereas Kant is bold in conjuring up future millions of centuries, he is very careful, on account of Lutheran authorities, not to tamper with the few thousands of years which their reading of the Bible allowed to have passed since the moment of creation. Thus for the full development of Jupiter, Kant would allow only a few hundred years more than was the case with the earth (see pp. [71–72]).

27. This evolutionary view had already been fully orchestrated by Buffon and voiced by many long before him.

28. The mass had to be not only "outstanding" but simply infinite.

29. Here Kant voices the traditional Christian doctrine of creation in time, a doctrine to which he denied philosophical validity in the *Kritik*.

30. Actually, within the Kantian framework, Creation is bound to repeat itself in endless successions. On the Kantian cosmos as a treadmill of perpetual recurrence, see my *Science and Creation: From Eternal Cycles to an Oscillating Universe* (Edinburgh: Scottish Academic Press; New York: Science History Publications, 1974), pp. 289–90.

31. This is the first of two quotations from Albrecht von Haller's "Unvollkommene

Ode über die Ewigkeit" which first appeared in the third enlarged edition of Haller's *Versuch schweizerischer Gedichte* (Danzig: Anno 1743), pp. 149–53; for quotation see p. 151. Haller (1708–1777), who is today best remembered as a physiologist, was highly regarded in his time as a poet. This translation is based on Hastie's *Kant's Cosmogony*, p. 146) by making it more conform to the German original, handled by Hastie rather freely in places.

32. The use of triple negative in this sentence is anticipating the procedure of those how nowadays glibly assert the existence of solar systems and of life on them everywhere in the universe, while at the same time try to appear very cautious thinkers, a feature all too obvious, say, in Carl Sagan's writings on the topic.

33. Unfortunately, mere reliance on analogy can be most misleading.

34. Kant fails to realize that the distribution in question implies infinite density at the center and zero density at infinity.

35. Once more Kant pre-empts, implicitly at least, the contingency of creation.

36. A favorite topic with Kant, whose *Physische Geographie* contains a section "on the history of the great changes which the earth has already suffered and will still suffer" (see AA 9:296–305).

37. Kant is oblivious to his previous declaration (p. [105]) that no finite quantity bears a relation to the infinite; see also p. [122].

38. From what follows it is obvious that Kant does not use here "universal" in a strict sense, that is, in a sense valid for the entire infinite universe as such.

39. Kant has in mind the Scholium of the *Principia* in which Newton emphatically declares that we know God "by his most wise and excellent contrivances of things" and that therefore, to discourse of God "from the appearances of things, does certainly belong to Natural Philosophy." See Var. Ed. 2:763–74.

40. Although Newton stated in the *Principia* (Bk. III, Prop. x, Theor. x) that planets and comets would continue their motions "for an immense stretch of times" in the celestial regions void of air and exhalations, and he even calculated in the *Opticks* (Query 22) that the resistance of an ether 700,000 times thinner than the air would not sensibly alter those motions in 10,000 years, in Query 31 he emphatically declared that owing to the mutual perturbation of planets the time will inevitably come when "this System [of planets] wants a Reformation." See Dover edition of the *Opticks* (New York, 1952), pp. 368 and 402.

41. Kant seems to imply that living beings, unlike formations of inert matter, reveal a direct action of God. See note 29 to Opening Discourse.

42. Somewhat rhetorical statement. Cities, but not entire nations, were known to have been destroyed by natural disasters. Even the Lisbon earthquake, still half a year away (Nov. 1, 1755), which struck an irreparable blow at the Leibnizian optimism exuding from this passage, did not wipe out the Portuguese nation, and not even the whole of Lisbon.

43. These lines in Brockes' translation (pp. 10–11) correspond to lines 87–90 of Epistle I of *Essay on Man* with the exception of the line in brackets, simply ignored by Brockes:

> Who sees with equal eye, as God of all,
> A hero perish, or a sparrow fall,
> [Atoms or systems into ruin hurled],
> And now a bubble burst, and now a world.

44. The statement invites comparison with a similar statement on p. [105].

45. Kant is once more evasive concerning nature as a whole.

46. In the manner of a priori thinkers, Kant is not serious about his protestations of diffidence.

47. Kant did not demonstrate at all that such material was the best fuel for fire. He should have rather noted that Newton had already voiced in the *Principia* the commonly held view that comets, by falling into the sun, rejuvenate its heat. See Bk. III, Prop. xlii; Var. Ed. 2:757.

48. Although Kant's cosmogony does not merit comparison with this or that aspect of modern astrophysics, a collapse of so many stars would undoubtedly result not in a new superstar but in a gigantic black hole with an apparent end to all further processes.

49. Obviously, Lovejoy did not keep in mind this and other passages (see esp. p. [136]) when he somewhat lamely claimed (*The Great Chain of Being*, p. 365) that Kant asserted only once, and even then inconsistently and not wholly explicitly, that the entire nature was subject to alternate cycles of evolution and dissolution. Lovejoy would certainly have profited by a remark of Kant's French translator, Charles Wolf, who singled out (*Les hypothèses cosmogoniques*, p. ix) as most eloquent and philosophically profound those pages in the *Allgemeine Naturgeschichte* in which Kant "sets forth his ideas on the successive formation of worlds in the indefinite extent of chaos, their perishing and their resurrection." Most revealing should seem the fact that Kant failed to rebut Weitenkampf, who throughout his *Lehrgebäude* (see note 11 above) kept arguing against the eternity of the world and against its irrevocable decay, let alone annihilation. The final prospect for the universe was, according to Weiten-kampf, an entirely new type of physical existence, in harmony with the supernatural resurrection of all. The idea of a cyclic cosmos could only be abhorrent to Weitenkampf, who quoted from a report of Danish missionaries in East India about the cyclic views prevailing there. In the report, as quoted by Weitenkampf, pointed reference was made to the Kaliyuga, a world-period stretching for 432,000 years, of which, according to Hindu belief, only 4337 years had so far passed by. For the report, see pp. 246–50 in the first (1754) edition, and pp. 231–34 of the second improved edition (1762, same publisher and place).

50. The basic independence of soul from body, which here underlies Kant's discourse, will be considerably weakened by his speculations in the Third Part.

51. "Unvollkommene Ode über die Ewigkeit", in *Versuch*, p. 152. Here too Hastie considerably departed in places from the original.

52. Perhaps Kant merely wanted to reassure Lutheran divines, whose ministration he was to refuse on his deathbed.

53. This is the memorable conclusion of Addison's essay on gratitude toward God in *Spectator* (Nr. 453, Aug. 9, 1712), which found a most competent translator in Johann Christoph Gottsched (1700–1766), a native of Königsberg, who had a considerable influence as a translator, playwright, critic, lexicographer, and finally as a professor of philosophy in Leipzig. Contrary to Rahts (AA 1:557), the translation is not from *Der Aufseher* (*Guardian*) but from *Der Zuschauer* (9 vols; 2d improved ed.; Leipzig; B. C. Breitkopf, 1749–51).

Addition to the Seventh Section

1. The meaning of "complete cosmogony," an expression remarkable in itself, will reveal its fullness in a subsequent remark of Kant (p. [141]) that he *must* discourse on the physical and intellectual characteristics of the denizens of planets.

2. The claim that only the first principles need to be recalled to explain this or that outstanding feature of a world-edifice (a claim which Kant had already made in connection with the zodiacal light, with Saturn's ring, to mention only two examples), will appear to be an old one to anyone familiar with the parlance of Aristotle and Descartes, authors of two markedly a priori cosmologies. It seems that the inner logic of one's presuppositions does not fail to set the pattern of one's diction.

3. According to Kant the orbital momentum of particles was the result of their mutual collisions. Therefore, very light particles could easily acquire the small amount of that momentum required at very great distances from the sun where they originally had been located, and thus most of them would have never fallen into the sun.

4. A generally shared preconception with little if any scientific merit.

5. In respect to its measure of confidence, obscurity, and categories this phrase emulates many a statement of Aristotle in his *Meteorologica*. Kant obviously thinks of himself as an authority on fire, possibly because while he was writing the *Allgemeine Naturgeschichte* he was preparing his Latin dissertation on fire (AA 1:369–84) for the degree of magister, which he defended on May 13, 1755, hardly two months after the *Allgemeine Naturgeschichte* left the press.

6. Only an Aristotle and a Descartes (and some moderns) could resolve so quickly a major point of cosmogony.

7. Kant is obviously eager to create an impressive background for his dicta. Contrary to his claim, the constitution of distant celestial bodies was not a widely discussed topic, nor were his reasons any stronger than the one offered by others.

8. In the theory of Buffon, who imagined the material forming the masses of planets to have been torn out from the sun by a comet, the sun had to be in such a hot molten condition. Kant does not reveal that his theory of the flaming condition of the sun (when taken together with his subsequent contentions about the solidity of the sun's surface and of the negligible effectiveness of fire in the downward direction) is essentially identical with the view that the sun is a dark body, as are the planets, though surrounded with a flaming atmosphere. In this view the sun could be seen as inhabited and this was in part the reason of its popularity with, for instance, Bode and Herschel, whose dicta are quoted by Adickes as a "dark" background for Kant's "enlightened" theory (*Kant als Naturforscher*, 2:278–79).

9. This statement, so markedly Aristotelian, will not appear strange in view of the heavily scholastic trend which, in part under Wolff's influence, still prevailed at that time in German universities.

10. As his dissertation on fire indicates, Kant was familiar with at least the most important pieces of literature on the subject and could have easily produced other "reasons."

11. Whereas at the beginning of this paragraph Kant firmly stated the flaming character of the sun, one (long, to be sure) sentence later he proposes the same only with probability.

12. Kant most likely had in mind his previous statement (p. [99]) that on the sun's equator the gravitational force exceeded by a factor of about 40,000 the centrifugal force. According to Newton, the respective weights of a body on the sun, Jupiter, Saturn and the earth would be as the series 10,000, 997, 791, and 435. See *Principia*, Bk. III, Prop. viii, Theor. viii; Var. Ed. 2:581.

13. To a systematizer as Kant no situation is without some resource.

14. The experiments in question are a part of Stephen Hales' (1677–1761) *Vegetable Staticks* (1727), which contained according to its long subtitle also a *Specimen of an Attempt to Analyse the Air, by a Great Variety of Chymio-Statical Experiments*. Its French translation by Buffon in 1735 may have acquainted Kant with its contents. Especially relevant is experiment 121; see S. Hales, *Vegetable Staticks*, with a foreword by M. A. Hoskin (London: Macdonald, 1969), pp. 172–80.

15. Somewhat different was Hales' general conclusion: "However, we may with pleasure see what immense treasures of this noble and important element [of air], endued with a most active principle, the all-wise Providence of the great Author of nature has provided: the constant waste of it being abundantly supplied by heat and fermentation from innumerable dense bodies; and that probably from many of those bodies, which when they had their ascending fumes confined in my Glasses, absorbed more air than they generated, but would be in a more free, open space generate more than they absorbed" (ibid., p. 177).

16. Evidences to the contrary could have been easily found by Kant, had he not been attached too much to the perspective set by his cosmogony.

17. The ease with which Kant discourses about deep gorges inside the sun is worth noting.

18. A candor which would have been appropriate about much of his cosmogony.

19. Salpeter or nitre is often mentioned in Hales' *Vegetable Staticks* (see, for instance, pp. 129, 133, 175). Patently naive is Oettingen's remark: "The mention of salpeter is indeed surprising for that time, 1755, as it had to be based on a knowledge of the production of gunpowder." See p. 157 in his edition (1898) of the *Allgemeine Naturgeschichte*. Had gunpowder not been produced in vast quantities for centuries before Kant?

20. The appeal of that theme to Kant was already evidenced by his brief essay on the question whether the earth was ageing, published in six instalments in a Königsberg weekly between August 10 and September 14, 1754, a period which saw the manuscript of the *Allgemeine Naturgeschichte* rapidly advancing toward its completion.

21. Not at all. In the Kantian universe there will be a star at an infinite number of times at any place.

22. The novae and variable stars. The explanation is rather similar to the one offered by Descartes in his *Principes de la philosophie*. See *Planets and Planetarians*, p. 43.

23. Kant could not have stated more clearly his belief in the cyclic character of everything in the universe.

24. Imagination can often help a scientist, but Kant relies on it too heavily and with an, at times, poetical penchant as shown by the passage to follow.

25. Since Johann Fabricius first discussed sunspots in print in 1611, many offered mostly brief speculations on them which, like those of Kant, were entirely conjectural and could easily fit, as was the case with him, almost any preconcieved scheme.

26. Kant's main, if not sole reason in describing the sun as an essentially solidified globe is to ward off the prospect of a sun still in hot flaming stage, which could have called for a theory of fire other than the one he advocated, tied as this was to the all-purpose role played by the "lightest stuff" in his cosmogony.

27. Underlying Kant's argument is the law, already stated by Kepler, of the decrease

of the intensity of light according to the inverse square law. In this perspective alone, and assuming the sun and Sirius to be similar stars, his argument is valid. Kant, however, should have taken into consideration the number of stars in the Milky Way. It seems that just as he lectured on physical geography without ever leaving the province (let alone the state) of Prussia, he discoursed on the Milky Way without ever looking at it through a telescope, which even in its modest pre-Herschelian stage would have shown him enormous quantities of stars. He should have at least remembered that the summary of Wright's *Original Theory* in the *Freye Urtheile* (and also in the *Hamburgisches Magazin*) contained Wright's estimate of the number of stars in the belt of the Milky Way as being close to 4 million and the warning that this was only a small portion of the sky. Therefore, and also in view of the lopsided ratio of the sun's mass to that of the planets, Kant should have spoken of a central body not 10,000 but many millions of times larger than the sun. No wonder that Lambert postulated those central bodies to be dark (see *Cosmological Letters*, pp. 109–110, 125–26) for a reason which combined both the optical and gravitational aspects of the problem. Kant and his admirers failed to react when in 1796 Laplace claimed that a star as dense as the earth but with a radius 250 times that of the sun would become opaque because owing to its gravitational field the escape velocity on its surface would exceed the speed of light. See *Planets and Planetarians*, p. 126.

28. According to Lambert, that center was in Orion, and probably was the great nebula there (see *Cosmological Letters*, pp. 138–39 and 180–81). This discrepancy between Lambert's and Kant's views was not noted by Utenhove in his comments on the French translation of the *Cosmologische Briefe* (see note 70 to Section IV of the Introduction).

29. A rather confusing explanation and statement, as according to Kant the sun was near the center of the system.

30. Instead, Kant might have simply stated that Sirius (α Canis Maioris) was in the middle of that widest part of the Milky Way, a point all too evident on a glance at a star chart most of which showed, long before Kant, the belt of the Milky Way.

31. A very clumsy way of stating that the planes of the ecliptic and of the Milky Way do not exactly coincide.

32. An unjust remark on the part of one unable to see the true character of his speculations on the physical and intellectual character of the denizens of planets.

33. But he claimed freedom to speculate in respect of a subject far less esoteric. See p. [135].

34. Wright, whose discourse has just been characterized by Kant as "fanatical" (p. [140]).

35. The Third Part is indeed a "must" according to Kant, whose former remark about "complete cosmogony" receives thereby its full meaning. In this respect he is certainly a forerunner of those who today allocate to the subject of extraterrestrial inteligence an integral part in their cosmogonical speculations.

36. This figure of speech to denote the gradation of perfection in every facet of existence had been a commonplace long before Kant. In making use of the degrees of perfection on behalf of his demonstration of the existence of God, Matthew Barker wrote: "These degrees in Nature are by learned Men called the Scale of Nature; and we must come to some top in the Scale or Ladder, and not ascend in Infinitum, though we must into Infinity, which is the

Infinite God. For, as I said before, where there . . . are degrees of Perfection, there must needs be some greatest Perfection, and what can that be but God" (*Natural Theology, or The knowledge of God, from the Works of Creation, Accommodated, and Improved, to the Service of Christianity* [London: printed for Nathaniel Ranew, 1674], p. 27). Unfortunately, there is very little about Nature in Barker's book.

37. This principle of the mind-body relationship is set forth in detail in the Third Part.

Eighth Section

1. The title, "General Overview," would have better fitted this Section, which Kant recommended (p. [c6v]) as a piece that would favorably predispose those uneasy about the boldness of his approach. The word certainty in the title should be seen in the light of Kant's repeated assertions in the rest of the *Allgemeine Naturgeschichte* of the unquestionable correctness of his cosmogony.

2. A gross exaggeration. There were still around many Cartesians who certainly believed in the universal explanatory power of mechanical laws (be it of their own brand), and no Newtonian would have made a recourse to God's direct intervention in order to explain, say, the spherical shape of celestial bodies, or the bending of the tail of comets, or the flattening of rotating bodies, to mention only a few examples. The *Principia* was in fact an enormous advance in reducing numerous and varied phenomena to the same inverse square law of gravitation. Rule I and Rule II at the very start of the Third Book of the *Principia* are a declaration of such a "reductionist" program in natural philosophy. Kant clearly exaggerates, in order to make his achievement appear more spectacular.

3. Kant could hardly name a thinker of any consequence who had taken such a stance.

4. The statement is not entirely free of traces of pantheism toward which Kant's thought was increasingly gravitating and which came through very clearly in the writings of most of those who claimed themselves to be the legitimate successors of his thought.

5. The spaced out type (equivalent to italics), in which this phrase was set in the original, meant to emphasize Kant's conviction about the truth of his cosmogony.

6. The "certain" cause, being a slight asymmetry coupled with chance collisions, could not have been more "uncertain" in producing the desired effect.

7. The lack of any qualification in this statement speaks for itself not only because Kant implicitly contradicts his repeated assertions about the perishable character of all features of the cosmos, but also because shortly afterwards (p. [152]) he refers to the mutual perturbations of planets.

8. See note 2 to the First Section of Second Part.

9. Kant probably meant orbital velocity, which indeed shows a steady though small decrease from Mercury (29.77 miles per second) to Saturn (5.8 miles per second) and beyond. He was patently wrong if he meant *force*, that is, centrifugal force.

10. A rather arbitrary presupposition, characteristic of a priori thinking.

11. See note 40 to Seventh Part of Second Section.

12. This rather naive distinction between "perfect" and "imperfect" geometrical

figures is a pivotal point of Kant's reasoning and had already been commented upon.

13. A statement attributed to Plato since antiquity.

14. This why Newton stated in Query 31 of his *Opticks* (New York: Dover, 1952, p. 402) that it was "unphilosophical to . . . pretend that it [the world] might arise out of a Chaos by the mere Laws of Nature," a statement which Kant should have mentioned.

15. Newton and others spoke rather of the divine arm. See Section II of the Introduction.

16. An exercise in vagueness in respect of Newton and in inexactness in respect of Kant. The former's "doctrine" (of inverse square law) was not a cosmogony, whereas the latter held his cosmogony to be the only one which is acceptable scientifically and philosophically.

17. Another noteworthy index of Kant's self-appraisal.

18. See note 7 above.

19. A statement befitting an amateur.

20. Clearly, Kant's erstwhile protestations of diffidence were a mere device of rhetoric.

21. See note 6 to Second Section of Second Part. The value 67 for Saturn is possibly a printing error, or more likely a carelessness on Kant's part.

22. Only a layman would be impressed by this estimate, or rather by its quantitative character. Even a layman would have, however, wondered about the correctness or experimental reliability of Kant's statement, had Kant informed him that one millionth of the earth's volume corresponds to that part of the entire outer crust of the earth which has a depth of about 2 meters from its surface. Could Kant refer to any experiment that showed that depth to be the limit of the heating effectiveness of the sun's rays?

23. It is characteristic of the particularly sweeping manner of Kant's argumentation in this Section that he does not care to recall his previous warnings (pp. [45] and [47]) that the increase must stop beyond a point.

24. Kant, on account of this reasoning, excludes the possibility of a planet between Mars and Jupiter (p. [179]). He does not mention that the presence of a planet there had been repeatedly conjectured ever since Kepler made bold to suggest it in his *Mysterium cosmographicum* (1596). On the other hand, the smallness of the combined mass of asteroids (less than 1/100th of the mass of Mars) would have presented no major problem for Kant's theory.

25. There is no such calculation in the *Principia*, because it contains only the values of the masses of the sun, earth, moon, Jupiter and Saturn. None of the three modern annotators of the *Allgemeine Naturgeschichte* (Rahts, Oettingen, and Ebert) cared to notice this fact. What Newton calculated was the ratio of the difference of the forces of gravity of the sun towards Saturn, and of Jupiter towards Saturn, to the force of Jupiter towards the sun as being 1/2409 (Book III, Prop. xiii; Var. Ed. 2:589), and added that the perturbations of other orbits are far less, except in the noticeable alteration of the earth's orbit by the moon.

26. The use of "often" could not have been more inappropriate, as in the entire solar system only the Mars-Jupiter-Saturn relation could be invoked by Kant in support of his contention, a classic case of the "one-stock-argument."

27. See remark in note 23 above.

28. Actually, Venus' mass is 0.81 of the earth's mass. Kant's throwing in the moon's mass is misleading because long before him it was known that the moon's

mass barely exceeded 1/100th of the earth's mass. Underlying Kant's estimate lie both his theory that the densities increase with closeness to the sun and the estimate widely accepted in his time that Venus' diameter was equal to that of the earth. On this latter point see, for instance, the Table of the data of planets in N. de Lacaille, *Leçons élémentaires d'astronomie géométrique et physique* (Paris: chez les Frères Guerin, 1746, p. 95; new rev. ed. 1761, p. 110).

29. Uranus turned out to be twice as distant as Saturn, but only with 1/7th of Saturn's mass, hardly a favorable outcome for Kant's theory. Even worse for it was the case of Neptune which, though not as distant in proportion, has a larger mass than Uranus. Kant, who made a first with these speculations on the physical cause of planetary distances, failed to notice a pattern of them which was to be discovered within ten years by Johann Daniel Titius, professor at Wittenberg. On the genesis of that discovery, see my "The Early History of the Titius-Bode Law," *American Journal of Physics*, 40 (1972): 1014–1023.

30. An intimation that for Kant the basic laws of mechanics were necessary laws, an idea which had been in the air since Descartes.

31. As Kant triumphantly surveys his cosmogony, he is prompted to declare his superiority over Buffon, a rather daring act in view of Buffon's tremendous renown. In Buffon's theory the ratio is used to show merely that the masses of planets were taken from the sun, as evidence of the common origin of solar system.

32. Hence the reason of Kant's wrong estimate of Venus' mass, which could have been avoided with a slight attention and consistency on his part.

33. Apart from the fact that in relation to Jupiter and Saturn, even the earth (to say nothing of the moon whose mass is only 1/100th of the earth's mass) is negligible, the statement contradicts Kant's foregoing remark on Venus' mass.

34. This estimate is not to be taken any more seriously than the one discussed in note 22 above. Through barometric experiments it had long been known that water was almost 1000 times denser than air (in the *Principia* the value 850 is given, Bk. III, Prop. xli; Var. Ed. 2:740), but no substance was known to be 15 times denser than water. Raht's remark (AA 1:557) that platinum is 15,000 times denser than air is typical of most commentators on Kant, who, instead of evaluating his statements in the contemporary context, try to justify them with references to modern data and findings.

35. Newton, so highly praised by Kant (see pp. [120] and [156]), was far more modest in his claims.

36. An estimate hardly befitting an allegedly scientific treatise.

37. Unless, of course, these universal laws are of a priori necessity. See note 30 above.

38. See p. [68] and note 19 to Fourth Section of Second Part.

39. A reference to the irregularity of comets.

40. Kant's idea of defect and deviation smacks of subjectivism and anthropomorphism.

41. That nature produces physical and moral characteristics in the same way as she does physical features, is a claim with a naturalistic ring, potentially destructive of Kant's natural theology.

Third Part

1. This Third Part first appeared in my translation as Appendix in *Cosmology,*

History and Theology, edited by W. Yourgrau and A. D. Breck (New York: Plenum Press, 1977), pp. 387–403. It is given here with some modifications to make it conform to the principles followed throughout this translation.

2. These lines, translated from Brockes' translation (pp. 4–5), correspond to lines 23–28 of Epistle I of *Essay on Man:*

> He, who through vast immensity can pierce,
> See worlds on worlds compose one universe,
> Observe how system into system runs,
> What other planets circle other suns,
> What varied Being peoples every star,
> May tell why Heaven has made us as we are.

Once more Kant gave Brockes' text with some variation , of which the most noteworthy was his replacing in the first line word "Regeln" (rules) with "Welten" (worlds). Had Kant done this with an eye on the English original, he must have also noticed several other glaring discrepancies between the original and Brockes' translation of it. Lovejoy's statement in his *Great Chain of Being* (p. 355), that "Kant's cosmology is a prose amplification and extension of the First Epistle of the *Essay on Man*," is certainly appropriate in connection with this Third Part.

3. Tempted as one may be to smile at Kant's smug estimate of the value of his own propositions, they for the most part appear very sober (if not reasonable) in comparison with all major publications on the topic that saw print prior to 1755 and with which Kant was undoubtedly familiar. In Fontenelle's *Entretiens*, in Huygens' *Cosmotheoros*, to say nothing of some earlier works, too many specifics are ascribed to denizens of other planets, a fact which hardly makes their portrayal appear "well grounded," to use Kant's expression. Even when served up by such a protagonist of sheer rationality as Christian Wolff, and in dry textbooks, such as his *Elementa matheseos universae* (a five-volume work, first published in 1715, of which the third volume contained the *Elementa astronomiae*; see new ed.; Geneva: apud Henricum-Albertum Gosse et Socios, 1740, pp. 437–38, for the scholion to the thesis that "nothing prevents that all planets may be viewed as being inhabited by animals and men"), too concrete description of extraterrestrial beings could hardly retain credibility for too long. Even within a rationalist milieu sold on "purely logical" inferences, their chain could appear the weaker, the further it was stretched. In such chains, forged by Wolff with a vengeance, each link seemed to be perfectly reasonable together with its connection to the immediately following link. What objection could be raised against inferring the pupil's size from the intensity of light, the size of the eyeball from that of the pupil, the size of the head from that of the eyeball, and finally from the latter the tallness of the body supporting it? Nothing at all could be objected to Wolff's presentation of the ratio, 26 to 5, of the distances of Jupiter and earth to the sun, as a ratio determining the respective intensity of sunlight on them. Still that 13-feet tall Jovian, which was the last link of the chain, could hardly look convincing in spite of Wolff's references to giants mentioned in Genesis, to the length of cubits as used by the Hebrews, and last but not least, by a Jesuit, that our earth cannot be the sole abode of life in the universe. Familiar as Kant must have been with these specifics offered by Wolff, he did not take them for a model. Much less was he willing to appear a student of Swedenborg,

293

although he still had a secret admiration for him when years later, in 1766, he parodied him in a booklet, as was convincingly shown in F. Sewall's introduction to E. F. Goerwitz's translation of Kant's *Dreams of a Spirit-Seer Illustrated by Dreams of Metaphysics* (London: Swan Sonnenschein, 1900). Years earlier Kant was eagerly waiting for and purchasing the expensive quarto volumes of Swedenborg's *Arcana coelestia*, an alleged commentary on Genesis and Exodus, but actually a verbose account of Swedenborg's private revelations. In the first volume of the commentary on Exodus, which came out in 1753, Swedenborg described his communications with the inhabitants of the moon, Mercury, Venus, and Mars, whereas in the next volume published in 1754, he dealt with the inhabitants of Jupiter and Saturn. According to Swedenborg the moon's inhabitants were of small stature and made a thunderlike noise as they spoke; those on Mercury preferred not to use vocal discourse; those on Venus were so many giants in body but dwarfs in intellect; those on Mars spoke through their Eustachian tubes and clothed themselves in garments made of barks; those in the warm zone of Jupiter went around in loincloths and hopped instead of walking; those on Saturn were protected against cold by an unusually thick skin. (For these and other details, see the names of various planets in *Index to Words, Names and Subjects in the Heavenly Arcana Disclosed by Emanuel Swedenborg*, Rotch Edition, vol. XX. (Boston; Massachusetts New Church Union, 1907). Of such details Kant kept aloof. He tried to remain on the level of principles as befitted a man of reason. He avoided historical and literary details that had been gathered with great diligence in the dissertation which Johann Christian Henning published in Kiel in 1738 under the title *Specimen planetographiae physicae, inquirens praecipue an planetae sint habitabiles* (71 pp; typis Godofr. Bartschii). But Kant was so much a man of the age of reason that he rated all possible objections worthy of no more than a brief ironic story. No wonder that all his reasoning proved to be an exercise in unreason to such an extent that the Third Part appeared to its French translator a piece characterized by a surprising measure of absence of logic (see Wolf, *Hypothèses cosmogoniques*, p. ix). What Wolf failed to see was that the absence in question was a logical part of the entire work. That he nevertheless translated that Third Part was also part of a logic not much more creditable. He hoped that exposure to it of the French reader would make clear to the latter the difference between "the work of the German philosopher" and "the exposition so sober and purely scientific which Laplace made of his famous and immortal hypothesis." Such was the logic of chauvinism, the highest form of logic available at a time which saw the accounts by Camille Flammarion, a professional astronomer by training, of the inhabitants of other planets being sold in hundreds of thousands of copies, and heard Anatole France declare (without provoking the slightest criticism) about Mars that "it is infinitely probably that it is inhabited" (see "Mysticism and Science" in *On Life and Letters. Fourth Series*, translated by B. Miall [New York: Gabriel Wells 1924], p. 46). Such statements and claims (as well as their present-day counterparts) only prove that infatuation with extraterrestrial intelligence demands that kind of logic whose nature is to go wrong with confidence.

4. The possibility that the shoe of madness may have been on the other foot, will not, of course, be seen even today by those, who in spite of what has been found out about the surface of Mars, or rather in spite of what has not been

found there, urge the spending of billions of dollars on projects aimed at detecting extraterrestrial intelligence.

5. See notes 25 and 30 to Fourth Section of Second Part.

6. See the same notes.

7. A point emphasized by Kant in Seventh Section of Second Part.

8. In spite of considerable efforts, I have not been able to identify that author. He is certainly not Huygens, author of *Cosmotheoros*. Perusal of philosophical and scientific works of Dutch authors active during the first half of the eighteenth century led me, however, to some interesting finds relating to the subject. One of them is W. J. 'sGravesande's criticism of the use of the principle of probability on behalf of the existence of intelligent beings on other planets in his *Introduction à la philosophie* (1737) where he states: "Those who pretend that there are inhabitants on the planets rest their case on the similarities that exist between the planets and our earth; similarities which prove the possibility of their assertion. But the probability that the planets are inhabited is to the certainty [that they are inhabited] as this [specific] use[fulness] of the planets, that is, as unity is to the number of use[fulnesses] to which the planets may have been destined. Now who would dare to assert that this [latter] number is not infinite?" See *Oeuvres philosophiques et mathématiques de Mr. G. J. 'sGravesande*, rassemblées & publiées par Jean Nic. Seb. Allemand, qui y a ajouté l'Histoire de la Vie & des Écrits de l'Auteur (Amsterdam: chez Marc Michel Rey, 1744), 2:87. The remark strikes, of course, at the very core of Kant's (and many others') argument based precisely on the view that planets would be purposeless if not inhabited.

9. In the original R., which Rahts transcribed (AA 1:353) without any explicit justification, as Reiche (kingdom). It may, however, be that Kant wished to indicate his source, that is, one of the periodicals whose title starts with such words as Relationes, Repertoire, and the like. My perusal of all the 13 volumes of *Relationes de libris novis* (Göttingen, 1752–55) led me to no positive result.

10. A reference to Fontenelle's imaginary ventures to other planets in his *Entretiens*.

11. See note 24 to the Eighth Section of Second Part.

12. Unlike Kant, Lambert firmly held that all comets must be inhabited. He was not altogether facetious when he postulated that astronomers were the inhabitants of those comets which wandered from one planetary system to another. See *Cosmological Letters*, pp. 73, 79.

13. Alexander the Great.

14. Exaggerated teleology is hardly different from pre-empting purpose, which happens when men, free and purposive beings, are viewed as necessary complements to physical conditions compatible with life.

15. Unexplored, of course, if "exploration" becomes equivalent to quantitative measurements.

16. The createdness of the intellect (soul) will be abandoned when mental properties become mere mirror images of physical properties.

17. The psychology of Wolff, who coined the word and founded that science which already in its Wolffian form left little logical room for a specially created soul.

18. Such premises could lend themselves only to conclusions which de la Mettrie had already drawn in his *L'homme machine* (1748).

19. In view of Kant's hasty conclusions, his physical state must have indeed contained much resistance.

20. Clearly, Kant's declarations of diffidence cannot be taken seriously.

21. No specific conditions were established by Newton's calculation of the densities of some of the planets.
22. Practically certain, to wit.
23. On the popularity of this notion before Kant, see Lovejoy, *The Great Chain of Being*, pp. 195–99, with quotations from Epistle II of *Essay on Man*. What should seem most relevant in this connection is the review which Kant wrote in 1785 (AA 8:45–55) of the First Part of Herder's *Ideen zur Philosophie der Geschichte der Menschheit* (see note 32 to Section IV of Introduction). In the second chapter of the First Book of the *Ideen* Herder made much of the "middle position" occupied by the earth in the planetary system in a manner very similar to Kant's reasoning in this Third Part. It was not, however, mentioned by Herder, or by Kant, although the first part of his review offered long quotations from that second chapter. Equally revealing is the second, or critical part of Kant's review. Whereas he criticized Herder for trying to specify man's mental features from empirical data, that is, from the conditions of matter on earth, he failed to note that such had precisely been his own procedure in the *Allgemeine Naturgeschichte*, a procedure declared to be "uncritical" by the author of the *Kritik*. In addition to Kant's resolve to be remembered only as its author, his criticism of that aspect of Herder's *Ideen* may have also been prompted by Herder's negative attitude towards the *Kritik*. For its initial failure to make impact Kant laid part of the blame on Herder's influence.
24. These lines in Brockes' translation (pp. 34–35) correspond to lines 30–34 of Epistle II of *Essay on Man:*

> Superior beings, when of late they saw
> A mortal Man unfold all Nature's law,
> Admired such wisdom in an earthly shape
> And showed a NEWTON as we show an Ape.

25. An astonishing conception of what a physical treatise ought to be, especially on the part of one who wished to be the Newton of cosmogony.
26. Indeed, it followed so naturally as to exclude anything but sheer naturalism.
27. See p. [80].
28. Kant clearly borrows from the chapter on the motion of moons around some planets in Derham's *Astrotheology* (Bk. IV, ch. v).
29. Here Kant left out several lines from Brockes' text (pp. 24–26), corresponding to the somewhat similar to lines 236–241 of Epistle I of *Essay on Man:*

> Vast chain of Being! which from God began,
> Natures ethereal, human, angel, man,
> Beast, bird, fish, insect, what no eye can see,
> No glass can reach; from Infinite to thee,
> From thee to Nothing.

30. Lines 197–98 of Book III of Haller's poem "Über den Ursprung des Übels".
31. See note 23 above.
32. A conclusion incompatible with Kant's repeated and emphatic assertions of the practical certainty of the ideas set forth in this Part.
33. This is not an evolutionary view of man, but a reference to the uncertainty surrounding man's state after death.
34. Perhaps Kant was toying with the idea of palingenesis. At any rate, in view of his statement, he had no right to criticize Wright (pp. [140–41]) for similar speculations.

Appendix

1. As no such rules are expounded in "The Only Possible Argument," Kant obviously refers to the *Allgemeine Naturgeschichte*, which he quotes at the end of the "Vorrede" as he regretfully mentions that not even the famous Lambert had learned of it.

2. See pp. [c5r]–[c6r] of the *Allgemeine Naturgeschichte*.

3. Since the very opposite of this view is argued at length in Lambert's *Cosmologische Briefe* (1761), Kant may not have yet learned of it.

4. See pp. [40]–[41] and [161] of the *Allgemeine Naturgeschichte*.

5. The statement is not only arbitrary with respect to the variation of density with distance, but also erroneous with respect to the variation with distance of the sun's heating effect. That the inverse square law was valid not only for gravitation but also for light and heat had been generally recognized long before Kant.

6. In 1763 de Mairan was already 85 and almost legendary for his stubborn allegiance to the Cartesian program of giving a mechanical explanation (such as the one based on vortex motion) to all physical phenomena.

7. In Milton's *Paradise Lost* such is the name of that part of the world where those in pursuit of vainglory, worldly or spiritual, were blown by a violent cross wind, as they boldly ascended towards Heaven:

   all these upwhirled aloft
   Fly o're the backside of the World farr off
   Into a *Limbo* large and broad, since calld
   The Paradise of Fools, to few unknown
   Long after, now unpeopl'd, and untrod (III, 493–97).

   Ironically, Kant describes shortly afterwards as a limbo that ring-shaped space around Saturn where particles ascending from its equatorial belt settle in stable orbits. The pride which Kant took in that futile explanation of the formation of Saturn's ring was hardly different from that vainglory for which Milton's limbo was the appropriate reward.

8. This figure is in flagrant discrepancy with the one given in the *Allgemeine Naturgeschichte* (p. [80]), that is, 6 hours, 23 minutes and 53 seconds, a discrepancy not noted either by Rahts, or by P. Menzer, editor and annotator of the *Einzig mögliche Beweisgrund* in the Akademie Ausgabe (2:63–163 and 470–75). The blame for that discrepancy clearly lies not with the typesetter but with Kant, who once more displays his carelessness with numerical data. Since in this section on cosmogony Kant found space for two unimportant footnotes, a similar note would have been most natural if the new figure had been the result of his having recalculated the period in question. Revealingly neither Kant nor Gensichen cared to recall this new figure, which had already seen print in three editions of the *Einzig mögliche Beweisgrund*, when in 1791 they collaborated on a much shortened version of the *Allgemeine Naturgeschichte* and took much pride in the value of the period of Saturn's rotation given there.

INDEX OF NAMES